PART II

# STUDENT'S SOLUTIONS MANUAL

# CALCULUS AND ANALYTIC GEOMETRY 7TH

## THOMAS/FINNEY

ALEXIA B. LATIMER
BENITA H. ALBERT
JUDITH BROADWIN

ADDISON-WESLEY PUBLISHING COMPANY, INC.
Reading, Massachusetts · Menlo Park, California · New York
Don Mills, Ontario · Wokingham, England · Amsterdam · Bonn
Sydney · Singapore · Tokyo · Madrid · San Juan

Reproduced by Addison-Wesley from camera-ready copy supplied by the authors.

ISBN 0-201-16326-8



ABCDEFGHIJ-BA-898

# CHAPTER 11

# INFINITE SEQUENCES AND INFINITE SERIES

## 11.1 SEQUENCES OF NUMBERS

1. $a_1 = \frac{2}{3}$; $a_2 = \frac{3}{5}$; $a_3 = \frac{4}{7}$; $a_4 = \frac{5}{9}$; $\lim_{x \to \infty} \frac{n+1}{2n+1} = \frac{1}{2}$

3. $a_1 = -\frac{1}{3}$; $a_2 = -\frac{3}{5}$; $a_3 = -\frac{5}{7}$; $a_4 = -\frac{7}{9}$; $\lim_{x \to \infty} \frac{1-2n}{1+2n} = -1$

5. $a_1 = \frac{1}{2}$; $a_2 = \frac{1}{2}$; $a_3 = \frac{1}{2}$; $a_4 = \frac{1}{2}$; $\lim_{x \to \infty} \frac{2^n}{2^{n+1}} = \frac{1}{2}$

7. $x_1 = 1$; $x_{n+1} = x_n + \left(\frac{1}{2}\right)^n$; $x_2 = 1 + \frac{1}{2} = \frac{3}{2}$; $x_3 = \frac{3}{2} + \left(\frac{1}{2}\right)^2 = \frac{7}{4}$;

$$x_4 = \frac{7}{4} + \left(\frac{1}{2}\right)^3 = \frac{15}{8};\ x^5 = \frac{15}{8} + \left(\frac{1}{2}\right)^4 = \frac{31}{16};\ x_6 = \frac{31}{16} + \left(\frac{1}{2}\right)^5 = \frac{63}{32}$$

9. $x_1 = 2$; $x_{n+1} = \frac{x_n}{2}$; $x_2 = \frac{2}{2} = 1$; $x_3 = \frac{1}{2}$; $x_4 = \frac{\frac{1}{2}}{2} = \frac{1}{4}$;

$$x_5 = \frac{\frac{1}{4}}{2} = \frac{1}{8};\ x_6 = \frac{\frac{1}{8}}{2} = \frac{1}{16}$$

11. $x_1 = x_2 = 1$; $x_{n+2} = x_{n+1} + x_n$; $x_3 = 1+1 = 2$; $x_4 = 2+1 = 3$;

$x_5 = 3+2 = 5$; $x_6 = 5+3 = 8$

13. (a) $(1)^2 - 2(1)+2 = -1$; $(3)^2 - 2(2)^2 = 1$; If $a^2 - 2b^2 = 1$, then

$(a + 2b)^2 - 2(a + b)^2 = a^2 - 4ab + 4b^2 - 2a^2 - 4ab - 2b^2 =$

$2b^2 - a^2 = -1$. If $a^2 - 2b^2 = -1$, then $(a + 2b)^2 - 2(a + b)^2$

$2b^2 - a^2 = -(a^2 - 2b^2) = -(-1) = 1$

(b) $\left(\frac{a+2b}{a+b}\right)^2 - 2 = \frac{a^2 + 4ab + 4b^2}{a^2 + 2ab + b^2} - 2 = \frac{2b^2 - a^2}{(a+b)^2} = \frac{\pm 1}{(y_n)^2}$

$$= \lim_{n\to\infty} r_n = \lim_{n\to\infty} \sqrt{2 \pm \left(\frac{1}{y_n}\right)^2} = \sqrt{2}$$

15. Let $f(x) = \cos x - x$. $f'(x) = -\sin x - 1$ and using the formula $x_{n+1} = x_n - \frac{f(x_n)}{f'(x_n)}$, we have $x_1 = 0.755222417$, $x_2 = 0.739141666$, $x_3 = 0.739085134$, $x_4 = 0.739085133$.

17. 0.876726216; $x^2 - \sin x = 0$

19. (a) Using $y = \tan x - 2x$, the root is $x = 1.65561185$

(b) Yes, $\frac{\pi}{3} \approx 1.05 < 1.66$

(c) If $x < \tan x < 2x$ for all $0 < x < b$,

then $\int x\,dx < \int \tan x\,dx < \int 2x\,dx$ or $\frac{x^2}{2} < \ln|\sec x| < x^2$

## 11.2 LIMIT THEOREMS

1. $0, -\frac{1}{4}, -\frac{2}{9}, -\frac{3}{16}$; converges to 0

3. $\frac{1}{3}, \frac{1}{9}, \frac{1}{27}, \frac{1}{81}$; converges to 0

5. $1, -\frac{1}{3}, \frac{1}{5}, -\frac{1}{7}$; converges to 0

7. 0,-1,0,1,0; diverges

9. $1, -\frac{1}{\sqrt{2}}, \frac{1}{\sqrt{3}}, -\frac{1}{2}$; converges to 0

11. converges to 0

13. converges to 1

15. diverges because the terms oscillate between ±1.

17. converges to $-\frac{2}{3}$

19. $\sqrt{\frac{2n}{n+1}} = \sqrt{\frac{2}{1+\frac{1}{n}}}$ converges to $\sqrt{2}$

21. converges to 0

23. diverges, terms oscillate between 1 and -1

25. $\frac{n^2}{(n+1)^2} = \left(\frac{n}{n+1}\right)^2$ converges to 1

27 $\lim \frac{1 - 5n^4}{n^4 + 8n^3} = \frac{\frac{1}{n^4} - 5}{1 + \frac{8}{n}} = -5$

29. $\lim\limits_{n\to\infty} \tanh n = \lim\limits_{n\to\infty} \frac{e^n - e^{-n}}{e^n + e^{-n}} = \lim\limits_{n\to\infty} \frac{1 - \frac{1}{e^{2n}}}{1 + \frac{1}{e^{2n}}} = 1$

31. $\lim_{n\to\infty} \frac{2(n+1)+1}{2n+1} = \lim_{n\to\infty} \frac{2n+3}{2n+1} = \lim_{n\to\infty} \frac{2+\frac{3}{n}}{2+\frac{1}{n}} = 1$

33. $\lim_{n\to\infty} 5 = 5$

35. $\lim_{n\to\infty} (.5)^n = \lim_{n\to\infty} \left(\frac{1}{2}\right)^n = 0$

37. $\lim_{n\to\infty} \frac{n^n}{(n+1)^{n+1}} = \lim_{n\to\infty} \left(\frac{n}{n+1}\right)^n \left(\frac{1}{n+1}\right) = (1)(0) = 0$

39. $\lim_{n\to\infty} \sqrt{2-\frac{1}{n}} = \sqrt{2}$

41. $\lim_{n\to\infty} \frac{3^n}{n^3} = \lim_{n\to\infty} \frac{(\ln 3)3^n}{3n^2} = \lim_{n\to\infty} \frac{(\ln 3)^2 3^n}{6n} = \lim_{n\to\infty} \frac{(\ln 3)^3 3^n}{6} = \infty$

43. $\lim_{n\to\infty} (\ln n - \ln (n+1)) = \lim_{n\to\infty} \ln \left(\frac{n}{n+1}\right) = \ln \lim_{n\to\infty} \left(\frac{n}{n+1}\right) = \ln 1 = 0$

45. $\lim_{n\to\infty} \frac{n^2-2n+1}{n-1} = \lim_{n\to\infty} \frac{1-\frac{2}{n}+\frac{1}{n^2}}{\frac{1}{n}-\frac{1}{n^2}} = \frac{1}{0} = \infty$

47. $\lim_{n\to\to\infty} \left(-\frac{1}{2}\right)^n = 0$

49. $\lim_{n\to\infty} \tan^{-1} n = \frac{\pi}{2}$

51. $\lim_{n\to\infty} n\sin\frac{1}{n} = \lim_{n\to\infty} \frac{\sin\frac{1}{n}}{\frac{1}{n}} = \lim_{n\to\infty} \frac{\cos\frac{1}{n}\left(-\frac{1}{n^2}\right)}{-\frac{1}{n^2}} = \cos 0 = 1$

53. $\lim_{n\to\infty} \frac{n^2}{2n-1}\sin\frac{1}{n} = \lim_{n\to\infty} \left(\frac{n}{2n-1}\right)\left(n\sin\frac{1}{n}\right) = \left(\frac{1}{2}\right)(1) = \frac{1}{2}$

55. Note that $\frac{n!}{n^n} = \frac{1\cdot 2\cdot 3\cdot \ldots \cdot n}{n\cdot n\cdot n \ldots \cdot n} < \frac{1}{n}$ since $\frac{2\cdot 3\cdot \ldots \cdot n}{n\cdot n\cdot \ldots \cdot n} < 1$

$\therefore\ 0 < \lim_{n\to\infty} \frac{n!}{n^n} < \lim_{n\to\infty} \frac{1}{n} = 0$

57. $\lim_{n\to\infty} (x)^{1/n} = 1$ for all $x > 0$. Fix $x > 0$ and consider $a_n = x^{1/n}$.

$\lim_{n\to\infty} (\ln a_n) = \lim_{n\to\infty} \frac{1}{n} \ln x = \ln x \lim_{n\to\infty} \frac{1}{n} = 0$. Therefore,

$\lim_{n\to\infty} (x)^{1/n} = \lim_{n\to\infty} e^{\frac{1}{n}\ln x} = e^0 = 1$

59. $\lim_{n\to\infty} nf\left(\frac{1}{n}\right) = \lim_{n\to\infty} \frac{f\left(\frac{1}{n}\right)}{\frac{1}{n}} = \lim_{n\to\infty} \frac{f'\left(\frac{1}{n}\right)\left(-\frac{1}{n^2}\right)}{-\frac{1}{n^2}} = \lim_{n\to\infty} f'\left(\frac{1}{n}\right) = f'(0)$

61. Let $f(\frac{1}{n}) = e^{\frac{1}{n}} - 1$. Then $f(x) = e^x - 1$ and $f'(x) = e^x$.

$$\lim_{n\to\infty} (e^{\frac{1}{n}} - 1) = 1 \text{ since } f'(0) = 1$$

63. Suppose that $\{a_n\}$ converges to some finite value L. Let $\varepsilon = 1$ be given. There exists $N_1 > 0$ for which

(1) $|a_n - L| < 1$ or $a_n < L + 1$ for all $n > N_1$.

There also exists $N_2 > 0$ for which

(2) $f(n) = a_n > L + 1$ for all $n > N_2$.

Let $N > \max\{N_1, N_2\}$. For all $n > N$, both equations (1) and (2) are true, which cannot be. Thus the sequence $\{a_n\}$ cannot converge, and hence must diverge.

65. The conclusion is that $|f(a_n) - f(L)| < \varepsilon$, so that the sequence $\{f(a_n)\}$ converges to $f(L)$.

## 11.3 LIMITS THAT ARISE FREQUENTLY

1. $\lim_{n\to\infty} \frac{1 + \ln n}{n} = \lim_{n\to\infty} \left(\frac{1}{n} + \frac{\ln n}{n}\right) = 0 + 0 = 0$

3. $\lim_{n\to\infty} \frac{(-4)^n}{n!} = 0$ by Formula 6 with $x = -4$.

5. $\lim_{n\to\infty} (.5)^n = 0$ by Formula 4 for $x = 0.5$.

7. $\lim_{n\to\infty} \left(1 + \frac{7}{n}\right)^n = e^7$, by Formula 5, for $x = 7$

9. $\lim_{n\to\infty} \frac{\ln(n+1)}{n} = \lim_{n\to\infty} \frac{\frac{1}{n+1}}{1} = 0$

11. $\lim_{n\to\infty} \frac{n!}{10^{6n}} = \lim_{n\to\infty} \frac{1}{\frac{10^{6n}}{n!}} = \infty$.

13. $\lim_{n\to\infty} \sqrt[2n]{n} = \lim_{n\to\infty} \left(n^{\frac{1}{n}}\right)^{\frac{1}{2}} = 1$

15. $\lim_{n\to\infty} \frac{1}{3^{2n-1}} = 0$

17. $\lim_{n\to\infty} \left(\frac{n}{n+1}\right)^n = \lim_{n\to\infty} \left(\frac{n+1}{n}\right)^{-n} = \lim_{n\to\infty} \left[\left(1 + \frac{1}{n}\right)^n\right]^{-1} = e^{-1}$

19. $\lim_{n\to\infty} \frac{\ln(2n+1)}{n} = \lim_{n\to\infty} \frac{\frac{2}{2n+1}}{1} = 0$

21. $\lim_{n\to\infty}\sqrt[n]{\dfrac{x^n}{2n+1}}$, $x > 0$, $= x\left(\lim_{n\to\infty}\sqrt[n]{\dfrac{1}{2n+1}}\right) = x$

23. Consider $a_n = \ln(n^2+n)^{1/n}$. $\lim_{n\to\infty}\ln(n^2+n)^{1/n} = \lim_{n\to\infty}\dfrac{1}{n}\ln(n^2+n)^{1/n} =$

$\lim_{n\to\infty}\dfrac{2n+1}{n^2+n} = 0$. $\therefore \lim_{n\to\infty} e^{\frac{1}{n}\ln(n^2+n)} = e^0 = 1$.

25. $\lim_{n\to\infty}\left(\dfrac{3}{n}\right)^{\frac{1}{n}} = \lim_{n\to\infty}\dfrac{3^{1/n}}{n^{1/n}} = 1$

27. $\lim_{n\to\infty}\left(1-\dfrac{1}{n}\right)^n = e^{-1}$

29. $\lim_{n\to\infty}\dfrac{\ln(n^2)}{n} = \lim_{n\to\infty}\dfrac{2\ln n}{n} = 2\lim_{n\to\infty}\dfrac{\ln n}{n} = 0$

31. Diverges, since $\lim_{n\to\infty}\ln n = \infty$ and $\lim_{n\to\infty} n^{1/n} = 1$.

33. $\displaystyle\int_1^n \frac{1}{x^p}\,dx = \left.\frac{x^{-p+1}}{-p+1}\right]_1^n = \frac{1}{-p+1}[n^{-p+1}-1]$. For $p > 1$,

$\dfrac{1}{-p+1}\lim_{n\to\infty}[n^{-p+1}-1] = (-1)\dfrac{1}{-p+1} = \dfrac{1}{p-1}$.

35. $N \geq 9124$

37. $|\sqrt[c]{n} - 1| < \varepsilon \Leftrightarrow \dfrac{1}{n^c} < \varepsilon \Leftrightarrow n^c > \dfrac{1}{\varepsilon}$ or $n > \sqrt[c]{\dfrac{1}{\varepsilon}}$

$\therefore$ Let $N = \varepsilon^{-\frac{1}{c}}$. For $n > N$, $0 < \dfrac{1}{n^c} < \varepsilon$ so $\dfrac{1}{n^c}$ converges to 0.

About the hint: $\dfrac{1}{n^{0.04}} < .001 \Leftrightarrow n^{0.04} > 10^3 \Leftrightarrow n > (10^3)^{25} = 10^{75}$

## 11.4 INFINITE SERIES

1. $S_n = \dfrac{2\left(1-\left(\frac{1}{3}\right)^n\right)}{1-\frac{1}{3}} = 3\left(1-\left(\frac{1}{3}\right)^n\right)$. $r = \dfrac{1}{3} < 1$, so $S = \dfrac{2}{1-\frac{1}{3}} = 3$

3. $S_n = \dfrac{1(1-e^{-n})}{1-e^{-1}}$. $r = \dfrac{1}{e} < 1$ so $S = \dfrac{1}{1-\frac{1}{e}} = \dfrac{e}{e-1}$

5. $S_n = \frac{1(1-(-2)^n)}{1-(-2)} = \frac{1-(-2)^n}{3}$. $r=-2$, $|r|>1$ so series diverges.

7. $\ln\frac{1}{2} + \ln\frac{2}{3} + \ln\frac{3}{4} + \ldots + \ln\frac{n}{n+1} =$

$\ln 1 - \ln 2 + \ln 2 - \ln 3 + \ln 3 - \ln 4 + \ldots + \ln n - \ln(n+1)$

$\therefore \lim_{n\to\infty} S_n = \lim_{n\to\infty}(-\ln(n+1)) = -\infty$. so series diverges

9. (a) $\sum_{n=-2}^{\infty} \frac{1}{(n+4)(n+5)}$ (b) $\sum_{n=0}^{\infty} \frac{1}{(n+2)(n+3)}$ (c) $\sum_{n=5}^{\infty} \frac{1}{(n-3)(n-2)}$

11. $S = \frac{1}{1-\frac{1}{4}} = \frac{4}{3}$

13. $S = \frac{\frac{7}{4}}{1-\frac{1}{4}} = \frac{7}{3}$

15. $S = \frac{5}{1-\frac{1}{2}} + \frac{1}{1-\frac{1}{3}} = 10 + \frac{3}{2} = \frac{23}{2}$

17. $S = \frac{1}{1-\frac{2}{5}} = \frac{5}{3}$

19. $\sum_{n=1}^{\infty} \frac{4}{(4n-3)(4n+1)} = \sum_{n=1}^{\infty}\left(\frac{1}{4n-3} - \frac{1}{4n+1}\right) =$

$\left(1-\frac{1}{5}\right)+\left(\frac{1}{5}-\frac{1}{9}\right)+\left(\frac{1}{9}-\frac{1}{13}\right)+\ldots+\left(\frac{1}{4n-3}-\frac{1}{4n+1}\right)+\ldots$

$\therefore \lim_{n\to\infty} S_n = \lim_{n\to\infty}\left(1-\frac{1}{4n+1}\right) = 1$

21. $\sum_{n=3}^{\infty} \frac{4}{(4n-3)(4n+1)} = \sum_{n=3}^{\infty}\left(\frac{1}{4n-3} - \frac{1}{4n+1}\right) =$

$\left(\frac{1}{9}-\frac{1}{13}\right)+\left(\frac{1}{13}-\frac{1}{17}\right)+\ldots+\left(\frac{1}{4n-3}-\frac{1}{4n+1}\right)+\ldots$

$\therefore \lim_{n\to\infty} S_n = \lim_{n\to\infty}\left(\frac{1}{9}-\frac{1}{4n+1}\right) = \frac{1}{9}$

23. (a) $0.234234234\ldots = \frac{234}{10^3} + \frac{234}{10^6} + \ldots$

$$S = \frac{\frac{234}{10^3}}{1-\frac{1}{10^3}} = \frac{234}{999} = \frac{26}{111}$$

(b) Yes, every repeating decimal is a geometric series, with ratio $= 10^{-n}$, where n is the number of repeating digits.

27. $\sum_{n=1}^{\infty} (-1)^{n+1} \frac{3}{2^n} = \frac{\frac{3}{2}}{1-\left(-\frac{1}{2}\right)} = 1$

29. $\sum_{n=0}^{\infty} \cos n\pi = 1 - 1 + 1 - 1 + 1 \ldots$ diverges because $\lim_{n\to\infty} (-1)^n \neq 0$

31. $\sum_{n=0}^{\infty} e^{-2n} = \frac{1}{1-e^{-2}} = \frac{e^2}{e^2 - 1}$

33. $\sum_{n=1}^{\infty} (-1)^{n+1} n$ diverges because $\lim_{n\to\infty} (-1)^{n+1} n \neq 0$

35. $\sum_{n=0}^{\infty} \frac{2^n - 1}{3^n} = \sum_{n=0}^{\infty} \left(\frac{2}{3}\right)^n - \sum_{n=0}^{\infty} \left(\frac{1}{3}\right)^n = \frac{1}{1-\frac{2}{3}} - \frac{1}{1-\frac{1}{3}} = \frac{3}{2}$

37. $\sum_{n=0}^{\infty} \frac{n!}{1000^n}$ diverges because $\lim_{n\to\infty} \frac{n!}{1000^n} = \infty$

39. $a = 1$ and $r = -x$, since $\frac{1}{1+x} = \frac{1}{1-(-x)} = \sum_{n=0}^{\infty} (-1)^n x^n$, $|x| < 1$.

41. The area of each square is one-half that of the preceding square. Thererore, the sum of the areas is
$S = 4 + 2 + \frac{1}{2} + \ldots = \frac{4}{1 - \frac{1}{2}} = 8$.

43. Let $\sum_{n=1}^{\infty} n$ and $\sum_{n=1}^{\infty} (-n)$ be the two divergent series. But the sum $\sum_{n=1}^{\infty} (n + (-n)) = \sum_{n=0}^{\infty} 0$ converges.

45. Let $\sum_{n=1}^{\infty} \frac{1}{2^n} = 1$ and $\sum_{n=1}^{\infty} \frac{1}{3^n} = \frac{1}{2}$ be the two convergent series.

Then $\sum_{n=1}^{\infty} \frac{\frac{1}{2^n}}{\frac{1}{3^n}} = \sum_{n=1}^{\infty} \left(\frac{3}{2}\right)^n$ diverges.

47. If $\sum_{n=1}^{\infty} a_n$ converges, then $\lim_{n\to\infty} a_n = 0$. Therefore, $\lim_{n\to\infty}\left(\frac{1}{a_n}\right) \neq 0$ and $\sum_{n=1}^{\infty}\left(\frac{1}{a_n}\right)$ diverges.

## 11.5 TESTS FOR CONVERGENCE OF SERIES WITH NONNEGATIVE TERMS

Note: The reasons given for convergence may not be the only ones that apply.

1. $\sum_{n=1}^{\infty} \frac{1}{10^n}$ converges. Geometric series with $r = \frac{1}{10} < 1$.

3. $\sum_{n=1}^{\infty} \frac{\sin^2 n}{2^n}$ converges, since $\sin^2 n \le 1 \Rightarrow \frac{\sin^2 n}{2^n} \le \frac{1}{2^n}$ and $\sum_{n=1}^{\infty} \frac{1}{2^n}$ converges.

5. $\sum_{n=1}^{\infty} \frac{1+\cos n}{n^2}$ converges by comparison with $\sum_{n=1}^{\infty} \frac{2}{n^2} =$ $2\sum_{n=1}^{\infty} \frac{1}{n^2}$ which is a multiple of a p-series with $p = 2 > 1$.

7. $\sum_{n=1}^{\infty} \frac{\ln n}{n}$ diverges since $\ln n > 1$ for $n > e \Rightarrow \frac{\ln n}{n} > \frac{1}{n}$ and $\sum_{n=1}^{\infty} \frac{1}{n}$ diverges.

9. $\sum_{n=1}^{\infty} \frac{2^n}{3^n}$ converges, geometric series with $r = \frac{2}{3} < 1$.

11. $\sum_{n=1}^{\infty} \frac{1}{1+\ln n}$ diverges by comparison with $\sum_{n=1}^{\infty} \frac{1}{1+n}$, since $\ln n < n$ for $n > 1 \Rightarrow 1 + \ln n < 1 + n \Rightarrow \frac{1}{1+\ln n} > \frac{1}{1+n}$.

13. $\sum_{n=1}^{\infty} \frac{2^n}{n+1}$ diverges, since $\lim_{n\to\infty} \frac{2^n}{n+1} \neq 0$.

15. $\sum_{n=1}^{\infty} \frac{1}{\sqrt{n^3+1}}$ converges, since $\sum_{n=1}^{\infty} \frac{1}{n^{3/2}}$ converges and

$$\lim_{n\to\infty} \frac{\dfrac{1}{\sqrt{n^3+1}}}{\dfrac{1}{\sqrt{n^3}}} = \lim_{n\to\infty} \sqrt{\frac{n^3}{n^3+1}} = 1.$$

17. $\sum_{n=1}^{\infty} \frac{n}{n^2+1}$ diverges by comparison with $\sum_{n=1}^{\infty} \frac{1}{n}$, since

$$\lim_{n\to\infty} \frac{\frac{n}{n^2+1}}{\frac{1}{n}} = \lim_{n\to\infty} \frac{n^2}{n^2+1} = 1.$$

19. $\sum_{n=1}^{\infty} \left(1+\frac{1}{n}\right)^n$ diverges, since $\lim_{n\to\infty} \left(1+\frac{1}{n}\right)^n = e \neq 0$.

21. $\sum_{n=1}^{\infty} \frac{1-n}{n \cdot 2^n}$ converges, because it is the difference of

$\sum_{n=1}^{\infty} \frac{1}{n \cdot 2^n}$ which converges because $\frac{1}{n \cdot 2^n} < \frac{1}{2^n}$ and $\sum_{n=1}^{\infty} \frac{1}{2^n}$.

23. $\sum_{n=1}^{\infty} \frac{1}{3^{n-1}+1}$ converges by comparison to $\sum_{n=1}^{\infty} \frac{1}{3^{n-1}} = \frac{3}{2}$.

25. $\sum_{n=1}^{\infty} \frac{1}{2n-1}$ diverges since $\int_1^{\infty} \frac{dx}{2x-1} = \lim_{t\to\infty} \int_1^t \frac{dx}{2x-1} =$

$$\lim_{t\to\infty} \frac{1}{2} \ln|2x-1| \Big]_1^t = \lim_{t\to\infty} \frac{1}{2}[2t-1] = \infty.$$

27. $S_n \leq 1 + \ln(365 \cdot 24 \cdot 60 \cdot 60 \cdot 13 \cdot 10^9) \approx 41.55$

29. For $n \geq 1$, $\frac{1}{n} \leq 1$ so $\frac{a_n}{n} \leq a_n$. $\therefore \sum_{n=1}^{\infty} \frac{a_n}{n}$ converges if $\sum_{n=1}^{\infty} a_n$ converges.

31. If $\{S_n\}$ is nonincreasing with lower bound M, then $\{-S_n\}$ is a nondecreasing sequence with upper bound -M. By Theorem 1, $\{-S_n\}$ converges, and hence $\{S_n\}$ converges. If $\{S_n\}$ has no lower bound, then $\{-S_n\}$ has no upper bound and diverges. Hence $\{S_n\}$ also diverges.

33. (a) $\sum_{n=2}^{\infty} \frac{1}{n \ln n}$ diverges, since $\sum_{n=2}^{\infty} 2^n \cdot \frac{1}{2^n \ln 2^n} = \sum_{n=2}^{\infty} \frac{1}{n \ln 2}$

$$= \frac{1}{\ln 2} \sum_{n=2}^{\infty} \frac{1}{n} \text{ diverges.}$$

(b) $\sum_{n=1}^{\infty} 2^n \cdot \frac{1}{(2^n)^p} = \sum_{n=1}^{\infty} 2^{n(1-p)}$ converges if $p > 1$ or $1 - p < 0$ and diverges if $p \leq 1$ or $1 - p \geq 0$.

35. Since $\sum_{n=2}^{\infty} \frac{1}{n \ln n}$ diverges, the limit comparison test and the fact that $\lim_{n\to\infty} \frac{n \ln n}{p_n} = 1$ states that $\sum_{n=1}^{\infty} \frac{1}{p_n}$ diverges.

## 11.6 SERIES WITH NONNEGATIVE TERMS: RATIO AND ROOT TESTS

Note: The reasons given fpr convergence may not be the only ones that apply.

1. $\sum_{n=1}^{\infty} \frac{n^2}{2^n}$ converges, since $\lim_{n\to\infty} \left| \frac{(n+1)^2}{2^{n+1}} \cdot \frac{2^n}{n^2} \right| = \lim_{n\to\infty} \frac{1}{2} \cdot \left(\frac{n+1}{n}\right)^2 = \frac{1}{2} < 1$.

3. $\sum_{n=1}^{\infty} \frac{n^{10}}{10^n}$ converges, since $\lim_{n\to\infty} \left(\frac{n^{10}}{10^n}\right)^{\frac{1}{n}} = \frac{1}{10}(1)^{10} = \frac{1}{10} < 1$.

5. $\sum_{n=1}^{\infty} \left(\frac{n-2}{n}\right)^n$ diverges since $\lim_{n\to\infty} \left(\frac{n-2}{n}\right)^n = e^{-2} \neq 0$.

7. $\sum_{n=1}^{\infty} n!e^{-n}$ diverges since $\lim_{n\to\infty} \left| \frac{(n+1)!}{e^{n+1}} \cdot \frac{e^n}{n!} \right| = \lim_{n\to\infty} \frac{n+1}{e} = \infty$.

9. $\sum_{n=1}^{\infty} \left(\frac{n-3}{n}\right)^n$ diverges since $\lim_{n\to\infty} \left(1 - \frac{3}{n}\right)^n = e^{-3} \neq 0$.

11. $\sum_{n=1}^{\infty} \sin\frac{1}{n}$ diverges, since $\lim_{n\to\infty} \frac{\sin\frac{1}{n}}{\frac{1}{n}} = \lim_{n\to\infty} \frac{\left(-\frac{1}{n^2}\right)\cos\frac{1}{n}}{-\frac{1}{n^2}} = \cos 0 = 1$.

13. $\sum_{n=1}^{\infty} \left(1 - \cos\frac{1}{n}\right)$ converges, since $\lim_{n\to\infty} \frac{1 - \cos\frac{1}{n}}{\frac{1}{n^2}} = \lim_{n\to\infty} \frac{\left(-\frac{1}{n^2}\right)\sin\frac{1}{n}}{-\frac{2}{n^3}}$

$= \lim_{n\to\infty} \frac{n \sin\frac{1}{n}}{2} = \frac{1}{2} \lim_{n\to\infty} \frac{\sin\frac{1}{n}}{\frac{1}{n}} = \frac{1}{2}$.

15. $\sum_{n=1}^{\infty} \tan\left(\frac{\ln n}{n}\right)$ diverges, since $\lim_{n\to\infty} \frac{\tan\left(\frac{\ln n}{n}\right)}{\frac{\ln n}{n}}$

$$= \lim_{n\to\infty} \frac{\sec^2\left(\frac{\ln n}{n}\right) D\left(\frac{\ln n}{n}\right)}{D\left(\frac{\ln n}{n}\right)} = \sec^2 0 = 1 \text{ and } \sum_{n=1}^{\infty} \frac{\ln n}{n} \text{ diverges.}$$

17. $\sum_{n=1}^{\infty} \ln \frac{n+2}{n+1} = \sum_{n=1}^{\infty} [\ln(n+2) - \ln(n+1)]$ diverges since

$\ln 3 - \ln 2 + \ln 4 - \ln 3 + \ln 5 - \ln 4 + \ldots + \ln(n+1) - \ln n + \ln(n+2) - \ln(n+1)$

$= -\ln 2 + \ln(n+2) = \infty$

19. $\sum_{n=1}^{\infty} n \sin\left(\frac{1}{n^2}\right)$ diverges, because $\lim_{n\to\infty} \frac{n \sin\left(\frac{1}{n^2}\right)}{\frac{1}{n}}$

$$= \lim_{n\to\infty} \frac{\sin\left(\frac{1}{n^2}\right)}{\frac{1}{n^2}} = \lim_{n\to\infty} \frac{\cos\left(\frac{1}{n^2}\right) D_n(n^{-2})}{D_n(n^{-2})} = \cos 0 = 1$$

21. $\sum_{n=1}^{\infty} \frac{(n+1)(n+2)}{n!}$ converges because

$$\lim_{n\to\infty} \frac{(n+2)(n+3)}{(n+1)!} \cdot \frac{n!}{(n+1)(n+2)} = \lim_{n\to\infty} \frac{n+3}{(n+1)^2} = 0 < 1$$

23. $\sum_{n=1}^{\infty} \frac{(n+3)!}{3!n!3^n}$ converges because

$$\lim_{n\to\infty} \frac{(n+4)!}{3!(n+1)!3^{n+1}} \cdot \frac{3!n!3^n}{(n+3)!} = \lim_{n\to\infty} \frac{n+4}{3(n+1)} = \frac{1}{3} < 1$$

25. $\sum_{n=1}^{\infty} \frac{1}{(2n+1)!}$ converges because $\lim_{n\to\infty} \frac{(2n+1)!}{(2n+3)!} =$

$$\lim_{n\to\infty} \frac{1}{(2n+2)(2n+3)} = 0 < 1$$

27. $\sum_{n=1}^{\infty} \frac{|nx^n|}{2^n}$ converges for $-2 < x < 2$, because:

$$\lim_{n\to\infty} \left| \frac{(n+1)x^{n+1}}{2^{n+1}} \cdot \frac{2^n}{nx^n} \right| = \lim_{n\to\infty} \frac{n+1}{n} \cdot \frac{1}{2} \cdot |x| < 1 \Leftrightarrow |x| < 2$$

If $x = \pm 2$, $\sum_{n=1}^{\infty} |n|$ diverges because $\lim_{n\to\infty} |n| = \infty$.

29. $\sum_{n=1}^{\infty}\left(\frac{x^2+1}{3}\right)^n$ converges for $-\sqrt{2} < x < \sqrt{2}$, because a geometric series converges for $|r| < 1$. $\frac{x^2+1}{3} < 1 \Leftrightarrow x^2+1 < 3 \Leftrightarrow x^2 < 2$ or $|x| < \sqrt{2}$

31. $\sum_{n=1}^{\infty}\frac{x^{2n+1}}{n^2}$ converges for $-1 \le x \le 1$ because:

$$\lim_{n\to\infty}\frac{x^{2n+3}}{(n+1)^2}\cdot\frac{n^2}{x^{2n+1}} = \lim_{n\to\infty}\left(\frac{n}{n+1}\right)^2\cdot x^2 < 1 \Leftrightarrow |x| < 1$$

If $x = 1$, $\sum_{n=1}^{\infty}\frac{1}{n^2}$ converges, and if $x = -1$, $\sum_{n=1}^{\infty}\frac{(-1)^{2n+1}}{n^2}$ converges.

33. Converges, because $\lim_{n\to\infty}\left|\frac{a_{n+1}}{a_n}\right| = \lim_{n\to\infty}\left|\frac{\frac{(1+\sin n)a_n}{n}}{a_n}\right| = \lim_{n\to\infty}\frac{1+\sin n}{n} = 0 < 1$

35. Diverges, because $a_1 = 3$, $a_2 = \frac{3}{2}$, $a_3 = 1$, $a_4 = \frac{3}{4}$, ... is the series $\sum_{n=1}^{\infty}\frac{3}{n}$.

37. Converges, because $\lim_{n\to\infty}\left|\frac{a_{n+1}}{a_n}\right| = \lim_{n\to\infty}\left|\frac{(1+\ln n)a_n}{na_n}\right| = \lim_{n\to\infty}\frac{1+\ln n}{n} = \lim_{n\to\infty}\frac{\frac{1}{n}}{1} = 0 < 1$

39. $\sum_{n=1}^{\infty}\frac{2^n n!n!}{(2n)!}$ converges, because $\lim_{n\to\infty}\frac{2^{n+1}(n+1)!(n+1)!}{(2n+2)!}\cdot\frac{(2n)!}{2^n n!n!}$

$$= \lim_{n\to\infty}\frac{2(n+1)^2}{(2n+1)(2n+2)} = \frac{1}{2} < 1.$$

41. $a_1 = 1$; $a_2 = \frac{1\cdot 2}{3\cdot 4}$; $a_3 = \frac{2\cdot 3}{4\cdot 5}\frac{1\cdot 2}{3\cdot 4}$; $a_4 = \frac{3\cdot 4}{5\cdot 6}\cdot\frac{2\cdot 3}{4\cdot 5}\frac{1\cdot 2}{3\cdot 4}$;

$a_5 = \frac{4\cdot 5}{6\cdot 7}\frac{3\cdot 4}{5\cdot 6}\cdot\frac{2\cdot 3}{4\cdot 5}\frac{1\cdot 2}{3\cdot 4}$; $a_n = \frac{12}{(n+1)(n+3)(n+2)^2}$

$\sum_{n=1}^{\infty}\frac{12}{(n+1)(n+3)(n+2)^2}$ converges by comparison with $\sum_{n=1}^{\infty}\frac{12}{n^4}$

## 11.7 ABSOLUTE CONVERGENCE

1. $\sum_{n=1}^{\infty}\frac{1}{n^2}$ converges absolutely, p-series with $p = 2 > 1$.

3. $\sum_{n=1}^{\infty}\left|\frac{1-n}{n^2}\right|$ diverges, since it can be expressed as

$\sum_{n=1}^{\infty}\frac{1}{n^2}$ which converges, and $\left(-\sum_{n=1}^{\infty}\frac{1}{n}\right)$ which diverges.

5. $\sum_{n=1}^{\infty}\frac{-1}{n^2+2n+1}$ converges absolutely, since $\sum_{n=1}^{\infty}\frac{1}{(n+1)^2}$

converges by comparison to $\sum_{n=1}^{\infty}\frac{1}{n^2}$.

7. $\sum_{n=1}^{\infty}\frac{|\cos n\pi|}{n\sqrt{n}} = \sum_{n=1}^{\infty}\frac{1}{n^{3/2}}$ is a p-series for $p = \frac{3}{2} > 1$ and hence

converges. Therefore $\sum_{n=1}^{\infty}\frac{\cos n\pi}{n\sqrt{n}}$ converges absolutely.

9. $\sum_{n=1}^{\infty}\frac{(-1)^n}{(2n)!}$ converges absolutely, since $\lim_{n\to\infty}\left|\frac{(-1)^{n+1}}{(2n+2)!}\cdot\frac{(2n)!}{(-1)^n}\right| =$

$\lim_{n\to\infty}\frac{1}{(2n+2)(2n+1)} = 0 < 1.$

11. $\sum_{n=1}^{\infty}\left|(-1)^n\frac{n}{n+1}\right|$ is divergent, since $\lim_{n\to\infty}\frac{n}{n+1} \neq 0$.

13. $\sum_{n=1}^{\infty}(5)^{-n}$ converges, geometric series with $r = \frac{1}{5} < 1$

15. $\sum_{n=1}^{\infty}\frac{(-100)^n}{n!}$ converges absolutely, since $\lim_{n\to\infty}\left|\frac{(-100)^{n+1}}{(n+1)!}\cdot\frac{n!}{(-100)^n}\right|$

$= \lim_{n\to\infty} 100\cdot\frac{1}{n+1} = 0 < 1$

17. $\sum_{n=1}^{\infty}\frac{2-n}{n^3} = 1 + \sum_{n=2}^{\infty}\frac{n-2}{n^3}$ converges absolutely, because $\sum_{n=2}^{\infty}\frac{1}{n^2}$ is a

p-series, $p = 2 > 1$, and $-2\sum_{n=2}^{\infty}\frac{1}{n^3}$ is a multiple of a p-series, $p=3 > 1$.

19. Since $|a_n| \geq a_n$, if $\sum_{1}^{\infty}a_n$ diverges then $\sum_{1}^{\infty}|a_n|$ must diverge.

21. Let $\sum_1^{\infty} a_n$ and $\sum_1^{\infty} b_n$ converge absolutely. Then

(a) $|a_n + b_n| \le |a_n| + |b_n| \Rightarrow \sum_1^{\infty} |a_n + b_n| \le \sum_1^{\infty} |a_n| + \sum_1^{\infty} |b_n|$

and hence $\sum_1^{\infty} (a_n + b_n)$ converges absolutely.

(b) $|a_n - b_n| = |a_n + (-b_n)| \le |a_n| + |-b_n| = |a_n| + |b_n|$.

Hence $\sum_1^{\infty} |a_n - b_n|$ converges and $\sum_1^{\infty} (a_n - b_n)$ converges absolutely.

(c) $|ka_n| = |k||a_n| \Rightarrow \sum_1^{\infty} |ka_n| = |k| \sum_1^{\infty} |a_n|$ converges. Hence

$\sum_1^{\infty} ka_n$ converges absolutely.

## 11.8 ALTERNATING SERIES AND CONDITIONAL CONVERGENCE

1. $\sum_{n=1}^{\infty} (-1)^{n+1} \frac{1}{n^2}$ converges because it converges absolutely, since

$\sum_{n=1}^{\infty} \frac{1}{n^2}$ converges (p–series for $p = 2 > 1$).

3. $\sum_{n=1}^{\infty} (-1)^{n-1} = \sum_{n=1}^{\infty} (-1)^{n-1}(1)$ diverges, since $\lim_{n\to\infty} (1) = 1 \neq 0$.

5. $\sum_{n=1}^{\infty} (-1)^{n+1} \frac{\sqrt{n}+1}{n+1}$ converges since $\lim_{n\to\infty} \frac{\sqrt{n}+1}{n+1} = \lim_{n\to\infty} \frac{\frac{1}{\sqrt{n}} + \frac{1}{n}}{1 + \frac{1}{\sqrt{n}}} = 0$

and $\left\{\frac{\sqrt{n}+1}{n+1}\right\}$ is a decreasing sequence.

7. $\sum_{n=1}^{\infty} (-1)^{n+1} \frac{1}{n^{3/2}}$ converges since it converges absolutely.

9. $\sum_{n=1}^{\infty}(-1)^n \ln\left(1+\frac{1}{n}\right)$ converges because $\lim_{n\to\infty} \ln\left(1+\frac{1}{n}\right) = \ln 1 = 0$.

If $f(x) = \ln\left(1+\frac{1}{x}\right)$ then $f'(x) = \frac{x}{x+1}\cdot\frac{x(1)-(x+1)(1)}{x^2} =$

$\frac{-1}{x(x+1)} < 0$ for $x > 1$. Hence $\left\{\ln\left(1+\frac{1}{n}\right)\right\}$ is decreasing.

11. $\sum_{n=1}^{\infty}(-1)^{n-1}(0.1)^n$ converges absolutely because it is a geometric series with $r = .1 < 1$.

13. $\sum_{n=1}^{\infty}(-1)^{n+1}\frac{n}{n^3+1}$ converges absolutely by comparison with $\sum_{n=1}^{\infty}\frac{1}{n^2}$, since $n^3 \le n^3 + 1 \Rightarrow \frac{1}{n^3+1} \le \frac{1}{n^3} \Rightarrow \frac{n}{n^3+1} \le \frac{n}{n^3} = \frac{1}{n^2}$

15. $\sum_{n=1}^{\infty}(-1)^{n+1}\frac{1}{n+3}$ converges conditionally, since $\left\{\frac{1}{n+3}\right\}$ is a decreasing sequence with limit 0, but $\sum_{n=1}^{\infty}\frac{1}{n+3}$ diverges.

17. $\sum_{n=1}^{\infty}(-1)^{n+1}\frac{3+n}{5+n}$ diverges since $\lim_{n\to\infty}\frac{3+n}{5+n} = 1 \ne 0$.

19. $\sum_{n=1}^{\infty}(-1)^{n+1}\frac{1+n}{n^2}$ converges conditionally, since $\left\{\frac{1+n}{n^2}\right\}$ is a decreasing sequence converging to 0. But the series $\sum_{n=1}^{\infty}\frac{1+n}{n^2}$ diverges by comparison to $\sum_{n=1}^{\infty}\frac{1}{n}$ since $\lim_{n\to\infty}\frac{\frac{1+n}{n^2}}{\frac{1}{n}} = \lim_{n\to\infty}\frac{1+n}{n} = 1$.

21. $\sum_{n=1}^{\infty} n^2\left(\frac{2}{3}\right)^n$ converges absolutely since $\lim_{n\to\infty}\frac{(n+1)^2\left(\frac{2}{3}\right)^{n+1}}{n^2\left(\frac{2}{3}\right)^2}$

$= \lim_{n\to\infty}\frac{2}{3}\cdot\left(\frac{n+1}{n}\right)^2 = 1$.

23. $\sum_{n=1}^{\infty}(-1)^n\frac{\tan^{-1}n}{n^2+1}$ converges absolutely, since $|\tan^{-1}n| < \frac{\pi}{2}$

$$\Rightarrow \sum_{n=1}^{\infty}\left|\frac{\tan^{-1}n}{n^2+1}\right| \le \frac{\pi}{2}\sum_{n=1}^{\infty}\frac{1}{n^2+1} \le \frac{\pi}{2}\sum_{n=1}^{\infty}\frac{1}{n^2}.$$

25. $\sum_{n=1}^{\infty}\left(\frac{1}{n}-\frac{1}{2n}\right) = \frac{1}{2}\sum_{n=1}^{\infty}\frac{1}{n}$ diverges.

27. $\sum_{n=1}^{\infty}(-1)^{n+1}(\sqrt{n+1}-\sqrt{n})$ converges conditionally since:

$\frac{\sqrt{n+1}-\sqrt{n}}{1}\cdot\frac{\sqrt{n+1}+\sqrt{n}}{\sqrt{n+1}+\sqrt{n}} = \frac{1}{\sqrt{n+1}+\sqrt{n}}$ and $\left\{\frac{1}{\sqrt{n+1}+\sqrt{n}}\right\}$ is a decreasing sequence which converges to 0. But $\frac{1}{\sqrt{n+1}+\sqrt{n}} \ge \frac{1}{3\sqrt{n}}$

so $\sum_{n=1}^{\infty}\frac{1}{\sqrt{n+1}+\sqrt{n}}$ diverges.

29. $a_5 = \frac{1}{5}$; error $\le 0.2$

31. $a_5 = \frac{(10^{-10})}{5}$; error $\le 2 \times 10^{-11}$

33. If $n = 5$, $\frac{1}{9!} = .0000028 = 2.8 \times 10^{-6}$. Therefore the sum of the first 4 terms is sufficiently accurate.

$1 - \frac{1}{2!} + \frac{1}{4!} - \frac{1}{4!} + \frac{1}{8!} = 0.540302579.$

35. (a) The condition $a_n \ge a_{n+1}$ is not met.

(b) $S = \frac{\frac{1}{3}}{1-\frac{1}{3}} - \frac{\frac{1}{2}}{1-\frac{1}{2}} = \frac{1}{2} - 1 = -\frac{1}{2}$

37. $\sum_{j=n+1}^{\infty}(-1)^{j+1}a_j = (-1)^{n+1}(a_{n+1}-a_{n+2}) + (-1)^{n+3}(a_{n+3}-a_{n+4}) + \ldots$

$= (-1)^{n+1}(a_{n+1}-a_{n+2}) + (a_{n+3}-a_{n+4}) + \ldots$

Each grouped term is positive, so the remainder has the same sign as $(-1)^{n+1}$, which is the sign of the first unused term.

39. Let $a_n = b_n = (-1)^n\frac{1}{\sqrt{n}}$. Then $\sum_{1}^{\infty}(-1)^n\frac{1}{\sqrt{n}}$ converges but

$\sum_{1}^{\infty}a_nb_n = \sum_{1}^{\infty}\frac{1}{n}$ diverges.

41. The rearranged sequences of partial sums would be:

$-\frac{1}{2}$ with $S_1 = -\frac{1}{2}$

$-\frac{1}{2} + 1$ with $S_2 = \frac{1}{2}$

$-\frac{1}{2} + 1 - \frac{1}{4} - \frac{1}{6} - \frac{1}{8}$ with $S_5 = -\frac{1}{24}$

$-\frac{1}{2} + 1 - \frac{1}{4} - \frac{1}{6} - \frac{1}{8} + \frac{1}{3} + \frac{1}{5} + \frac{1}{7}$ with $S_8 = \frac{498}{840}$

## 11.9 RECAPITULATION

1. $\sum_{n=1}^{\infty}(-1)^{n-1}\frac{1}{\ln(n+1)}$ converges since $\lim_{n\to\infty}\frac{1}{\ln(n+1)} = 0$ and $\frac{1}{\ln(n+2)} \le \frac{1}{\ln(n+1)}$ for all n.

3. This is the series $\sum_{n+1}^{\infty}(-1)^{n+1}\frac{1}{n}$ which converges.

5. Diverges, because $\lim_{n\to\infty}\frac{(n+1)^{n+1}}{(n+1)!}\cdot\frac{n!}{n^n} = \lim_{n\to\infty}\frac{(n+1)^n(n+1)}{(n+1)n!}\cdot\frac{n!}{n^n}$

$= \lim_{n\to\infty}\left(\frac{n+1}{n}\right)^n = e > 1$

7. Converges, because $\lim_{n\to\infty}\frac{(n+1)^2}{2^{n+1}}\cdot\frac{2^n}{n^2} = \frac{1}{2} < 1.$

9. Converges; it is the geometric series $\sum_{n=1}^{\infty}\left(\frac{1}{2}\right)^n.$

11. Diverges; it is the series $2\sum_{n=1}^{\infty}\frac{1}{n}.$

13. Diverges; $a_n \le 1 \Rightarrow 1 + a_n \le 2 \Rightarrow \frac{1}{1+a_n} \ge \frac{1}{2}$. Thus $\lim_{n\to\infty} a_{n+1} \ne 0.$

15. Diverges; $\lim_{n\to\infty} na_n = \infty \ne 0.$

17. Diverges; $\lim_{n\to\infty} a_n \ne 0$ since $a_n$ = either +1 or −1.

19. Converges by comparison to $\sum_{n=1}^{\infty}\frac{1}{n^2}$ since $|\sin n| \le 1.$

21. (a) Let $t_1 = c_1$, $t_2 = c_1 + c_2 \Rightarrow c_2 = t_2 - t_1$, $t_3 = c_1 + c_2 + c_3 \Rightarrow$

$c_3 = t_3 - (c_1 + c_2) = t_3 - t_2$, and in general, $t_n - t_{n-1} = \sum_{k=1}^{n} c_k$.

$$s_{2n+1} = \sum_{k=1}^{2n+1} \frac{c_k}{k} = c_1(1) + c_2\left(\frac{1}{2}\right) + \ldots + c_{2n+1}\left(\frac{1}{2n+1}\right)$$

$$= t_1(1) + \frac{1}{2}(t_2 - t_1) + \ldots + t_{2n}\left(\frac{1}{2n} - \frac{1}{2n+1}\right) + t_{2n+1}\left(\frac{1}{2n+1}\right)$$

$$= \sum_{k=1}^{2n} \frac{t_k}{k(k+1)} + \frac{t_{2n+1}}{2n+1}$$

$\sum_{k=1}^{2n} \left| \frac{t_k}{k(k+1)} \right| \le M \sum_{k=1}^{2n} \frac{1}{k(k+1)}$ converges absolutely, and $\lim_{n\to\infty} \frac{t_{2n+1}}{2n+1} = 0$,

so $\lim_{n\to\infty} s_{2n+1}$ exists. If $s_{2n} = \sum_{k=1}^{2n} \frac{c_k}{k}$, then $\lim_{n\to\infty} (s_{2n+1} - s_{2n})$

$= \lim_{n\to\infty} \frac{c_{2n+1}}{2n+1} = 0$, so $\sum_{k=1}^{\infty} \frac{c_k}{k}$ converges to $\sum_{k=1}^{\infty} \frac{t_k}{k(k+1)}$.

$$= t_1(1) + \frac{1}{2}(t_2 - t_1) + \ldots + t_{2n}\left(\frac{1}{2n} - \frac{1}{2n+1}\right) + t_{2n+1}\left(\frac{1}{2n+1}\right)$$

$$= \sum_{k=1}^{2n} \frac{t_k}{k(k+1)} + \frac{t_{2n+1}}{2n+1}$$

(b) In $\sum_{n=1}^{\infty} (-1)^{n+1}\frac{1}{n}$, take $\{c_k\} = \{1, -1, 1, -1, \ldots\}$ so that

$\sum_{k=1}^{n} c_k \le 1$, so that the alternating harmonic series converges.

(c) If $\{c_k\} = \{1, -1, -1, 1, 1, -1, -1, 1, 1, \ldots\}$ then $\sum_{k=1}^{n} c_k \le 1$, so

the series converges.

## 11.10 ESTIMATING THE SUM OF A SERIES

3. The ratios $\frac{a_{n+1}}{a_n} = \frac{n+1}{3n}$ form a decreasing sequence which converges to $\frac{1}{3}$. Take $r_1 = \frac{1}{3}$ and $r_2 = \frac{N+1}{3N}$.

(a) $\frac{10}{3^{10}}\cdot\frac{\frac{1}{3}}{1-\frac{1}{3}} \le R_{10} \le \frac{10}{3^{10}}\cdot\frac{\frac{11}{30}}{1-\frac{11}{30}}$; $8.47\times10^{-5} \le R_{10} \le 1.07\times10^{-5}$

(b) $\frac{100}{3^{100}}\cdot\frac{\frac{1}{3}}{1-\frac{1}{3}} \le R_{100} \le \frac{100}{3^{100}}\cdot\frac{\frac{101}{300}}{1-\frac{101}{300}}$; $9.70\times10^{-47} \le R_{100} \le 9.85\times10^{-47}$

## 11.M MISCELLANEOUS

1. $$\sum_{k=2}^{n} \ln\left(1-\frac{1}{k^2}\right) = \sum_{k=2}^{n}\left[\ln\left(1+\frac{1}{k}\right)+\ln\left(1-\frac{1}{k}\right)\right] =$$

$$\sum_{k=2}^{n}[\ln(k+1)-\ln k+\ln(k-1)-\ln k] = \ln(n+1)-\ln n-\ln 2$$

$$= \ln\frac{n+1}{2n}. \quad \therefore \lim_{n\to\infty}\ln\frac{n+1}{2n} = \ln\frac{1}{2}.$$

3. $$\sum_{n=1}^{\infty}(x_{n+1}-x_n) = \lim_{n\to\infty}\sum_{j=1}^{n}(x_{j+1}-x_j) = \lim_{n\to\infty}(x_{n+1}-x_1) =$$

$\left(\lim_{n\to\infty} x_{n+1}\right) - x_1$. Therefore, the series and the sequence either both converge or both diverge.

5. $\frac{1}{1-x} = -\frac{\frac{1}{x}}{1-\frac{1}{x}}$. Using $a = r = \frac{1}{x}$, this equals

$-\left(\frac{1}{x}+\frac{1}{x^2}+\frac{1}{x^3}+\ldots+\frac{1}{x^n}+\ldots\right)$ for $\frac{1}{|x|} < 1$ or $|x| > 1$.

7. $\sum_{n=1}^{\infty}(-1)^n \tanh n$ diverges because:

$$\lim_{n\to\infty}\tanh n = \lim_{n\to\infty}\frac{\sinh n}{\cosh n} = \lim_{n\to\infty}\frac{e^x-e^{-x}}{e^x+e^{-x}} = \lim_{n\to\infty}\frac{e^{2x}-1}{e^{2x}+1} = \lim_{n\to\infty}\frac{2e^{2x}}{2e^{2x}} = 1 \ne 0$$

9. $\sum_{n=1}^{\infty}\frac{n}{2(n+1)(n+2)}$ diverges because $\sum_{n=1}^{\infty}\frac{1}{n}$ diverges and

$$\lim_{n\to\infty}\frac{\frac{n}{2(n+1)(n+2)}}{\frac{1}{n}} = \lim_{n\to\infty}\frac{n^2}{2(n^2+3n+2)} = \frac{1}{2}$$

11. $\sum_{n=2}^{\infty} \frac{1}{n(\ln n)^2}$ converges because $\int_2^{\infty} \frac{dx}{x(\ln x)^2} = \lim_{t\to\infty} \int_2^t \frac{dx}{x(\ln x)^2}$

$= \lim_{t\to\infty}\left[-\frac{1}{\ln x}\right]_2^t = \lim_{t\to\infty}\left[-\frac{1}{\ln t} + \frac{1}{\ln 2}\right] = \frac{1}{\ln 2}$

13. $\sum_{n=1}^{\infty} \frac{n}{1000n^2 + 1}$ diverges by comparison to $\sum_{n=1}^{\infty} \frac{1}{n}$, since

$\lim_{n\to\infty} \frac{n}{1000n^2 + 1} \cdot \frac{n}{1} = \frac{1}{1000}$

15. $\sum_{n=1}^{\infty} \frac{1}{n\sqrt{n^2+1}}$ converges by comparison to $\sum_{n=1}^{\infty} \frac{1}{n^2}$ because $\lim_{n\to\infty} \frac{1}{n\sqrt{n^2+1}} \cdot \frac{n^2}{1} = 1$

17. Diverges, because $\frac{1\cdot 3\cdot 5\cdot \ldots \cdot(2n-1)}{2\cdot 4\cdot 6\cdot \ldots \cdot(2n)} \geq \frac{1\cdot 2\cdot 4\cdot \ldots \cdot(2n-2)}{2\cdot 4\cdot 6\cdot \ldots \cdot(2n)} = \frac{1}{2n}$

and $\frac{1}{2}\sum_{n=1}^{\infty} \frac{1}{n}$ diverges.

19. $\sum_{n=1}^{\infty} \frac{n+1}{n!}$ converges because $\lim_{n\to\infty} \frac{n+2}{(n+1)!} \cdot \frac{n!}{n+1} = 0 < 1$

21. (a) $\sum_{n=1}^{\infty} \frac{a_n}{n} = a_1 + \frac{1}{2}a_2 + \frac{1}{3}a_3 + \frac{1}{4}a_4 + \frac{1}{5}a_5 + \frac{1}{6}a_6 + \ldots + \frac{1}{n}a_n + \ldots$

$\geq a_1 + \frac{1}{2}a_2 + \frac{1}{3}a_4 + \frac{1}{4}a_4 + \frac{1}{5}a_8 + \frac{1}{6}a_8 + \frac{1}{7}a_8 + \frac{1}{8}a_8 + \ldots + \frac{1}{n}a_n + \ldots$

$= a_1 + \frac{1}{2}a_2 + \left(\frac{1}{3} + \frac{1}{4}\right)a_4 + \left(\frac{1}{5} + \frac{1}{6} + \frac{1}{7} + \frac{1}{8}\right)a_8 + \left(\frac{1}{9} + \frac{1}{10} + \ . + \frac{1}{16}\right)a_{16} + ..$

$\geq \frac{1}{2}(a_2 + a_4 + a_8 + a_{16} + \ldots)$ which diverges.

(b) Let $a_n = \frac{1}{\ln n}$, $n \geq 2$. Then

(i) $a_2 \geq a_3 \geq a_4 \geq \ldots$ and

(ii) $\frac{1}{\ln 2} + \frac{1}{\ln 4} + \frac{1}{\ln 8} + \frac{1}{\ln 16} + .. = \frac{1}{\ln 2} + \frac{1}{2\ln 2} + \frac{1}{3\ln 2} + \frac{1}{4\ln 4} + ..$

$= \frac{1}{\ln 2}\left(1 + \frac{1}{2} + \frac{1}{3} + \frac{1}{4} + \ldots\right)$ which diverges.

By part (a), $1 + \sum_{n=2}^{\infty} \frac{1}{n\ln n}$ diverges.

23. $\sum_{n=3}^{\infty} \frac{1}{n\ln n\,(\ln(\ln n))^p}$ converges since $\int_3^{\infty} \frac{dx}{x\ln x\,(\ln(\ln x))^p} =$

$\frac{1}{-p+1}(\ln(\ln x))^{-p+1}\Big]_3^{\infty}$ converges only for $p < 1$.

# CHAPTER 12

# POWER SERIES

## 12.2 TAYLOR POLYNOMIALS

1.

| n | $f^n(x)$ | $f^n(0)$ |
|---|---|---|
| 0 | $e^{-x}$ | 1 |
| 1 | $-e^{-x}$ | -1 |
| 2 | $e^{-x}$ | 1 |
| 3 | $-e^{-x}$ | -1 |
| 4 | $e^{-x}$ | 1 |

$$P_3(x) = 1 - x + \frac{x^2}{2} - \frac{x^3}{6}$$

$$P_4(x) = 1 - x + \frac{x^2}{2} - \frac{x^3}{6} + \frac{x^4}{24}$$

3.

| n | $f^n(x)$ | $f^n(0)$ |
|---|---|---|
| 0 | cosx | 1 |
| 1 | -sinx | 0 |
| 2 | -cosx | -1 |
| 3 | sinx | 0 |
| 4 | cosx | 1 |

$$P_3(x) = 1 - \frac{x^2}{2}$$

$$P_4(x) = 1 - \frac{x^2}{2} + \frac{x^4}{24}$$

5.

| n | $f^n(x)$ | $f^n(0)$ |
|---|---|---|
| 0 | sinhx | 0 |
| 1 | coshx | 1 |
| 2 | sinhx | 0 |
| 3 | coshx | 1 |
| 4 | sinhx | 0 |

$$P_3(x) = x + \frac{x^3}{6}$$

$$P_4(x) = x + \frac{x^3}{6}$$

7.

| n | $f^n(x)$ | $f^n(0)$ |
|---|---|---|
| 0 | $x^4 - 2x + 1$ | 1 |
| 1 | $4x^3 - 2$ | -2 |
| 2 | $12x^2$ | 0 |
| 3 | $24x$ | 0 |
| 4 | 24 | 24 |

$$P_3(x) = 1 - 2x$$

$$P_4(x) = 1 - 2x + x^4$$

9.

| n | $f^n(x)$ | $f^n(0)$ |
|---|---|---|
| 0 | $x^2 - 2x + 1$ | 1 |
| 1 | $2x - 2$ | -2 |
| 2 | 2 | 2 |
| 3 | 0 | 0 |
| 4 | 0 | 0 |

$$P_3(x) = 1 - 2x + x^2$$

$$P_4(x) = P_3(x)$$

11. $f(x) = x^2;\ f'(x) = 2x; f''(x) = 2;\ f^n(x) = 0$ for $n > 2$
$f(0) = 0; f'(0) = 0; f''(0) = 2$

$$x^2 = 0 + 0x + \frac{2}{2}x^2 + 0 + \ldots = x^2$$

13. $f(x) = (1+x)^{\frac{3}{2}}$ $\qquad f(0) = 1$

$f'(x) = \frac{3}{2}(1+x)^{\frac{1}{2}}$ $\qquad f'(0) = \frac{3}{2}$

$f''(x) = \frac{1}{2}\cdot\frac{3}{2}(1+x)^{-\frac{1}{2}}$ $\qquad f''(0) = \frac{1\cdot 3}{2^2}$

$f'''(x) = -\frac{1}{2}\cdot\frac{1}{2}\cdot\frac{3}{2}(1+x)^{-\frac{3}{2}}$ $\qquad f'''(0) = \frac{(-1)\cdot 1\cdot 3}{2^3}$

$f^4(x) = \frac{3\cdot 1\cdot(-1)(-3)}{2^4}(1+x)^{-\frac{5}{2}}$ $\qquad f^4(x) = \frac{3\cdot 1\cdot(-1)(-3)}{2^4}$

$$f(x) = 1 + \sum_{n=1}^{\infty} \frac{(5-2n)}{n!2^n}x^n$$

15. $f(x) = e^{10} + e^{10}(x-10) + \frac{e^{10}}{2!}(x-10)^2 + ..$

$$= \sum_{n=0}^{\infty} \frac{e^{10}}{n!}(x-10)^n$$

17.

| n | $f^n(x)$ | $f^n(1)$ |
|---|---|---|
| 0 | ln x | 0 |
| 1 | $x^{-1}$ | 1 |
| 2 | $-x^{-2}$ | -1 |
| 3 | $2x^{-3}$ | 2 |
| 4 | $-3\cdot 2x^{-4}$ | -6 |

$$\ln x = \ln 1 + \frac{1}{1}(x-1) - \frac{1}{1^2\cdot 2}(x-1)^2 + \frac{2}{1^3\cdot 3!}(x-1)^3 - \ldots$$

$$= \sum_{n=1}^{\infty}(-1)^{n-1}\frac{(x-1)^n}{n}$$

19.

| n | $f^n(x)$ | $f^n(-1)$ |
|---|---|---|
| 0 | $x^{-1}$ | -1 |
| 1 | $-x^{-2}$ | -1 |
| 2 | $2x^{-3}$ | -2 |
| 3 | $-3\cdot 2x^{-4}$ | -6 |
| 4 | $4\cdot 3\cdot 2x^{-5}$ | -24 |

$$f(x) = -\sum_{n=0}^{\infty}(x+1)^n$$

21. $f(x) = \tan x$ $\qquad f(\frac{\pi}{4}) = 1$

$f'(x) = \sec^2 x$ $\qquad f'(\frac{\pi}{4}) = 2$

$f''(x) = 2\sec^2 x\tan x$ $\qquad f''(\frac{\pi}{4}) = 4$

$\tan x = 1 + 2(x - \frac{\pi}{4}) + 2(x - \frac{\pi}{4})^2 + \ldots$

## 12.3 TAYLOR'S THEOREM WITH REMAINDER: SINES, COSINES, AND $e^x$

1. $e^{\frac{x}{2}} = \sum_{n=0}^{\infty}\left(\frac{x}{2}\right)^n \cdot \frac{1}{n!} = \sum_{n=0}^{\infty} \frac{x^n}{2^n n!}$

3. $5\cos\frac{x}{\pi} = 5\sum_{n=0}^{\infty}(-1)^n\left(\frac{x}{\pi}\right)^{2n}\frac{1}{(2n)!} = 5\sum_{n=0}^{\infty}(-1)^n\frac{x^{2n}}{\pi^{2n}(2n)!}$

5. $\frac{x^2}{2} - 1 + \cos x = \frac{x^2}{2} - 1 + 1 - \frac{x^2}{2} + \frac{x^4}{4!} - \ldots = \sum_{n=2}^{\infty}(-1)^n\frac{x^{2n}}{(2n)!}$

7. (a) $\cos(-x) = \sum_{n=0}^{\infty}(-1)^n\frac{(-x)^{2n}}{(2n)!} = \sum_{n=0}^{\infty}(-1)^n\frac{x^{2n}}{(2n)!} = \cos x$

(b) $\sin(-x) = \sum_{n=0}^{\infty}(-1)^n\frac{(-x)^{2n+1}}{(2n+1)!} = -\sum_{n=0}^{\infty}(-1)^n\frac{x^{2n+1}}{(2n+1)!} = -\sin x$

9. Using the formula for a geometric series with a = 1 and r = -x:

$\frac{1}{1+x} = 1 - x + x^2 + R_n(x)$

11. $f(x) = (1+x)^{\frac{1}{2}}$; $f(0) = 1$; $f'(x) = \frac{1}{2}(1+x)^{-\frac{1}{2}}$; $f'(0) = \frac{1}{2}$

$f''(x) = -\frac{1}{4}(1+x)^{-\frac{3}{2}}$; $f''(0) = -\frac{1}{4}$

$(1+x)^{\frac{1}{2}} \approx 1 + \frac{1}{2}x - \frac{1}{8}x^2 + R_n(x)$

13. $\left|\frac{x^5}{5!}\right| < 5\times10^{-4} \Leftrightarrow |x^5| < 120\cdot5\times10^{-4} = .06 \Leftrightarrow |x| < 0.5697$

15. (a) $R_2(x) = \frac{-\cos c}{3!}x^3$. $\therefore |R_2(x)| = \frac{\cos c}{6}|x|^3$. If $|x| < 10^{-3}$,

then $|R_2(x)| \le \frac{1}{6}(10^{-3})^3 < 1.67 \times 10^{-10}$.

(b) $-10^{-3} < x < 10^{-3} \Rightarrow \cos c > 0 \Rightarrow -\cos c < 0$.

If $-10^{-3} < x < 0$, $\frac{-\cos c}{3!}x^3 < 0 \Rightarrow x > \sin x$

If $10^{-3} > x > 0$, $\frac{-\cos c}{3!}x^3 > 0 \Rightarrow \sin x > x$

17. If $|x| < 0.1$, then $e^c < e^{.1}$. Therefore,

$|R_2(x)| \le \frac{e^{.1}(.1)^3}{3!} < 0.000184$.

19. $|R_4(x)| \le \frac{|\sinh c||x^5|}{5!} = \frac{.521(0.5)^5}{5!} < 0.0003$

21. $(f+g)(x) = \sum_{n=0}^{\infty}\frac{(f+g)^n(0)}{n!}x^n = \sum_{n=0}^{\infty}\frac{f^n(0)+g^n(0)}{n!}x^n$.

23. (a) $e^{i\pi} = \cos\pi + i\sin\pi = -1 + 0i$

(b) $e^{\frac{i\pi}{4}} = \cos\frac{\pi}{4} + i\sin\frac{\pi}{4} = \frac{\sqrt{2}}{2} + \frac{\sqrt{2}}{2}i$

(c) $e^{-\frac{i\pi}{2}} = \cos\left(-\frac{\pi}{2}\right) + i\sin\left(-\frac{\pi}{2}\right) = 0 - i$

(d) $e^{i\pi} \cdot e^{-\frac{i\pi}{2}} = e^{\frac{i\pi}{2}} = \cos\frac{\pi}{2} + i\sin\frac{\pi}{2} = 0 + i$

25. $\cos^3\theta = \left(\frac{e^{i\theta} + e^{-i\theta}}{2}\right)^3 = \frac{1}{8}(e^{3i\theta} + 3e^{2i\theta}e^{-i\theta} + 3e^{i\theta}e^{-2i\theta} + e^{-3i\theta})$

$= \frac{1}{8}(\cos3\theta + i\sin3\theta + 3[\cos\theta + i\sin\theta] + 3[\cos(-\theta) + i\sin(-\theta)] + \cos(-3\theta) + i\sin(-3\theta))$

$= \frac{1}{8}(2\cos3\theta + 6\cos\theta) = \frac{1}{4}\cos3\theta + \frac{3}{4}\cos\theta$

$\sin^3\theta = \left(\frac{e^{i\theta} - e^{-i\theta}}{2i}\right)^3 = \frac{1}{8i^3}(e^{3i\theta} - 3e^{2i\theta}e^{-i\theta} + 3e^{i\theta}e^{-2i\theta} - e^{-3i\theta})$

$= -\frac{1}{8i}(\cos3\theta + i\sin3\theta - 3[\cos\theta + i\sin\theta] + 3[\cos(-\theta) + i\sin(-\theta)] - \cos(-3\theta) - i\sin(-3\theta))$

$= -\frac{1}{8i}(2i\sin3\theta - 6i\sin\theta) = -\frac{1}{4}\sin3\theta + \frac{3}{4}\sin\theta$

27. $\int e^{(a+ib)x}dx = \frac{1}{a+ib}e^{(a+ib)x} + C = \frac{a-ib}{a^2+b^2}e^{(a+ib)x} + C$

$$= \frac{a}{a^2+b^2}e^{(a+ib)x} + \frac{-ib}{a^2+b^2}e^{(a+ib)x}$$

$$= \frac{ae^{ax}}{a^2+b^2}\cos bx - \frac{ib\,e^{ax}}{a^2+b^2}\cos bx + \frac{iae^{ax}}{a^2+b^2}\sin bx + \frac{be^{ax}}{a^2+b^2}\sin bx$$

$$= \frac{1}{a^2+b^2}e^{ax}(a\cos bx + b\sin bx) + \frac{i}{a^2+b^2}e^{ax}(a\sin bx - b\cos bx)$$

$$\int e^{(a+ib)x}dx = \int e^{ax}(\cos bx + i\sin bx)dx = \int e^{ax}\cos bx\,dx + i\int e^{ax}\sin bx\,dx$$

Equating real part to real part and imaginary part to imaginary part in the two expressions for the integral, we have:

$$\int e^{ax}\cos bx\,dx = \frac{1}{a^2+b^2}e^{ax}(a\cos bx + b\sin bx)$$

$$\int e^{ax}\sin bx\,dx = \frac{1}{a^2+b^2}e^{ax}(a\sin bx - b\cos bx)$$

## 12.4 EXPANSION POINTS, THE BINOMIAL THEOREM, ARCTANGENTS & $\Pi$

1. $31^\circ = \frac{31\pi}{180} \approx 0.5411$ radians.

$\cos 31^\circ = 1 - \frac{(.5411)^2}{2} + \frac{(.5411)^4}{24} \approx 0.857$ with error

$|R_5(x)| \leq \frac{(.5411)^6}{6!} < 0.000035$

3. Using $\sin(2\pi + x) = \sin x$, $\sin 6.3 = \sin(2\pi + 0.0168) = \sin 0.0168$

We need only the first term $\sin 0.0168 = 0.0168$ with error

$|R_2(x)| \leq \frac{(0.0168)^3}{6} < 7.9 \times 10^{-7}$

5. $\ln 1.25 = \ln(1 + .25) = .25 - \frac{(.25)^2}{2} + \frac{(.25)^3}{3} - \frac{(.25)^4}{4} = .223$

with error $|R_5(x)| \leq \frac{(.25)^5}{5} < 0.0002$

7. $\ln(1+2x) = 2x - \frac{(2x)^2}{2} + \frac{(2x)^3}{3} - \ldots = \sum_{n=1}^{\infty} (-1)^{n-1} \frac{2^n x^n}{n}$ converges

for all $-1 < 2x \leq 1$ or $-\frac{1}{2} < x \leq \frac{1}{2}$.

9. $$\int_0^{0.1} \frac{\sin x}{x} dx = \int_0^{0.1} \frac{1}{x}\left(x - \frac{x^3}{3!} + \frac{x^5}{5!} - \ldots\right)dx$$

$$= \int_0^{0.1} \left(1 - \frac{x^2}{3!} + \frac{x^4}{5!} - \frac{x^6}{7!} + \ldots\right)dx$$

$$= x - \frac{x^3}{3 \cdot 3!} + \frac{x^5}{5 \cdot 5!} - \Big]_0^{0.1} = 0.1$$

with error $|R_2(x)| \leq \frac{(0.1)^3}{18} = 0.00006$

11. The parabola $x^2 = 2a(y - a)$ solved for y is $y = a + \frac{x^2}{2a}$

These are the first two terms of the Maclaurin's Series for $y = \cosh x$. The remainder is:

$$|R_3(x)| \leq \frac{|a|\,|\cosh c|}{4!3^4} = 0.0005|a|$$

13. This is the series for $\ln(1 + x)$ evaluated at $x = \frac{1}{2}$, which converges to $\ln(\frac{3}{2})$

15. $\pi = 48\tan^{-1}\frac{1}{18} + 32\tan^{-1}\frac{1}{57} - 20\tan^{-1}\frac{1}{239} =$

$$= 48\left[.0556 - \frac{(.0556)^3}{3}\right] + 32\left[.0175 - \frac{(.0175)^3}{3}\right] - 20\left[.0042 - \frac{(.0042)^3}{3}\right]$$

$= 2.66604 + 0.55994 - 0.0839 = 3.142$

17. $a_0 = 1$ $\qquad b_0 = \dfrac{1}{\sqrt{2}} \approx 0.707107$

$$a_1 = \frac{1 + \frac{1}{\sqrt{2}}}{2} = 0.853553 \qquad b_1 = \sqrt{\frac{1}{\sqrt{2}}} = 0.840896$$

$$a_2 = \frac{a_1 + b_1}{2} = 0.847225 \qquad b_2 = \sqrt{a_1 b_1} = 0.847201$$

$$a_3 = \frac{a_2 + b_2}{2} = 0.847213 \qquad b_3 = \sqrt{a_2 b_2} = 0.847213$$

$$c_3 = \frac{4a_3b_3}{1 - 4(a_1^2 - b_1^2) - 8(a_2^2 - b_2^2) - 16(a_3^2 - b_3^2)}$$

$$= \frac{2.871079}{1 - .085788 - .000325 - 0} = 3.1416127$$

19. By dividing $1 - t^2$ into 1, and expressing the answer as quotient plus remainder over divisor, we obtain the identity

$$\frac{1}{1 - t^2} = 1 + t^2 + t^4 + \ldots + t^{2n} + \frac{t^{2n+2}}{1 - t^2}$$

Another way of obtaining this identity is to use the formula for the $n^{th}$ partial sum of a geometric series

$$1 + t^2 + t^4 + \ldots + t^{2n} = \frac{1 - (t^2)^{n+1}}{1 - t^2}$$

Then

$$\int_0^x \frac{dt}{1-t^2} = \int_0^x \left[1 + t^2 + t^4 + \ldots + t^{2n} + \frac{t^{2n+2}}{1-t^2}\right] dt$$

$$= t + \frac{t^3}{3} + \frac{t^5}{5} + \ldots + \frac{t^{2n+1}}{2n+1}\Bigg]_0^x + \int_0^x \frac{t^{2n+2}}{1-t^2} dt$$

Thus $\tanh^{-1} x = x + \dfrac{x^3}{3} + \dfrac{x^5}{5} + \ldots + \dfrac{x^{2n+1}}{2n+1} + R$, with

$$R = \int_0^x \frac{t^{2n+2}}{1-t^2} dt$$

21. (a) $\dfrac{d}{dx}(1 - x)^{-1} = \dfrac{d}{dx}\left(1 + x + x^2 + \ldots + x^n + \dfrac{x^{n+1}}{1 - x}\right)$

$(1 - x)^{-2} = 1 + 2x + 3x^2 + \ldots + nx^{n-1} + R$, where

$$R = \frac{(1 - x)(n + 1)x^n + x^{n+1}}{(1 - x)^2}$$

(b) $\lim\limits_{n\to\infty} x^{n+1} = 0$ for $|x| < 1$. We consider $\lim\limits_{n\to\infty}(n + 1)x^n =$

$$\lim_{n\to\infty} \frac{n+1}{x^{-n}} = \lim_{n\to\infty} \frac{1}{-nx^{-n-1}} = \lim_{n\to\infty} \frac{x^{n+1}}{-n} = 0$$

(c) $\displaystyle\sum_{n=1}^{\infty} n\left(\frac{5}{6}\right)^{n-1}\left(\frac{1}{6}\right) = \frac{1}{6}\left(\frac{1}{\left(1 - \left(\frac{5}{6}\right)\right)^2}\right) = 6$

(d) $\displaystyle\sum_{n=1}^{\infty} np^{n-1}q = \frac{q}{(1-p)^2} = \frac{q}{q^2} = \frac{1}{q}$

## 12.5 CONVERGENCE OF POWER SERIES, INTEGRATION, DIFFERENTIATION, MULTIPLICATION AND DIVISION

1. $\sum_{n=0}^{\infty} x^n$ converges for $-1 < x < 1$ because $\lim_{n\to\infty} \frac{|x^{n+1}|}{|x^n|} = \lim_{n\to\infty} |x| < 1$

for all x such that $|x| < 1$. If $x = 1$, then $\sum_{n=0}^{\infty} (1)^n$ diverges, and

if $x = -1$, $\sum_{n=0}^{\infty} (-1)^n$ diverges.

3. $\sum_{n=0}^{\infty} \frac{nx^n}{2^n}$ converges for $-2 < x < 2$ because $\lim_{n\to\infty} \left| \frac{(n+1)x^{n+1}}{2^{n+1}} \cdot \frac{2^n}{nx^n} \right| =$

$\lim_{n\to\infty} \left| \frac{n+1}{n} \cdot \frac{1}{2} x \right| = \frac{1}{2} |x| < 1$ for all x such that $|x| < 2$. If $x = \pm 2$, then

$\sum_{n=0}^{\infty} \frac{n2^n}{2^n} = \sum_{n=0}^{\infty} n$ diverges, and $\sum_{n=0}^{\infty} \frac{n(-2)^n}{2^n} = \sum_{n=0}^{\infty} (-1)^n n$ diverges.

5. $\sum_{n=0}^{\infty} \frac{(-1)^n x^{2n+1}}{(2n+1)!}$ converges for all x because $\lim_{n\to\infty} \left| \frac{(n+1)x^{n+1}}{2^{n+1}} \cdot \frac{2^n}{nx^n} \right| =$

$\lim_{n\to\infty} \left| \frac{x^{2n+3}}{(2n+3)!} \cdot \frac{(2n+1)!}{x^{2n+1}} \right| = \lim_{n\to\infty} \frac{1}{(2n+3)(2n+1)} x^2 = 0 < 1$ for all x.

7. $\sum_{n=0}^{\infty} \frac{n^2 (x+2)^n}{2^n}$ converges for $-4 < x < 0$ because $\lim_{n\to\infty} \left| \frac{(n+1)^2 (x+2)^{n+1}}{2^{n+1}} \cdot \frac{2^n}{n^2 (x+2} \right.$

$\lim_{n\to\infty} \left| \left( \frac{n+1}{n} \right)^2 \cdot \frac{1}{2} (x+2) \right| < 1$ if $|x+2| < 2$ or $-4 < x < 0$.

$\sum_{n=0}^{\infty} \frac{n^2}{2^n} \cdot 2^n = \sum_{n=0}^{\infty} n^2$ diverges and $\sum_{n=0}^{\infty} \frac{n^2}{2^n} (-2)^n = \sum_{n=0}^{\infty} (-1)n^2$ diverges

9. $\sum_{n=0}^{\infty} \frac{(-1)^n x^{2n+1}}{2n+1}$ converges for $-1 < x < 1$ because

$\lim_{n\to\infty} \left| \frac{x^{2n+3}}{2n+3} \cdot \frac{2n+1}{x^{2n+1}} \right| = \lim_{n\to\infty} \left| \left( \frac{2n+3}{2n+1} \right) x^2 \right| < 1$ if $|x| < 1$.

$\sum_{n=0}^{\infty} (-1)^n \frac{1}{2n+1}$ converges by alternating series test.

$\sum_{n=0}^{\infty} (-1)^n \frac{(-1)^{2n+1}}{2n+1} = \sum_{n=0}^{\infty} (-1)^{n+1} \frac{1}{2n+1}$ also converges.

11. $\sum_{n=0}^{\infty} \frac{\cos nx}{2^n}$ converges absolutely for all x since

$\frac{|\cos nx|}{2^n} \le \frac{1}{2^n}$ and $\sum_{n=0}^{\infty} \frac{1}{2^n}$ converges.

13. $\sum_{n=0}^{\infty} \frac{x^n e^n}{n+1}$ converges for $-\frac{1}{e} \le x < \frac{1}{e}$ because $\lim_{n\to\infty} \left| \frac{x^{n+1}e^{n+1}}{n+2} \cdot \frac{n+1}{x^n e^n} \right| =$

$\lim_{n\to\infty} \left(\frac{n+1}{n+2}\right)|x|\, e < 1$ if $|x| < \frac{1}{e}$. If $x = \frac{1}{e}$, $\sum_{n=0}^{\infty} \frac{1}{n+1}$ diverges,

and if $x = -\frac{1}{e}$, $\sum_{n=0}^{\infty} (-1)^n \frac{1}{n+1}$ converges.

15. $\sum_{n=0}^{\infty} n^n x^n$ converges for $x = 0$ only because

$\lim_{n\to\infty} \sqrt[n]{n^n x^n} = \lim_{n\to\infty} |nx| = \infty$ for all x except $x = 0$.

17. $\sum_{n=0}^{\infty} (-2)^n (n+1)(x-1)^n$ converges for $\frac{1}{2} < x < \frac{3}{2}$ because

$\lim_{n\to\infty} \left| \frac{(-2)^{n+1}(n+2)(x-1)^{n+1}}{(-2)^n(n+1)(x-1)^n} \right| = \lim_{n\to\infty} |-2| \left(\frac{n+2}{n+1}\right)|x-1| < 1$ if

$|x-1| < \frac{1}{2}$. At $x = \frac{3}{2}$ and $\frac{1}{2}$, $\sum_{n=0}^{\infty} (-1)^n (n+1)$ and $\sum_{n=0}^{\infty} (n+1)$ both diverge .

19. $\sum_{n=0}^{\infty} \left(\frac{x^2-1}{2}\right)^n$ converges for $-\sqrt{3} < x < \sqrt{3}$ because $\lim_{n\to\infty} \left| \frac{(x^2-1)^{n+1}}{2^{n+1}} \cdot \frac{2^n}{(x^2-1)^n} \right| =$

$\lim_{n\to\infty} \frac{1}{2}|x^2-1| < 1$ if $|x^2-1| < 3$ or if $|x| < \sqrt{3}$.

At $x = \pm\sqrt{3}$, $\sum_{n=0}^{\infty} (1)^n$ diverges.

21. The series converges to $e^{3x} + 6$

23 (a) $\cos x = 1 - \frac{x^2}{2!} + \frac{x^4}{4!} + \ldots (-1)^n \frac{x^{2n}}{(2n)!}$

$\frac{d}{dx}(\cos x) = -\frac{2x}{2!} + \frac{4x^3}{4!} + \ldots (-1)^n (2n \frac{x^{2n-1}}{(2n-1)!}$

$= -1 + \frac{x^3}{3!} - \frac{x^5}{5!} + \ldots (-1) \frac{x^{2n-1}}{(2n-1)!} = -\sin x$

(b) $\int_0^x \cos t\,dt = \int_0^x (1 - \frac{t^2}{2!} + \frac{t^4}{4!} - \ldots + (1)^n \frac{t^{2n}}{(2n)!})\,dt$

$$= t - \frac{1}{3}\cdot\frac{t^3}{2!} + \frac{1}{5}\cdot\frac{t^5}{4!} - \ldots + (-1)^n \frac{1}{2n+1}\cdot\frac{t^{2n+1}}{(2n)!}\Bigg]_0^x$$

$$= x - \frac{x^3}{3!} + \frac{x^5}{5!} - \ldots + (-1)^n \frac{x^{2n+1}}{(2n+1)!} = \sin x$$

(c) $y = e^x = 1 + x + \frac{x^2}{2!} + \frac{x^3}{3!} + \ldots + \frac{x^n}{n!} + \ldots$

$$y' = 1 + \frac{2x}{2!} + \frac{3x^2}{3!} + \ldots + \frac{nx^{n-1}}{n!} + \ldots$$

$$= 1 + x + \frac{x^2}{2!} + \frac{x^3}{3!} + \ldots + \frac{x^n}{n!} + \ldots = e^x$$

25. $\frac{1}{1-x^2} = 1 + x^2 + x^4 + x^6 + \ldots + (x^{2n}) + \ldots = \sum_{n=0}^{\infty} x^{2n}$ , $|x| < 1$.

Note that $\frac{d}{dx}(1-x^2)^{-1} = \frac{2x}{(1-x^2)^2}$. So, for $|x| < 1$

$$\frac{2x}{(1-x^2)^2} = 2x + 4x^3 + 6x^5 + \ldots + 2nx^{2n-1} = \sum_{n=1}^{\infty}(2n)x^{2n-1}$$

27. $\int_0^{.2} \sin x^2\,dx = \int_0^{.2}\left(x^2 - \frac{x^6}{3!} + \frac{x^{10}}{5!} - \ldots\right)dx = \frac{1}{3}x^3 - \frac{1}{7\cdot 3!}x^7 - \ldots\Big]_0^{.2}$

$= 0.0027$ with error $|E| \le \frac{1}{7\cdot 3!}(.2)^7 = 3 \times 10^{-7}$

29. $\int_0^{.1} x^2 e^{-x^2}\,dx = \int_0^{.1} x^2\left(1 - x^2 + \frac{x^4}{2!} - \frac{x^6}{3!} + \ldots\right)dx = \int_0^{.1}\left(x^2 - x^4 + \frac{x^6}{2!} - \ldots\right)dx$

$$= \frac{1}{3}x^3 - \frac{1}{5}x^5 + \frac{1}{7\cdot 2!}x^7 - \ldots\Big]_0^{.1} = \frac{1}{3}(.1)^3 = 0.00033$$

with error $|E| \le \frac{1}{5}(.1)^5 = 2 \times 10^{-6}$

31. $\int_0^{.4} \frac{1-e^{-x}}{x}\,dx = \int_0^{.4} \frac{1}{x}\left[1 - \left(1 - x + \frac{x^2}{2} - \frac{x^3}{3!} + \ldots\right)\right]dx$

$$= \int_0^{.4}\left(1 - \frac{x}{2!} + \frac{x^2}{3!} - \frac{x^3}{4!} + \ldots\right)dx = 1 - \frac{1}{2\cdot 2!}x^2 + \frac{1}{3\cdot 3!}x^3 - \frac{1}{4\cdot 4!}x^4 + \ldots\Big]_0^{.4}$$

$= 0.3636$ with error $|E| \le \frac{(.4)^4}{4\cdot 4!} < 0.0003$

33. $\displaystyle\int_0^{.1} \frac{1}{\sqrt{1+x^4}}dx = \int_0^{.1}\left(1 - \frac{1}{2}x^4 + \frac{\left(-\frac{1}{2}\right)\left(-\frac{3}{2}\right)}{2}x^8 \ldots\right)dx$

$$= \int_0^{.1}\left(1 - \frac{1}{2}x^4 + \frac{3}{8}x^8 - \ldots\right)dx = x - \frac{1}{10}x^5 + \frac{3}{72}x^9 - ..\Big]_0^{.1}$$

$= 0.1$ with error $|E| \le 1 \times 10^{-6}$

35. (a) $\displaystyle\sinh^{-1}x = \int_0^x \frac{dt}{\sqrt{1+t^2}} = \int_0^x\left(1 - \frac{1}{2}t^2 + \frac{3}{8}t^4 - \frac{5}{16}t^6 + \ldots\right)dt$

$$= t - \frac{1}{6}t^3 + \frac{3}{40}t^5 - \frac{5}{112}t^7 + \ldots\Big]_0^x = x - \frac{1}{6}x^3 + \frac{3}{40}x^5 - \frac{5}{112}x^7 + \ldots$$

(b) $\sinh^{-1}.25 = .25 - \dfrac{(.25)^3}{6} = 0.247$

with error $|E| \le \dfrac{3(.25)^5}{40} = 0.00007$

37. Problem 15 of this section is an example of a series which converges only for $x = 0$.

39. We are given that $\sum a_n$ converges for $-r < x < r$. Let a be any point such that $-r < a < r$. There exists $r_1$ such that $-r < -r_1 < a < r_1 < r$. The $\sum a_n$ converges for $r_1$ and hence absolutely for a, by Theorem 1. But a was any point between -r and r, and hence the series converges absolutely for all x such that $-r < x < r$.

41. $\displaystyle e^x\sin x = (1 + x + \frac{x^2}{2!} + \frac{x^3}{3!} + .+\frac{x^n}{n!})(x - \frac{x^3}{3!} + \frac{x^5}{5!} - .+(-1)^n\frac{x^{2n+1}}{(2n+1)!})$

$$=1(x - \frac{x^3}{3!} + \frac{x^5}{5!} - \ldots) + x(x - \frac{x^3}{3!} + \frac{x^5}{5!} - \ldots) +$$

$$\frac{x^2}{2}(x - \frac{x^3}{3!} + \frac{x^5}{5!} - \ldots) + \frac{x^3}{3!}(x - \frac{x^3}{3!} + ..) + \frac{x^4}{4!}(x - \frac{x^3}{3!} + ..)$$

$$= (x - \frac{x^3}{3!} + \frac{x^5}{5!} - ..) + (x^2 - \frac{x^4}{3!} + ..) + (\frac{x^3}{2} - \frac{x^5}{2\cdot 3!} + \ldots)$$

$$+ (\frac{x^4}{3!} + ..) + (\frac{x^5}{4!} - ..)$$

$$= x + x^2 + \frac{1}{3}x^3 - \frac{1}{30}x^5 \ldots$$

Check: $\displaystyle(e^x)(e^{ix}) = e^{(1+i)x} = 1 + (1+i)x + \frac{(1+i)^2x^2}{2} + \frac{(1+i)^3x^3}{3!}$

$$+ \frac{(1+i)^4x^4}{4!} + \frac{(1+i)^5x^5}{5!} + \ldots.$$

$$= 1 + (1+i)x + \frac{2ix^2}{2} + \frac{(2i-2)x^3}{3!} - \frac{4x^4}{4!} + \frac{(-4-4i)x^5}{5!} + ..$$

The imaginary part of this series is the same as the one obtained in the first part of the problem.

43. $$\int_0^x \tan t\,dt = \int_0^x \left(t+\frac{t^3}{3}+\frac{2t^5}{15}+\dots\right)dt = \left.\frac{1}{2}t^2+\frac{1}{12}t^4+\frac{2}{90}t^6+\dots\right]_0^x$$

$$\ln|\sec x| = \frac{1}{2}x^2+\frac{1}{2}x^4+\frac{1}{45}x^6+\,..$$

45. (a) $$\frac{r_2}{r_1} = \sec\frac{\pi}{3}$$

$$\frac{r_3}{r_2} = \sec\frac{\pi}{4}$$

$$\frac{r_4}{r_3} = \sec\frac{\pi}{5}$$

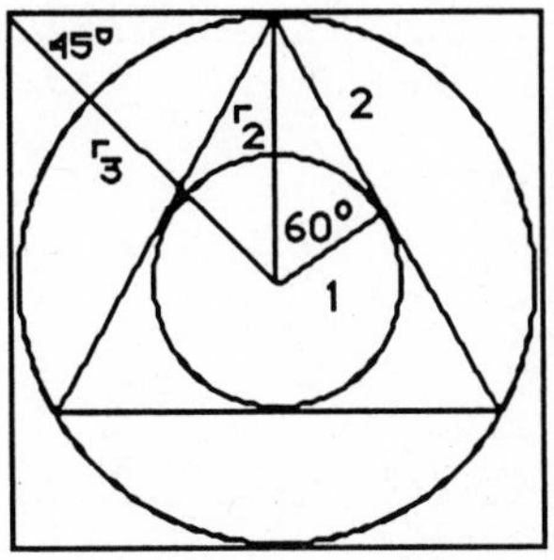


In general, if a (n+1)-sided polygon is inscribed in a circle, the central angle is $\frac{2\pi}{n+1}$ and the ratio is $\frac{r_n}{r_{n-1}} = \sec\frac{1}{2}\left(\frac{2\pi}{n+1}\right)$

(b) $$r_n = r_{n-1}\sec\frac{\pi}{n+1} = \sec\frac{\pi}{n+1}\left(r_{n-2}\sec\frac{\pi}{n}\right) = \sec\frac{\pi}{n+1}\sec\frac{\pi}{n}\left(r_{n-3}\sec\frac{\pi}{n-1}\right)$$

$$=\sec\frac{\pi}{n+1}\sec\frac{\pi}{n}\sec\frac{\pi}{n-1}\dots\sec\frac{\pi}{4}\left(r_1\sec\frac{\pi}{3}\right)$$

$$\ln r_n = \ln r_1 + \ln\sec\frac{\pi}{3} + \ln\sec\frac{\pi}{4} + \dots + \ln\sec\frac{\pi}{n+1}$$

(c) $$\lim_{n\to\infty}\frac{\ln\sec\frac{\pi}{n}}{\frac{1}{n^2}} = \lim_{n\to\infty} n^2\left(\frac{\pi^2}{2n^2}+\frac{\pi^4}{12n^4}+\dots\right) = \frac{\pi^2}{2}.$$

$$\sum_{n=3}^{\infty}\ln\sec\frac{\pi}{n} \text{ converges by comparison to } \sum_{n=1}^{\infty}\frac{1}{n^2}.$$

## 12.6 INDETERMINATE FORMS

1. $$\lim_{h\to0}\frac{\sinh}{h} = \lim_{h\to0}\frac{h-\frac{h^3}{3!}+\frac{h^5}{5!}-\,..}{h} = \lim_{h\to0}\left(1-\frac{h^2}{3!}-\frac{h^4}{5!}-\,..\right) = 1$$

3. $$\lim_{t\to0}\frac{1-\cos t-\frac{t^2}{2}}{t^4} = \lim_{t\to0}\frac{1}{t^4}\left[1-\frac{t^2}{2}-\left(1-\frac{t^2}{2}+\frac{t^4}{4!}-\frac{t^6}{6!}+\,..\right)\right]$$

$$=\lim_{t\to0}\left[-\frac{1}{4!}+\frac{t^2}{6!}-\,..\right] = -\frac{1}{24}$$

5. $$\lim_{x\to0}\frac{x^2}{1-\cosh x} = \lim_{x\to0}\frac{x^2}{1-\left(1+\frac{x^2}{2!}+\frac{x^4}{4!}+\,..\right)} = \lim_{x\to0}\frac{1}{-\frac{1}{2}-\frac{x^2}{4!}-\,..} = -2$$

7. $$\lim_{x\to 0}\frac{1-\cos x}{\sin x} - \lim_{x\to 0}\frac{1-\left(1-\frac{x^2}{2}+\frac{x^4}{4!}-\ldots\right)}{x-\frac{x^3}{3!}+\frac{x^5}{5!}-\ldots} = \lim_{x\to 0}\frac{x^2\left(\frac{1}{2}-\frac{x^2}{4!}+\ldots\right)}{x\left(1-\frac{x^2}{3!}+\ldots\right)} = 0$$

9. $$\lim_{z\to 0}\frac{\sin(z^2)-\sinh(z^2)}{z^6} = \lim_{z\to 0}\frac{\left(z^2-\frac{z^6}{3!}+\frac{z^{10}}{5!}-\ldots\right)-\left(z^2+\frac{z^6}{3!}+\frac{z^{10}}{5!}+\ldots\right)}{z^6}$$

$$= \lim_{z\to 0}\frac{-\frac{2z^6}{3!}-\frac{2z^{10}}{5!}-\ldots}{z^6} = -\frac{1}{3}$$

11. $$\lim_{x\to 0}\frac{\sin x - x + \frac{x^3}{6}}{x^5} = \lim_{x\to 0}\frac{-x+\frac{x^3}{6}+\left(x-\frac{x^3}{3!}+\frac{x^5}{5!}-\frac{x^7}{7!}\ldots\right)}{x^5} = \frac{1}{120}$$

13. $$\lim_{x\to 0}\frac{x-\tan^{-1}x}{x^3} = \lim_{x\to 0}\frac{x-\left(x-\frac{x^3}{3}+\frac{x^5}{5}-\ldots\right)}{x^3} = \frac{1}{3}$$

15. $$\lim_{x\to\infty} x^2(e^{-1/x^2}-1) = \lim_{x\to\infty} x^2\left[\left(1-\frac{1}{x^2}+\frac{1}{2x^4}-\frac{1}{6x^6}+\ldots\right)-1\right] = -1$$

17. $$\lim_{x\to 0}\frac{\tan 3x}{x} = \lim_{x0}\frac{3x+\frac{(3x)^3}{3}+\frac{2(3x)^5}{15}+\ldots}{x} = 3$$

19. $$\lim_{x\to\infty}\frac{x^{100}}{e^x} = \lim_{x\to\infty}\frac{x^{100}}{1+x+\frac{x^2}{2!}+\ldots+\frac{x^{101}}{101!}+\ldots} = 0$$

21. (a) For $x \geq 0$, $e^{x^2} \geq 1$. Therefore, $\int_0^x e^{t^2}dt \geq \int_0^x dt = x$

and $\int_0^x e^{t^2}dt$ diverges.

(b) $$\lim_{x\to\infty} x\int_0^x e^{t^2-x^2}dt = \lim_{x\to\infty} x\int_0^x e^{t^2}e^{-x^2}dt = \lim_{x\to\infty} xe^{-x^2}\int_0^x e^{t^2}dt$$

$$= \lim_{x\to\infty}\frac{x\int_0^x e^{t^2}dt}{e^{x^2}} = \lim_{x\to\infty}\frac{\int_0^x e^{t^2}dt + xe^{x^2}}{2xe^{x^2}} = \lim_{x\to\infty}\frac{e^{x^2}+e^{x^2}+2x^2e^{x^2}}{4x^2e^{x^2}+2e^{x^2}}$$

$$= \lim_{x\to\infty}\frac{2+2x^2}{2+4x^2} = \frac{1}{2}$$

23.

| $x$ | $\sin x$ | $\frac{6x}{6+x^2}$ |
|---|---|---|
| $\pm 1.0$ | $\pm 0.84147$ | $\pm 0.85714$ |
| $\pm 0.1$ | $\pm 0.09983$ | $\pm 0.09983$ |
| $\pm 0.01$ | $\pm 0.00999$ | $\pm 0.00999$ |

$\mathrm{Sin}x \approx \frac{6x}{6+x^2}$ is better

## 12.M MISCELLANEOUS

1. (a) $\frac{x^2}{1+x^2} = x^2\left(\frac{1}{1-(-x)}\right) = x^2(1-x+x^2-x^3+..+(-1)^n x^n) = \sum_{n=0}^{\infty}(-1)^n x^{n+2}$.

(b) No, the radius of convergence for the series is $-1 < x < 1$.

3. $$e^{\sin x} = 1 + (x - \frac{x^3}{3!} + \frac{x^5}{5!} - \ldots) + \frac{1}{2}(x - \frac{x^3}{3!} + \frac{x^5}{5!} - \ldots)^2 + \frac{1}{6}(x - \frac{x^3}{3!} + \frac{x^5}{5!} - \ldots)^3 + \frac{1}{24}(x - \frac{x^3}{3!} + \frac{x^5}{5!} - \ldots)^4 + ..$$

$$= 1 + (x - \frac{x^3}{3!} + \frac{x^5}{5!} - \ldots) + \frac{1}{2}(x^2 - \frac{x^4}{3} + \frac{x^6}{36} - ..) + \frac{1}{6}(x^3 + 3x^2 . \frac{x^3}{3!} + .. + \frac{1}{24}(x^4 + \ldots) + \ldots$$

$$= 1 + x + \frac{1}{2}x^2 - \frac{1}{8}x^4 + \ldots$$

5 (a) $\ln(\cos x) = \ln[1 - (1 - \cos x)]$

$$= -\left(\frac{x^2}{2} - \frac{x^4}{24} + \frac{x^6}{720} - ..\right) - \frac{1}{2}\left(\frac{x^2}{2} - \frac{x^4}{24} + ..\right)^2 - \frac{1}{3}\left(\frac{x^2}{2} - \frac{x^4}{24} + ..\right)^3 - \ldots$$

$$= -\frac{x^2}{2} + \frac{x^4}{24} - \frac{x^6}{720} + \ldots - \frac{x^4}{8} + \frac{x^6}{48} - \ldots - \frac{x^6}{24} - \ldots$$

$$= -\frac{x^2}{2} - \frac{x^4}{12} - \frac{x^6}{45} - \ldots$$

(b) $\int_0^{.1} \ln(\cos x)\,dx = \int_0^{.1}\left(-\frac{x^2}{2} - \frac{x^4}{12} - \frac{x^6}{45} - \ldots\right)dx$

$$= -\frac{1}{6}x^3 - \frac{1}{60}x^5 - \frac{1}{315}x^7\Big]_0^{.1} = -0.00017$$

7. $\int_0^1 e^{-(x^2)}\,dx = \int_0^1\left(1 - x^2 + \frac{x^4}{2} - \frac{x^6}{6} + \frac{x^8}{24} - \ldots\right)dx$

$$= x - \frac{1}{3}x^3 + \frac{1}{10}x^5 - \frac{1}{42}x^7 + \frac{1}{216}x^9 - \ldots\Big]_0^1 = 0.747$$

9. $f(x) = \frac{1}{1-x}$ $\quad$ $f(2) = -1$

$f'(x) = \frac{1}{(1-x)^2}$ $\quad$ $f'(2) = 1$

$f''(x) = 2(1-x)^3$ $\quad$ $f''(2) = -2$

$f^{(n)}(x) = \frac{n!}{(1-x)^n}$ $\quad$ $f^{(n)}(2) = (-1)^{n+1} n!$

$f(x) = \sum_{n=0}^{\infty} (-1)^{n+1} (x-2)^n$ converges for $1 < x < 3$ since

$$\lim_{n\to\infty} \left| \frac{(x-2)^{n+1}}{(x-2)^n} \right| < 1 \Leftrightarrow |x-2| < 1$$

11. $f(x) = \cos x$ $\quad$ $f\left(\frac{\pi}{3}\right) = \frac{1}{2}$

$f'(x) = -\sin x$ $\quad$ $f\left(\frac{\pi}{3}\right) = -\frac{\sqrt{3}}{2}$

$f''(x) = -\cos x$ $\quad$ $f''\left(\frac{\pi}{3}\right) = -\frac{1}{2}$

$f'''(x) = \sin x$ $\quad$ $f'''\left(\frac{\pi}{3}\right) = \frac{\sqrt{3}}{2}$

$$\cos x = \frac{1}{2} - \frac{\sqrt{3}}{2}\left(x - \frac{\pi}{3}\right) - \frac{1}{2}\cdot\frac{1}{2}\left(x - \frac{\pi}{3}\right)^2 + \frac{1}{3!}\cdot\frac{\sqrt{3}}{2}\left(x - \frac{\pi}{3}\right)^3 + \ldots$$

$$= \frac{1}{2}\left(1 - \frac{1}{2}\left(x - \frac{\pi}{3}\right)^2 - \ldots\right) + \frac{\sqrt{3}}{2}\left(-\left(x - \frac{\pi}{3}\right) + \left(x - \frac{\pi}{3}\right)^3 - \ldots\right)$$

$$= \frac{1}{2}\sum_{n=0}^{\infty} \frac{(-1)^n}{(2n)!}\left(x - \frac{\pi}{3}\right)^n + \frac{\sqrt{3}}{2}\sum_{n=0}^{\infty} \frac{(-1)^{n+1}}{(2n+1)!}\left(x - \frac{\pi}{3}\right)^{2n+1}$$

13. $f'(x) = g(x) \Rightarrow f''(x) = g'(x) = f(x)$. Then $f'''(x) = f'(x) = g(x)$. In general, $f^{(2n+1)}(x) = g(x)$ and $f^{(2n)}(x) = f(x)$. Therefore,

$$f(x) = f(0) + f'(0)x + \frac{f''(0)}{2!}x^2 + \frac{f'''(0)}{3!}x^3 + \ldots.$$

$$= f(0) + g(0)x + \frac{f(0)}{2!}x^2 + \frac{g(0)}{3!}x^3 = 1 + \frac{1}{2}x^2 + \frac{1}{4!}x^4 + \frac{1}{6!}x^6 +$$

$f(1) = 1.543$

15. $f(x) = e^{(e^x)}$ $\qquad f(0) = e$

$f'(x) = e^x e^{(e^x)} = e^{(x+e^x)}$ $\qquad f'(0) = e$

$f''(x) = (1 + e^x)\, e^{(x+e^x)}$ $\qquad f''(0) = 2e$

$f'''(x) = e^x e^{(x+e^x)} + (1 + e^x)^2 e^{(x+e^x)}$ $\qquad f'''(0) = 5e$

$f(x) = e + ex + ex^2 + \frac{5e}{6}x^3 + \ldots$

17. $(1 + x)^{\frac{1}{3}} = 1 + \frac{1}{3}x + \frac{\left(\frac{1}{3}\right)\left(-\frac{2}{3}\right)}{2}x^2 - \ldots$ begins alternating after the first term, and the error $E \le \left|-\frac{1}{9}\left(\frac{1}{10}\right)^2\right| = 0.0011$

19. $\lim_{x\to 0}\left(\frac{\sin x}{x}\right)^{\frac{1}{x^2}} = e^{-1/6}$. To see this, consider $\lim_{x\to 0}\left[\ln\left(\frac{\sin x}{x}\right)^{\frac{1}{x^2}}\right]$

$$= \lim_{x\to 0}\left[\frac{1}{x^2}\ln\left(\frac{\sin x}{x}\right)\right] = \lim_{x\to 0}\left[\frac{\ln\left(\frac{\sin x}{x}\right)}{x^2}\right] = \lim_{x\to 0}\frac{\left(\frac{x}{\sin x}\right)\left(\frac{x\cos x - \sin x}{x^2}\right)}{2x}$$

$$= \lim_{x\to 0}\frac{x\cos x - \sin x}{2x^2\sin x} = \lim_{x\to 0}\frac{\cos x - x\sin x - \cos x}{4x\sin x + 2x^2\cos x}$$

$$= \lim_{x\to 0}\frac{-\sin x}{4\sin x + 2x\cos x} = \lim_{x\to 0}\frac{-\cos x}{4\cos x - 2x\sin x + 2\cos x} = -\frac{1}{6}$$

21. $\lim_{n\to\infty}\left|\frac{(x+2)^{n+1}}{3^{n+1}(n+1)}\cdot\frac{3^n n}{(x+2)^n}\right| = \lim_{n\to\infty}\left(\frac{n}{n+1}\right)\left(\frac{1}{3}\right)|x+2| < 1$

if $\frac{1}{3}|x+2| < 1$ or $-5 < x < 1$. At $x = 1$, $\sum_{n=1}^{\infty}\frac{1}{n}$ diverges, and

at $x = -5$, $\sum_{n=1}^{\infty}(-1)^n\frac{1}{n}$ converges. The convergenge is for $-5 \le x < 1$.

23. $\sum_{n=1}^{\infty}\frac{x^n}{n^n}$ converges for all x, since $\lim_{n\to\infty}\sqrt[n]{\left|\frac{x^n}{n^n}\right|} = 0$

25. $\sum_{n=0}^{\infty} \frac{n+1}{2n+1} \frac{(x-3)^n}{2^n}$ converges for $1 < x < 5$ because

$$\lim_{n\to\infty} \left| \frac{(n+2)(x-3)^{n+1}}{(2n+3)\,2^{n+1}} \cdot \frac{(2n+1)\,2^n}{(n+1)(x-3)^n} \right| = \lim_{n\to\infty} \left(\frac{n+2}{n+1}\right)\left(\frac{2n+1}{2n+3}\right)\left(\frac{1}{2}\right)|x-3| < 1$$

if $|x-3| < 1$ or is $1 < x < 5$. Since $\lim_{n\to\infty} \frac{n+1}{2n+1} = \frac{1}{2} \neq 0$, the series diverges at both endpoints.

27. $\sum_{n=1}^{\infty} \frac{(-1)^{n-1}(x-1)^n}{n^2}$ converges for $0 \leq x \leq 2$.

$$\lim_{n\to\infty} \left| \frac{(x-1)^{n+1}}{(n+1)^2} \cdot \frac{n^2}{(x-1)^n} \right| = \lim_{n\to\infty} \left(\frac{n+1}{n}\right)^2 |x-1| < 1 \text{ if } 0 < x < 2.$$

At $x = 0$, $\sum_{n=1}^{\infty} \frac{(-1)^{n-1}(-1)^n}{n^2} = \sum_{n=1}^{\infty} \frac{1}{n^2}$ converges (p-series, $p = 2$).

At $x = 2$, $\sum_{n=1}^{\infty} \frac{(-1)^{n-1}}{n^2}$ converges (alternating series test).

29. $\sum_{n=1}^{\infty} \frac{(x-2)^{3n}}{n!}$ converges for all x.

$$\lim_{n\to\infty} \left| \frac{(x-2)^{3n+3}}{(n+1)!} \cdot \frac{n!}{(x-2)^{3n}} \right| = \lim_{n\to\infty} \frac{1}{n+1} |x-2|^3 = 0 \text{ for all } x.$$

31. $\sum_{n=1}^{\infty} \frac{1}{n}\left(\frac{x-1}{x}\right)^n$ converges for all $x \geq \frac{1}{2}$.

$$\lim_{n\to\infty} \left| \frac{\left(\frac{x-1}{x}\right)^{n+1} \frac{1}{n+1}}{\left(\frac{x-1}{x}\right)^n \frac{1}{n}} \right| \lim_{n\to\infty} \left(\frac{n}{n+1}\right) \left| \frac{x-1}{x} \right| < 1 \Leftrightarrow -1 < \frac{x-1}{x} < 1.$$

Case I: $\frac{x-1}{x} < 1 \Leftrightarrow \frac{x-1}{x} - 1 < 0 \Leftrightarrow -\frac{1}{x} < 0 \Leftrightarrow x > 0$

Case II: $\frac{x-1}{x} > -1 \Leftrightarrow \frac{x-1}{x} + 1 > 0 \Leftrightarrow \frac{2x-1}{x} > 0 \Leftrightarrow x < 0 \text{ or } x > \frac{1}{2}$.

The intersection of these solutions sets is $x \geqslant \frac{1}{2}$.

At $x = \frac{1}{2}$, $\sum_{n=1}^{\infty} (-1)^n \frac{1}{n}$ converges.

33. If $\sum_{n=1}^{\infty} a_n$ converges and $a_n > 0$, show that $\sum_{n=1}^{\infty} \frac{a_n}{1+a_n}$ converges.

$$\lim_{n\to\infty} \frac{\frac{a_n}{1+a_n}}{a_n} = \lim_{n\to\infty} \frac{1}{1+a_n} = 1$$ since $\lim_{n\to\infty} a_n = 0$. By the Limit Comparison Test, $\sum_{n=1}^{\infty} \frac{a_n}{1+a_n}$ since $\sum_{n=1}^{\infty} a_n$ does.

35. If $\sum_{n=1}^{\infty} |a_n|$ converges, and $a_n > -1$, prove $\prod_{n=1}^{\infty} (1+a_n)$ converges.

The convergence of $\sum_{n=1}^{\infty} |a_n|$ means that $\lim_{n\to\infty} |a_n| = 0$. Let $N > 0$ be such that $|a_n| < \frac{1}{2}$ for all $n > N$ and consider $\sum_{n=N}^{\infty} \ln(1+a_n)$.

$$|\ln(1+a_n)| = |a_n - \frac{a_n^2}{2} + \frac{a_n^3}{3} - \frac{a_n^4}{4} + \ldots| \le |a_n| + |\frac{a_n^2}{2}| + |\frac{a_n^3}{3}| + |\frac{a_n^4}{4}| + .$$

$$< |a_n| + |a_n|^2 + |a_n|^3 + |a_n|^4 + \ldots.$$

$$= \frac{|a_n|}{1-|a_n|} < 2|a_n| \text{ since, for } n > N,\ 1-|a_n| \ge \frac{1}{2}.$$

Therefore, $\sum_{n=N}^{\infty} \ln(1+a_n) \le \left|\sum_{n=N}^{\infty} \ln(a_n)\right| \le \sum_{n=N}^{\infty} 2|a_n|$

$\le 2\sum_{n=1} |a_n|$ which is convergent. Hence $\prod_{n=1}^{\infty} (1+a_n)$ converges.

37. $$\frac{\tan^{-1}x}{1-x} = \frac{1}{1-x}\cdot\tan^{-1}x = (1+x+x^2+x^3+x^4+x^5+\ldots)\left(x-\frac{x^3}{3}+\frac{x^5}{5}-\ldots\right)$$

$$= x+x^2+x^3+x^4+x^5 - \frac{x^3}{3} - \frac{x^4}{3} - \frac{x^5}{3} + \frac{x^5}{5} + \ldots$$

$$= x+x^2+\frac{2}{3}x^3+\frac{2}{3}x^4+\frac{13}{15}x^5+\ldots$$

# CHAPTER 13

# VECTORS

## 13.1 VECTORS IN THE PLANE

1. See the sketches in the Answer Section of the textbook.

3. $P_3 = \left(\frac{-4+2}{2}, \frac{3-1}{2}\right) = (-1, 1)$; $\overrightarrow{OP_3} = -\mathbf{i} + \mathbf{j}$

5. $\overrightarrow{AB} = (2-1)\mathbf{i} + (0+1)\mathbf{j} = \mathbf{i} + \mathbf{j}$;

   $\overrightarrow{CD} = (-2+1)\mathbf{i} + (3-2)\mathbf{j} = -\mathbf{i} - \mathbf{j}$;

   $\overrightarrow{AB} + \overrightarrow{CD} = 0\mathbf{i} + 0\mathbf{j}$.

7. $\mathbf{u} = \cos(-30^\circ)\mathbf{i} + \sin(-30^\circ)\mathbf{j} = \frac{\sqrt{3}}{2}\mathbf{i} - \frac{1}{2}\mathbf{j}$

9. $y = x^2 \Rightarrow y' = 2x$. $y'(2) = 4 = \frac{4}{1}$. $\mathbf{v} = \mathbf{i} + 4\mathbf{j}$ is tangent to the curve.

   $|\mathbf{v}| = \sqrt{1+16} = \sqrt{17}$. $\therefore$ Either of the unit vectors $\mathbf{u} = \pm\frac{1}{\sqrt{17}}\mathbf{i} \pm \frac{4}{\sqrt{17}}\mathbf{j}$.

11. (a) $y = x^2 + 2x \Rightarrow y' = 2x + 2$. $y'(1) = 4 = \frac{4}{1}$. $\mathbf{v} = -\mathbf{i} - 4\mathbf{j}$

    is tangent to the curve. $|\mathbf{v}| = \sqrt{1+16} = \sqrt{17}$.

    $\therefore$ $\mathbf{u} = -\frac{1}{\sqrt{17}}\mathbf{i} - \frac{4}{\sqrt{17}}\mathbf{j}$ is the required unit vector.

    (b) $\mathbf{w} = -4\mathbf{i} + \mathbf{j}$ is orthogonal to $\mathbf{u}$, hence the normal is

    $\mathbf{n} = -\frac{4}{\sqrt{17}}\mathbf{i} + \frac{1}{\sqrt{17}}\mathbf{j}$.

13. $|\mathbf{i} + \mathbf{j}| = \sqrt{2}$. $\mathbf{u} = \frac{1}{\sqrt{2}}\mathbf{i} + \frac{1}{\sqrt{2}}\mathbf{j}$. $\cos\theta = \frac{1}{\sqrt{2}} \Rightarrow \theta = \frac{\pi}{4}$.

15. $|\sqrt{3}\mathbf{i} + \mathbf{j}| = 2$. $\mathbf{u} = \frac{\sqrt{3}}{2}\mathbf{i} + \frac{1}{2}\mathbf{j}$. $\cos\theta = \frac{\sqrt{3}}{2} \Rightarrow \theta = \frac{\pi}{6}$.

17. $|5\mathbf{i} + 12\mathbf{j}| = 13$. $\mathbf{u} = \frac{5}{13}\mathbf{i} + \frac{12}{13}\mathbf{j}$. $\theta = \tan^{-1}\left(\frac{12}{5}\right)$.

19. $\mathbf{v} = -4\mathbf{i} + 2\mathbf{j}$. $|\mathbf{v}| = \sqrt{16+4} = 2\sqrt{5}$.

21. $\mathbf{C} = 3\mathbf{i} + 6\mathbf{j}$ has $|\mathbf{C}| = \sqrt{40} = 2\sqrt{5}$ and direction $\mathbf{u} = \frac{1}{\sqrt{5}}\mathbf{i} + \frac{2}{\sqrt{5}}\mathbf{j}$.

    $\mathbf{D} = \frac{1}{2}\mathbf{i} - 2\mathbf{j}$ has $|\mathbf{D}| = \frac{\sqrt{5}}{2}$ and direction $\mathbf{v} = \frac{1}{\sqrt{5}}\mathbf{i} + \frac{2}{\sqrt{5}}\mathbf{j}$.

23. By definition, **A** and **B** have opposite directions if and only if $\frac{\mathbf{A}}{|\mathbf{A}|} = -\frac{\mathbf{B}}{|\mathbf{B}|}$. Then $\mathbf{A} = -\frac{|\mathbf{A}|}{|\mathbf{B}|}\mathbf{B} = -k\mathbf{B}$.

25. In ▱ ABCD, let N be the midpoint of AC, M be the midpoint of BD.

$$\mathbf{AN} = \frac{1}{2}\mathbf{AC} = \frac{1}{2}(\mathbf{AB} + \mathbf{BC}) = \frac{1}{2}\mathbf{AB} + \frac{1}{2}\mathbf{BC} = \frac{1}{2}\mathbf{AB} + \frac{1}{2}\mathbf{AD}.$$

$$\mathbf{AB} + \mathbf{BD} + \mathbf{DA} = 0 \Rightarrow \mathbf{BD} = -\mathbf{DA} - \mathbf{AB} = \mathbf{AD} - \mathbf{AB}.$$

$$\mathbf{AM} = \mathbf{AB} + \mathbf{BM} = \mathbf{AB} + \frac{1}{2}\mathbf{BD} = \mathbf{AB} + \frac{1}{2}(\mathbf{AD} - \mathbf{AB}) = \frac{1}{2}\mathbf{AB} + \frac{1}{2}\mathbf{AD} = \mathbf{AN}$$

Hence, $\mathbf{AM} = \mathbf{AN} \Rightarrow M = N$ so the diagonals bisect each other.

## 13.2 MODELING PROJECTILE MOTION

1. $x = (v_0 \cos \alpha)\, t$. $\therefore$ $(840 \text{ m/s})(\cos 60^\circ) = (21 \text{ km})\left(\frac{1000 \text{ m}}{1 \text{ km}}\right) \Rightarrow t = 50$ seconds.

3. (a) $t = \frac{2 v_0 \sin \alpha}{g} = \frac{2\,(500 \text{ m/sec})(\sin 45^\circ)}{9.8 \text{ m/sec}^2} \approx 72.2$ sec

$R = v_0 \cos \alpha\, t = (500 \text{ m/sec})(\cos 45^\circ)(72.2 \text{ sec}) \approx 25{,}510.2$ m

(b) $v_0 \cos \alpha\, t = R$, so $(500 \text{ m/sec})(\cos 45^\circ)\, t = 5000 \text{ m} \Rightarrow t = 10\sqrt{2}$ sec

$$y = v_0 \sin \alpha\, t - \frac{1}{2} g t^2$$

$$= (500 \text{ m})\left(\frac{1}{\sqrt{2}}\right)(10\sqrt{2} \text{ sec}) - 4.9 \text{ m/sec}^2\,(10\sqrt{2} \text{ sec})^2 = 4020 \text{ m}$$

(c) $$y_{max} = \frac{(v_0 \sin \alpha)^2}{2g} = \frac{\left(500 \cdot \frac{1}{\sqrt{2}}\right)^2}{2\,(9.8)} = 6{,}377.6 \text{ m}$$

5. Let $\beta = 90^\circ - \alpha$. Then $R = \frac{v_0^2}{g} \sin 2\beta = \sin 2\,(90^\circ - \alpha)$

$$= \frac{v_0^2}{g} \sin (180^\circ - 2\alpha) = \frac{v_0^2}{g} \sin 2\alpha.$$

7. $R = \frac{v_0^2}{g} \sin 2\alpha$. Then $v_0^2 \sin 90^\circ = (10 \text{ m})(9.8 \text{ m/sec}^2) \Rightarrow v_0 = 9.9$ m/sec

$(9.9 \text{ m/sec})^2 \sin 2\alpha = (6\text{m})(9.8 \text{ m/sec}^2) \Rightarrow \sin 2\alpha = 0.5999 \Rightarrow 2\alpha = 39.6^\circ$,

so $\alpha = 18.5^\circ$ or $90^\circ - 18.5^\circ = 71.6^\circ$.

9. $\frac{v_0^2}{32 \text{ ft/sec}^2}(\sin 18^\circ) = 248.8 \text{ yd}\left(\frac{3\text{ft}}{1 \text{ yd}}\right) \Rightarrow v_0 = 278 \text{ ft/sec} = 189.6$ mph

11. The maximum height $y_{max} = \dfrac{(v_0 \sin\alpha)^2}{g}$ is reached in $t_{max} = \dfrac{v_0 \sin\alpha}{g}$ sec.

The time required to reach $\frac{3}{4}$ the maximum height is:

$$(v_0 \sin\alpha)t - \frac{1}{2}gt^2 = \frac{3}{4}\frac{(v_0 \sin\alpha)^2}{g} \Rightarrow 4g^2t^2 - 8gv_0 \sin\alpha\, t + 3(v_0 \sin\alpha)^2 = 0$$

$$(2gt - v_0 \sin\alpha)(2gt - 3v_0 \sin\alpha\, t) = 0 \Rightarrow t = \frac{v_0 \sin\alpha}{2g} \text{ or } \frac{3v_0 \sin\alpha}{2g}$$

$\therefore\ t = \frac{1}{2}t_{max}$ (going up) or $\frac{3}{2}t_{max}$ (going down)

13. The time required to travel 135 feet is: $t = \dfrac{x}{v_0 \cos\alpha} = \dfrac{135}{45\sqrt{3}} = \sqrt{3}$ sec.

$$y = v_0 \sin\alpha\, t - \frac{1}{2}gt^2 = 90\left(\frac{1}{2}\right)\sqrt{3} - \frac{1}{2}(32)(\sqrt{3})^2 = 29.9 \text{ ft.}$$

The ball will not clear the 30 ft tree.

15. The time required to travel 315 feet is $t = \dfrac{315}{v_0 \cos 20^\circ}$

During this time, the ball rose to a height of 37 feet, i.e..

$y = v_0 \sin\alpha\, t + y_0 - \frac{1}{2}gt^2$ or

$$v_0 \sin 20^\circ\left(\frac{315}{v_0 \cos 20^\circ}\right) + 3 - 16\left(\frac{315}{v_0 \cos 20^\circ}\right)^2 = 37 \Rightarrow v_0 = 149.3 \text{ ft/sec}$$

The time $t = \dfrac{315}{v_0 \cos 20^\circ} = 2.25$ sec

17. For B: $y = R\tan\alpha - \frac{1}{2}gt^2$. For A: $y = v_0 \sin\alpha\, t - \frac{1}{2}gt^2$.

Since $t = \dfrac{R}{v_0 \cos\alpha}$, for A: $y = v_0 \sin\alpha\left(\dfrac{R}{v_0 \cos\alpha}\right) - \frac{1}{2}gt^2$

$= R\tan\alpha - \frac{1}{2}gt^2$. $\therefore$ A and B will collide regardless of $v_0$.

19. The distance to be traveled is $R = b + at$. $\therefore\ \dfrac{v_0^2 \sin 2\alpha}{g} = b + at$.

$t = \dfrac{2v_0 \sin\alpha}{g}$, so $\dfrac{v_0^2 \sin 2\alpha}{g} = b + a\left(\dfrac{2v_0 \sin\alpha}{g}\right)$, or

$v_0^2 \sin 2\alpha - bg - 2av_0 \sin\alpha = 0$.

## 13.3 COORDINATES AND VECTORS IN SPACE

1. The intersection of the plane $x = 2$ with the plane $y = 3$ to form a line parallel to the z-axis through the point (2,3,0).

3. The x-axis.

5. A circle in the xy-plane with center (0,0,0) and radius 2.

7. A circle in the xz-plane with center (0,0,0) and radius 2.

9. A circle in the xy-plane with center (0,0,0) and radius 1.

11. A circle in the xy-plane with center (0,0,0) and radius 4 formed by slicing the sphere with center (0,0,-3) and radius 5 by the plane $z = 0$.

13. (a) The first quadrant of the xy-plane.
    (b) The fourth quadrant of the xy-plane.

15. (a) The sphere with center (0,0,0) and radius 1, with its interior.
    (b) The exterior of the sphere in part (a).

17. (a) Hemisphere with center (0,0,0) and radius 1, lying above the xy-plane.
    (b) The hemisphere in part (a) with its interior.

19. (a) $x = 3$ (b) $y = -1$ (c) $z = -2$

21. (a) $z = 1$ (b) $x = 3$ (c) $y = -1$

23. (a) $x^2 + (y-2)^2 = 4,\ z = 0$ (b) $(y-2)^2 + z^2 = 4,\ x = 0$
    (c) $x^2 + z^2 = 4,\ y = 2$

25. (a) $y = 3,\ z = -1$ (b) $x = 1,\ z = -1$ (c) $x = 1, y = 3$

27. $x^2 + y^2 = 16,\ z = 3$

29. $0 \le z \le 1$

31. $z \le 0$

33. (a) $(x-1)^2 + (y-1)^2 + (z-1)^2 < 1$
    (b) $(x-1)^2 + (y-1)^2 + (z-1)^2 > 1$

35. $|2\mathbf{i} + \mathbf{j} - 2\mathbf{k}| = \sqrt{4+1+4} = 3;\ \mathbf{u} = \frac{2}{3}\mathbf{i} + \frac{1}{3}\mathbf{j} - \frac{2}{3}\mathbf{k}$

37. $|\mathbf{i} + 4\mathbf{j} - 8\mathbf{k}| = \sqrt{1+16+64} = 9;\ \mathbf{u} = \frac{1}{9}\mathbf{i} + \frac{4}{9}\mathbf{j} - \frac{8}{9}\mathbf{k}$

39. $|5\mathbf{k}| = 5;\ \mathbf{u} = \mathbf{k}$

41. $\left|\frac{1}{\sqrt{2}}\mathbf{i} - \frac{1}{\sqrt{2}}\mathbf{k}\right| = \sqrt{\frac{1}{2} + \frac{1}{2}} = 1;\ = \frac{1}{\sqrt{2}}\mathbf{i} - \frac{1}{\sqrt{2}}\mathbf{k}$

43. $\left|\frac{1}{\sqrt{3}}\mathbf{i} + \frac{1}{\sqrt{3}}\mathbf{j} + \frac{1}{\sqrt{3}}\mathbf{k}\right| = \sqrt{\frac{1}{3} + \frac{1}{3} + \frac{1}{3}} = 1;\ \mathbf{u} = \frac{1}{\sqrt{3}}\mathbf{i} + \frac{1}{\sqrt{3}}\mathbf{j} + \frac{1}{\sqrt{3}}\mathbf{k}$

45. $|6\mathbf{i}| = 6;\ \mathbf{u} = \mathbf{i}$

47. (a) $2\mathbf{i}$ (b) $-4\mathbf{j}$ (c) $\sqrt{3}\mathbf{k}$
    (d) $\frac{3}{10}\mathbf{j} + \frac{4}{10}\mathbf{k}$ (e) $6\mathbf{i} - 2\mathbf{j} + 3\mathbf{k}$ (f) $au_1\mathbf{i} + au_2\mathbf{j} + au_3\mathbf{k}$

49. $|\mathbf{i} + \mathbf{j} + \mathbf{k}| = \sqrt{3};\ \mathbf{u} = \frac{5}{\sqrt{3}}(\mathbf{i} + \mathbf{j} + \mathbf{k})$

51. $x^2+y^2+z^2+4x-4z=0 \Rightarrow x^2+4x+4+y^2+z^2-4z+4=8$

$(x+2)^2+y^2+(z-2)^2=8$; Center $(-2,0,2)$, radius $=2\sqrt{2}$

53. $x^2+y^2+z^2-2az=0 \Rightarrow x^2+y^2+z^2-2az+a^2=a^2$

$x^2+y^2+(z-a)^2=a^2$; Center $(0,0,a)$, radius $=a$

55. (a) $d_1=\sqrt{y^2+z^2}$

(b) $d_2=\sqrt{x^2+z^2}$

(c) $d_3=\sqrt{x^2+y^2}$

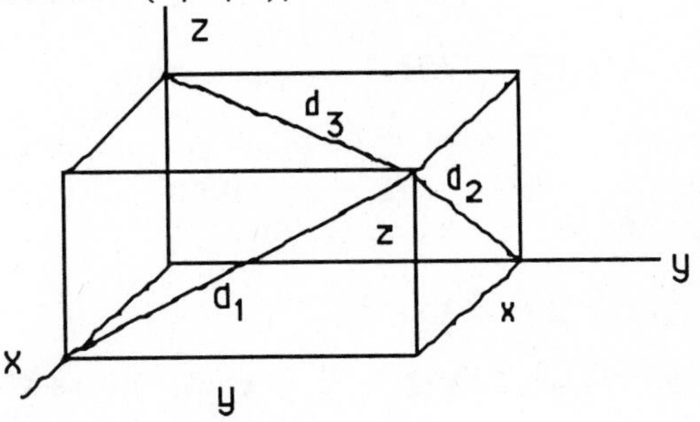


57. (a) $M=\left(\frac{4+1}{2},\frac{3+2}{2},\frac{0+0}{2}\right)=\left(\frac{5}{2},\frac{5}{2},0\right)$

$\vec{CM}=\left(\frac{5}{2}\mathbf{i}+\frac{5}{2}\mathbf{j}+0\mathbf{k}\right)-(\mathbf{i}+\mathbf{j}+3\mathbf{k})=\left(\frac{3}{2}\mathbf{i}+\frac{3}{2}\mathbf{j}-3\mathbf{k}\right)$

(b) $\mathbf{x}=\frac{2}{3}\left(\frac{3}{2}\mathbf{i}+\frac{3}{2}\mathbf{j}-3\mathbf{k}\right)=\mathbf{i}+\mathbf{j}-2\mathbf{k}$

(c) $\mathbf{v}=(\mathbf{i}+\mathbf{j}+3\mathbf{k})+(\mathbf{i}+\mathbf{j}-2\mathbf{k})=2\mathbf{i}+2\mathbf{j}+\mathbf{k}$.

The center of mass is the point $(2,2,1)$.

## 13.4 DOT PRODUCTS

1. $\mathbf{A}=3\mathbf{i}+2\mathbf{j}$; $\mathbf{B}=5\mathbf{j}+\mathbf{k}$

$\mathbf{A}\cdot\mathbf{B}=(3\mathbf{i}+2\mathbf{j}+0\mathbf{k})\cdot(0\mathbf{i}+5\mathbf{j}+\mathbf{k})=3\cdot0+2\cdot5\ 0\cdot1=10$

$|\mathbf{A}|=\sqrt{9+4}=\sqrt{13}$; $|\mathbf{B}|=\sqrt{25+1}=\sqrt{26}$

$\cos\theta=\frac{\mathbf{A}\cdot\mathbf{B}}{|\mathbf{A}||\mathbf{B}|}=\frac{10}{\sqrt{13}\sqrt{26}}=\frac{5\sqrt{2}}{13}$

$|\mathbf{B}|\cos\theta=\sqrt{26}\cdot\frac{10}{\sqrt{13}\sqrt{26}}=\frac{10}{\sqrt{13}}$

$\text{Proj}_{\mathbf{A}}\mathbf{B}=\left(\frac{\mathbf{A}\cdot\mathbf{B}}{\mathbf{A}\cdot\mathbf{A}}\right)\mathbf{A}=\frac{10}{13}(3\mathbf{i}+2\mathbf{j})=\frac{30}{13}\mathbf{i}+\frac{20}{13}\mathbf{j}$

3. $\mathbf{A} = 3\mathbf{i} - 2\mathbf{j} - \mathbf{k}$; $\mathbf{B} = -2\mathbf{j}$

$\mathbf{A} \cdot \mathbf{B} = (3\mathbf{i} - 2\mathbf{j} - \mathbf{k}) \cdot (0\mathbf{i} - 2\mathbf{j} + 0\mathbf{k}) = 3 \cdot 0 + (-2)(-2) + 0(-1) = 4$

$|\mathbf{A}| = \sqrt{9+4+1} = \sqrt{14}$; $|\mathbf{B}| = \sqrt{4} = 2$

$$\cos\theta = \frac{\mathbf{A} \cdot \mathbf{B}}{|\mathbf{A}||\mathbf{B}|} = \frac{4}{2\sqrt{14}} = \frac{2}{\sqrt{14}}$$

$$|\mathbf{B}|\cos\theta = 2 \cdot \frac{2}{\sqrt{14}} = \frac{4}{\sqrt{14}}$$

$$\text{Proj}_{\mathbf{A}}\mathbf{B} = \left(\frac{\mathbf{A} \cdot \mathbf{B}}{\mathbf{A} \cdot \mathbf{A}}\right)\mathbf{A} = \frac{2}{7}(3\mathbf{i} - 2\mathbf{j} - \mathbf{k}) = \frac{6}{7}\mathbf{i} - \frac{4}{7}\mathbf{j} - \frac{2}{7}\mathbf{k}$$

5. $\mathbf{A} = 5\mathbf{j} - 3\mathbf{k}$; $\mathbf{B} = \mathbf{i} + \mathbf{j} + \mathbf{k}$

$\mathbf{A} \cdot \mathbf{B} = (0\mathbf{i} + 5\mathbf{j} - 3\mathbf{k}) \cdot (\mathbf{i} + \mathbf{j} + \mathbf{k}) = (1)(0) + (5)(1) + (1)(-3) = 2$

$|\mathbf{A}| = \sqrt{25+9} = \sqrt{34}$; $|\mathbf{B}| = \sqrt{1+1+1} = \sqrt{3}$

$$\cos\theta = \frac{\mathbf{A} \cdot \mathbf{B}}{|\mathbf{A}||\mathbf{B}|} = \frac{2}{\sqrt{34}\sqrt{3}} = \frac{2}{\sqrt{102}}$$

$$|\mathbf{B}|\cos\theta = \sqrt{3} \cdot \frac{2}{\sqrt{102}} = \frac{2}{\sqrt{34}}$$

$$\text{Proj}_{\mathbf{A}}\mathbf{B} = \left(\frac{\mathbf{A} \cdot \mathbf{B}}{\mathbf{A} \cdot \mathbf{A}}\right)\mathbf{A} = \frac{1}{17}(5\mathbf{j} - 3\mathbf{k}) = \frac{5}{17}\mathbf{j} - \frac{3}{17}\mathbf{k}$$

7. $\mathbf{A} = -\mathbf{i} + \mathbf{j}$; $\mathbf{B} = \sqrt{2}\mathbf{i} + \sqrt{3}\mathbf{j} + 2\mathbf{k}$

$\mathbf{A} \cdot \mathbf{B} = (-\mathbf{i} + \mathbf{j} + 0\mathbf{k}) \cdot (\sqrt{2}\mathbf{i} + \sqrt{3}\mathbf{j} + 2\mathbf{k}) = (-1)(\sqrt{2}) + (1)(\sqrt{3}) + (0)(2) = \sqrt{3} - \sqrt{2}$

$|\mathbf{A}| = \sqrt{1+1} = \sqrt{2}$; $|\mathbf{B}| = \sqrt{2+3+4} = 3$

$$\cos\theta = \frac{\mathbf{A} \cdot \mathbf{B}}{|\mathbf{A}||\mathbf{B}|} = \frac{\sqrt{3} - \sqrt{2}}{3\sqrt{2}} = \frac{\sqrt{6} - 2}{6}$$

$$|\mathbf{B}|\cos\theta = 3 \cdot \frac{\sqrt{6} - 2}{6} = \frac{\sqrt{6} - 2}{2}$$

$$\text{Proj}_{\mathbf{A}}\mathbf{B} = \left(\frac{\mathbf{A} \cdot \mathbf{B}}{\mathbf{A} \cdot \mathbf{A}}\right)\mathbf{A} = \frac{\sqrt{3} - \sqrt{2}}{2}(-\mathbf{i} + \mathbf{j})$$

9. $\mathbf{A} = 2\mathbf{i} - 4\mathbf{j} + \sqrt{5}\mathbf{k}$; $\mathbf{B} = -2\mathbf{i} + 4\mathbf{j} - \sqrt{5}\mathbf{k}$

$$\mathbf{A} \cdot \mathbf{B} = (2\mathbf{i} - 4\mathbf{j} + \sqrt{5}\mathbf{k}) \cdot (-2\mathbf{i} + 4\mathbf{j} - \sqrt{5}\mathbf{k}) = (-2)(2) + (-4)(4) + (\sqrt{5})(-\sqrt{5}) = -25$$

$$|\mathbf{A}| = \sqrt{4 + 16 + 5} = 5;\ |\mathbf{B}| = \sqrt{4 + 16 + 5} = 5$$

$$\cos\theta = \frac{\mathbf{A} \cdot \mathbf{B}}{|\mathbf{A}|\,|\mathbf{B}|} = -1$$

$$|\mathbf{B}|\cos\theta = -5$$

$$\mathrm{Proj}_{\mathbf{A}}\mathbf{B} = \left(\frac{\mathbf{A} \cdot \mathbf{B}}{\mathbf{A} \cdot \mathbf{A}}\right)\mathbf{A} = -(2\mathbf{i} - 4\mathbf{j} + \sqrt{5}\mathbf{k}) = -2\mathbf{i} + 4\mathbf{j} - \sqrt{5}\mathbf{k}$$

11. $\mathbf{A} = 10\mathbf{i} + 11\mathbf{j} - 2\mathbf{k}$; $\mathbf{B} = 3\mathbf{j} + 4\mathbf{k}$

$$\mathbf{A} \cdot \mathbf{B} = (10\mathbf{i} + 11\mathbf{j} - 2\mathbf{k}) \cdot (3\mathbf{j} + 4\mathbf{k}) = (10)(0) + (11)(3) + (-2)(4) = 25$$

$$|\mathbf{A}| = \sqrt{100 + 121 + 4} = 15;\ |\mathbf{B}| = \sqrt{9 + 16} = 5$$

$$\cos\theta = \frac{\mathbf{A} \cdot \mathbf{B}}{|\mathbf{A}|\,|\mathbf{B}|} = \frac{1}{3}$$

$$|\mathbf{B}|\cos\theta = \frac{5}{3}$$

$$\mathrm{Proj}_{\mathbf{A}}\mathbf{B} = \left(\frac{\mathbf{A} \cdot \mathbf{B}}{\mathbf{A} \cdot \mathbf{A}}\right)\mathbf{A} = \frac{1}{9}(10\mathbf{i} + 11\mathbf{j} - 2\mathbf{k}) = \frac{10}{9}\mathbf{i} + \frac{11}{9}\mathbf{j} - \frac{2}{9}\mathbf{k}$$

13. $\overrightarrow{AC} = (1 + 1)\mathbf{i} + (-2 - 0)\mathbf{j} + (2 - 2)\mathbf{k} = 2\mathbf{i} - 2\mathbf{j}$

$$\overrightarrow{AB} = (2 + 1)\mathbf{i} + (1 - 0)\mathbf{j} + (-1 - 2)\mathbf{k} = 3\mathbf{i} + \mathbf{j} - 3\mathbf{k}$$

$$\cos\angle BAC = \frac{\mathbf{A} \cdot \mathbf{B}}{|\mathbf{A}|\,|\mathbf{B}|} = \frac{6 - 2}{\sqrt{8}\sqrt{19}} = \frac{4}{\sqrt{152}};\ \angle BAC \approx 71.1^\circ$$

$$\overrightarrow{BA} = -3\mathbf{i} - \mathbf{j} + 3\mathbf{k};\ \overrightarrow{BC} = -\mathbf{i} - 3\mathbf{j} + 3\mathbf{k}$$

$$\cos\angle CBA = \frac{3 + 3 + 9}{\sqrt{19}\sqrt{19}} = \frac{15}{19};\ \angle CBA \approx 37.9^\circ$$

$$\overrightarrow{CA} = -2\mathbf{i} + 2\mathbf{j};\ \overrightarrow{CB} = \mathbf{i} + 3\mathbf{j} - 3\mathbf{k}$$

$$\cos\angle CAB = \frac{-2 + 6 + 0}{\sqrt{19}\sqrt{8}} = \frac{4}{\sqrt{152}};\ \angle CAB \approx 71.1^\circ$$

15. $\cos\theta = \dfrac{(\mathbf{i} + \mathbf{j} + \mathbf{k}) \cdot (\mathbf{i} + \mathbf{k})}{\sqrt{3}\sqrt{2}} = \dfrac{2}{\sqrt{6}};\ \theta = 35.3^\circ$

17. $\mathbf{v} = OB = 2\mathbf{i} + 4\mathbf{j} - 3\mathbf{k}$; $\mathbf{w} = OA = \mathbf{i} + \mathbf{j}$ (contained in the line $y = x$)

$$\mathrm{Proj}_{\mathbf{w}}\mathbf{v} = \left(\frac{\mathbf{v} \cdot \mathbf{w}}{|\mathbf{w}|\,|\mathbf{w}|}\right)\mathbf{w} = \frac{2 + 4}{\sqrt{1 + 1}\sqrt{1 + 1}}(\mathbf{i} + \mathbf{j}) = 3\mathbf{i} + 3\mathbf{j}.$$ Thepoint is (3,3,0

19. We want to write $\mathbf{B} = \text{Proj}_{\mathbf{A}}\mathbf{B} + (\mathbf{B} - \text{Proj}_{\mathbf{A}}\mathbf{B})$

$$\text{Proj}_{\mathbf{A}}\mathbf{B} = \frac{(\mathbf{i}+\mathbf{j})\cdot(3\mathbf{j}+4\mathbf{k})}{\sqrt{2}\sqrt{2}}(\mathbf{i}+\mathbf{j}) = \frac{3}{2}\mathbf{i} + \frac{3}{2}\mathbf{j}$$

$$\therefore\ 3\mathbf{j} + 4\mathbf{k} = \left(\frac{3}{2}\mathbf{i} + \frac{3}{2}\mathbf{j}\right) + \left(-\frac{3}{2}\mathbf{i} + \frac{3}{2}\mathbf{j} + 4\mathbf{k}\right)$$

21. (a) $\mathbf{N} = \mathbf{i} + 3\mathbf{j}$ is normal to the line $x + 3y = 6$; $(0,2)$ is a point on the line and $\mathbf{v} = (2-0)\mathbf{i} + (8-2)\mathbf{j} = 2\mathbf{i} + 6\mathbf{j}$ is a vector from the point $(2,8)$ to the normal. The distance is

$$d = |\text{proj}_{\mathbf{N}}\mathbf{v}| = \left|\frac{(2\mathbf{i}+6\mathbf{j})\cdot(\mathbf{i}+3\mathbf{j})}{\sqrt{10}}\right| = 2\sqrt{10}$$

(b) $$d = \left|\frac{-2\mathbf{j}\cdot(\mathbf{i}+3\mathbf{j})}{\sqrt{10}}\right| = \frac{6}{\sqrt{10}}$$

23. We show that their dot products are 0.

$$\frac{1}{\sqrt{3}}(\mathbf{i}-\mathbf{j}+\mathbf{k})\cdot\frac{1}{\sqrt{2}}(\mathbf{j}+\mathbf{k}) = \frac{1}{\sqrt{6}}(0-1+1) = 0$$

$$\frac{1}{\sqrt{3}}(\mathbf{i}-\mathbf{j}+\mathbf{k})\cdot\frac{1}{\sqrt{6}}(-2\mathbf{i}-\mathbf{j}+\mathbf{k}) = \frac{1}{\sqrt{18}}(-2+1+1) = 0$$

$$\frac{1}{\sqrt{2}}(\mathbf{j}+\mathbf{k})\cdot\frac{1}{\sqrt{6}}(-2\mathbf{i}-\mathbf{j}+\mathbf{k}) = \frac{1}{\sqrt{12}}(0-1+1) = 0$$

25. $\mathbf{v} = \mathbf{i}+\mathbf{j}+\mathbf{k}$ goes from origin to $(1,1,1)$.

$W = |\mathbf{F}|\,|\mathbf{v}|\cos\theta = (-5\mathbf{k})\cdot(\mathbf{i}+\mathbf{j}+\mathbf{k}) = -5$ newton-meters

27. $W = (200\text{ N})(20\text{ m})\cos 30^\circ = 2000\sqrt{3}$ newton-meters

29. $(\mathbf{v}_1+\mathbf{v}_2)\cdot(\mathbf{v}_1-\mathbf{v}_2) = \mathbf{v}_1\cdot\mathbf{v}_1 + \mathbf{v}_1\cdot\mathbf{v}_2 - \mathbf{v}_2\cdot\mathbf{v}_1 + \mathbf{v}_2\cdot\mathbf{v}_2$

$= |\mathbf{v}_1|^2 - |\mathbf{v}_2|^2 = 0 \Leftrightarrow |\mathbf{v}_1| = |\mathbf{v}_2|$.

31. If $\mathbf{v}_1$ and $\mathbf{v}_2$ are the sides of a rectangle, then $(\mathbf{v}_1+\mathbf{v}_2)$ and $(\mathbf{v}_1-\mathbf{v}_2)$ are the two diagonals. By Problem 29, these are perpendicular if $|\mathbf{v}_1| = |\mathbf{v}_2|$ so that the rectangle is a square.

33. $3x + y = 5$ has slope $\frac{-3}{1} = \frac{\Delta y}{\Delta x}$ and direction $\mathbf{N}_1 = \frac{1}{\sqrt{10}}(\mathbf{i} - 3\mathbf{j})$;

$2x - y = 4$ has slope $\frac{2}{1}$ and direction $\mathbf{N}_2 = \frac{1}{\sqrt{5}}(\mathbf{i} + 2\mathbf{j})$.

$$\cos\theta = \mathbf{N}_1\cdot\mathbf{N}_2 = \frac{1}{\sqrt{50}}(1-6) = -\frac{1}{\sqrt{2}}.\quad \therefore\ \theta = \frac{\pi}{4}\left(\text{or } \frac{3\pi}{4}\right).$$

35. $\sqrt{\frac{3}{4}+x}=\sqrt{\frac{3}{4}-x}$ if $x=0$, $y=\sqrt{\frac{3}{4}}$. $\frac{d}{dx}\left(\sqrt{\frac{3}{4}+x}\right)=\frac{1}{2}\left(\frac{3}{4}+x\right)^{-1/2}=\frac{1}{\sqrt{3}}$

at $\left(0,\sqrt{\frac{3}{4}}\right)$; the tangent vector is $\mathbf{T}_1 = \sqrt{3}\mathbf{i} + \mathbf{j}$;

$\frac{d}{dx}\sqrt{\frac{3}{4}-x}=-\frac{1}{2}\left(\frac{3}{4}-x\right)^{-1/2}=-\frac{1}{\sqrt{3}}$ at $\left(0,\sqrt{\frac{3}{4}}\right)$; the tangent vector is

$\mathbf{T}_2 = \sqrt{3}\mathbf{i} - \mathbf{j}$. $\cos\theta = \frac{\mathbf{T}_1 \cdot \mathbf{T}_2}{|\mathbf{T}_1||\mathbf{T}_2|} = \frac{1}{2}$. $\therefore \theta = \frac{\pi}{3}$

37. $x^2 = x^{1/3}$ if $x=0$ or $1$. $\frac{d}{dx}(x^2) = 2x$ and $\frac{d}{dx}(x^{1/3}) = \frac{1}{3}x^{-2/3}$.

At $x=0$, the tangent vectors have slope 0 and undefined, so $\theta = \frac{\pi}{2}$.

At $x=1$, $y=x^2$ has $\frac{dy}{dx}=2$ and $\mathbf{T}_1 = \mathbf{i} + 2\mathbf{j}$; $y=x^{1/3}$ has $\frac{dy}{dx}=\frac{1}{3}$ amd

the tangent vector is $\mathbf{T}_2 = 3\mathbf{i}+\mathbf{j}$. $\cos\theta = \frac{\mathbf{T}_1 \cdot \mathbf{T}_2}{|\mathbf{T}_1||\mathbf{T}_2|} = \frac{1}{\sqrt{2}}$. $\therefore \theta = \frac{\pi}{4}$.

## 13.5 CROSS PRODUCTS

1. $\mathbf{A}\times\mathbf{B} = \begin{vmatrix} \mathbf{i} & \mathbf{j} & \mathbf{k} \\ 2 & -2 & -1 \\ 1 & 1 & 1 \end{vmatrix} = \mathbf{i}\begin{vmatrix} -2 & -1 \\ 1 & 1 \end{vmatrix} - \mathbf{j}\begin{vmatrix} 2 & -1 \\ 1 & 1 \end{vmatrix} + \mathbf{k}\begin{vmatrix} 2 & -2 \\ 1 & 1 \end{vmatrix} = -\mathbf{i} - 3\mathbf{j} + 4\mathbf{k}$

$|\mathbf{A}\times\mathbf{B}| = |\mathbf{B}\times\mathbf{A}| = \sqrt{1+9+16} = \sqrt{26}$

Direction of $\mathbf{A}\times\mathbf{B} = \frac{1}{\sqrt{26}}(-\mathbf{i} - 3\mathbf{j} + 4\mathbf{k})$; of $\mathbf{B}\times\mathbf{A} = \frac{1}{\sqrt{26}}(\mathbf{i} + 3\mathbf{j} - 4\mathbf{k})$

3. $\mathbf{A} = 2\mathbf{B} \Rightarrow |\mathbf{A}\times\mathbf{B}| = |\mathbf{B}\times\mathbf{A}| = 0\mathbf{i} + 0\mathbf{j} + 0\mathbf{k}$

5. $\mathbf{A}\times\mathbf{B} = 2\mathbf{i}\times(-3\mathbf{j}) = -6(\mathbf{i}\times\mathbf{j}) = -6\mathbf{k}$; $|-6\mathbf{k}| = 6$; direction of

$\mathbf{A}\times\mathbf{B} = -\mathbf{k}$; of $\mathbf{B}\times\mathbf{A} = \mathbf{k}$.

7. $\mathbf{A}\times\mathbf{B} = \begin{vmatrix} \mathbf{i} & \mathbf{j} & \mathbf{k} \\ -8 & -2 & -4 \\ 2 & 2 & 1 \end{vmatrix} = \mathbf{i}\begin{vmatrix} -2 & -4 \\ 2 & 1 \end{vmatrix} - \mathbf{j}\begin{vmatrix} -8 & -4 \\ 2 & 1 \end{vmatrix} + \mathbf{k}\begin{vmatrix} -8 & -2 \\ 2 & 2 \end{vmatrix} = 6\mathbf{i} - 12\mathbf{k}$

$|\mathbf{A}\times\mathbf{B}| = 6\sqrt{5}$; direction is $\frac{1}{\sqrt{5}}\mathbf{i} - \frac{2}{\sqrt{5}}\mathbf{k}$; direction of $\mathbf{B}\times\mathbf{A} = -\frac{1}{\sqrt{5}}\mathbf{i} + \frac{2}{\sqrt{5}}\mathbf{k}$

9. $\mathbf{A}\times\mathbf{B} = \mathbf{i}\times\mathbf{j} = \mathbf{k}$

11. $\mathbf{A} \times \mathbf{B} = \begin{vmatrix} \mathbf{i} & \mathbf{j} & \mathbf{k} \\ 1 & 0 & -1 \\ 0 & 1 & 1 \end{vmatrix} = \mathbf{i} - \mathbf{j} + \mathbf{k}$

13. $\mathbf{A} \times \mathbf{B} = \begin{vmatrix} \mathbf{i} & \mathbf{j} & \mathbf{k} \\ 1 & 3 & 2 \\ 0 & 0 & 1 \end{vmatrix} = 3\mathbf{i} - \mathbf{j}$

15. Let $\mathbf{A} = \overrightarrow{AB} = (2-1)\mathbf{i} + (0+1)\mathbf{j} + (-1-2)\mathbf{k} = \mathbf{i} + \mathbf{j} - 3\mathbf{k}$

$\mathbf{B} = \overrightarrow{AC} = (0-1)\mathbf{i} + (2+1)\mathbf{j} + (1-2)\mathbf{k} = -\mathbf{i} + 3\mathbf{j} - \mathbf{k}$

$\mathbf{N} = \mathbf{A} \times \mathbf{B} = \begin{vmatrix} \mathbf{i} & \mathbf{j} & \mathbf{k} \\ 1 & 1 & -3 \\ -1 & 3 & -1 \end{vmatrix} = 8\mathbf{i} + 4\mathbf{j} + 4\mathbf{k}$

17. From Problem 15, $\mathbf{N} = 2\mathbf{i} + \mathbf{j} + \mathbf{k}$. $OA = \mathbf{i} - \mathbf{j} + 2\mathbf{k}$.

Distance $= \overrightarrow{OA} \cdot \dfrac{\mathbf{N}}{|\mathbf{N}|} = (\mathbf{i} - \mathbf{j} + 2\mathbf{k}) \cdot \dfrac{2\mathbf{i} + \mathbf{j} + \mathbf{k}}{\sqrt{4+1+1}} = \sqrt{\dfrac{3}{2}}$

19. $\mathbf{A} \times \mathbf{B} = 2\mathbf{i} - 4\mathbf{j} + 4\mathbf{k}$. Area $= \dfrac{1}{2}|\mathbf{A} \times \mathbf{B}| = \dfrac{1}{2}\sqrt{4+16+16} = 3$

21. $\mathbf{A} \times \mathbf{B} = \begin{vmatrix} \mathbf{i} & \mathbf{j} & \mathbf{k} \\ 2 & -1 & 0 \\ 1 & 3 & -2 \end{vmatrix} = 2\mathbf{i} + 4\mathbf{j} + 7\mathbf{k}$

$(\mathbf{A} \times \mathbf{B}) \cdot \mathbf{A} = (2\mathbf{i} + 4\mathbf{j} + 7\mathbf{k}) \cdot (2\mathbf{i} - \mathbf{j} + 0\mathbf{k}) = 0$

$(\mathbf{A} \times \mathbf{B}) \cdot \mathbf{B} = (2\mathbf{i} + 4\mathbf{j} + 7\mathbf{k}) \cdot (\mathbf{i} + 3\mathbf{j} - 2\mathbf{k}) = 0$

23. $\mathbf{A} \cdot \mathbf{B} = (5\mathbf{i} - \mathbf{j} + \mathbf{k}) \cdot (0\mathbf{i} + \mathbf{j} - 5\mathbf{k}) = -6 \neq 0$

$\mathbf{A} \cdot \mathbf{C} = (5\mathbf{i} - \mathbf{j} + \mathbf{k}) \cdot (-15\mathbf{i} + 3\mathbf{j} - 3\mathbf{k}) = -81 \neq 0$

$\mathbf{B} \cdot \mathbf{C} = (0\mathbf{i} + \mathbf{j} - 5\mathbf{k}) \cdot (-15\mathbf{i} + 3\mathbf{j} - 3\mathbf{k}) = 18 \neq 0$; none are $\perp$

$\mathbf{C} = -3\mathbf{A} \Rightarrow \mathbf{C} \parallel \mathbf{A}$

25. Let $\overrightarrow{DA} = \mathbf{A}$, $\overrightarrow{DC} = \mathbf{C}$, $\overrightarrow{DB} = \mathbf{B}$, $\overrightarrow{AB} = \mathbf{E}$, and $\overrightarrow{AC} = \mathbf{F}$. Then the required sum is

$\mathbf{N} = (\mathbf{A} \times \mathbf{C}) + (\mathbf{C} \times \mathbf{B}) + (\mathbf{B} \times \mathbf{A}) + (\mathbf{E} \times \mathbf{F})$. Since $\mathbf{E} = \mathbf{B} - \mathbf{A}$ and $\mathbf{F} = \mathbf{C} - \mathbf{A}$,

$\mathbf{E} \times \mathbf{F} = (\mathbf{B} - \mathbf{A}) \times (\mathbf{C} - \mathbf{A}) = (\mathbf{B} \times \mathbf{C}) - (\mathbf{B} \times \mathbf{A}) - (\mathbf{A} \times \mathbf{C}) + (\mathbf{A} \times \mathbf{A})$

$\therefore\ \mathbf{N} = (\mathbf{A} \times \mathbf{C}) + (\mathbf{C} \times \mathbf{B}) + (\mathbf{B} \times \mathbf{A}) + (\mathbf{B} \times \mathbf{C}) - (\mathbf{B} \times \mathbf{A}) - (\mathbf{A} \times \mathbf{C}) + (\mathbf{A} \times \mathbf{A})$

$= (\mathbf{C} \times \mathbf{B}) - (\mathbf{C} \times \mathbf{B}) + (\mathbf{A} \times \mathbf{A}) = 0$

27. Let $\mathbf{A} = (0-1)\mathbf{i} + (1-0)\mathbf{j} = -\mathbf{i} + \mathbf{j}$; $\mathbf{B} = (0-1)\mathbf{i} + (-1-0)\mathbf{j} = -\mathbf{i} - \mathbf{j}$

$\mathbf{A} \times \mathbf{B} = (-\mathbf{i} + \mathbf{j}) \times (-\mathbf{i} - \mathbf{j}) = 2\mathbf{k}$. Area $= |2\mathbf{k}| = 2$.

29. Let $\mathbf{A} = (2+1)\mathbf{i} + (0-2)\mathbf{j} = 3\mathbf{i} - 2\mathbf{j}$; $\mathbf{B} = (4+1)\mathbf{i} + (3-2)\mathbf{j} = 5\mathbf{i} + \mathbf{j}$

$\mathbf{A}\times\mathbf{B} = (3\mathbf{i} - 2\mathbf{j}) \times (5\mathbf{i} + \mathbf{j}) = 13\mathbf{k}$. Area $= |13\mathbf{k}| = 13$.

31. Let $\mathbf{A} = (-2-0)\mathbf{i} + (3-0)\mathbf{j} = -2\mathbf{i} + 3\mathbf{j}$; $\mathbf{B} = (3-0)\mathbf{i} + (1-0)\mathbf{j} = 3\mathbf{i} + \mathbf{j}$

$\mathbf{A}\times\mathbf{B} = (-2\mathbf{i} + 3\mathbf{j}) \times (3\mathbf{i} + \mathbf{j}) = -11\mathbf{k}$. Area $= \frac{1}{2}|-11\mathbf{k}| = \frac{11}{2}$.

33. Let $\mathbf{A} = (1+5)\mathbf{i} + (-2-3)\mathbf{j} = 6\mathbf{i} - 5\mathbf{j}$; $\mathbf{B} = (6+5)\mathbf{i} + (-2-3)\mathbf{j} = 11\mathbf{i} - 5\mathbf{j}$

$\mathbf{A}\times\mathbf{B} = (6\mathbf{i} - 5\mathbf{j}) \times (11\mathbf{i} - 5\mathbf{j}) = 25\mathbf{k}$. Area $= \frac{1}{2}|25\mathbf{k}| = \frac{25}{2}$.

35. Let $\mathbf{A} = a_1\mathbf{i} + a_2\mathbf{j}$ = ; $\mathbf{B} = b_1\mathbf{i} + b_2\mathbf{j}$

$$\mathbf{A}\times\mathbf{B} = \begin{vmatrix} \mathbf{i} & \mathbf{j} & \mathbf{k} \\ a_1 & a_2 & 0 \\ b_1 & b_2 & 0 \end{vmatrix} = \begin{vmatrix} a_1 & a_2 \\ b_1 & b_2 \end{vmatrix}\mathbf{k}$$

Area $= \frac{1}{2}\,|\mathbf{A}\times\mathbf{B}| = \pm\frac{1}{2}\begin{vmatrix} a_1 & a_2 \\ b_1 & b_2 \end{vmatrix}$. The sign is controlled by the sign of $\mathbf{A}\times\mathbf{B}$

## 13.6 EQUATIONS FOR LINES, LINE SEGMENTS AND PLANES IN SPACE

1. $x = 3 + t$; $y = -4 + t$; $z = -1 + t$

3. $PQ = (-2-3)\mathbf{i} + (0-5)\mathbf{j} + (3+2)\mathbf{k} = -5\mathbf{i} - 5\mathbf{j} + 5\mathbf{k}$ is parallel to the line.

$\therefore$ $x = -2 - 5t$, $y = -5t$, $z = 3 + 5t$

5. $x = 0$, $y = 2t$, $z = t$

7. Take $\mathbf{k}$ as a parallel vector. $\therefore$ $x = 1$, $y = 1$, $z = 1 + t$

9. The normal $\mathbf{N} = \mathbf{i} + 2\mathbf{j} + 2\mathbf{k}$ is parallel to the line. Hence

$x = t$, $y = -7 + 2t$, $z = 2t$.

11. $x = t$, $y = 0$, $z = 0$

13. From $(0,0,0)$ to $(1,1,1)$: $x = t$, $y = t$, $z = t$, $0 \le t \le 1$.

15. From $(1,0,0)$ to $(1,1,0)$: $x = 1$, $y = t$, $z = 0$, $0 \le t \le 1$.

17. From $(0,1,1)$ to $(0,-1,1)$: $x = 0$, $y = 1 - 2t$, $z = 1$, $0 \le t \le 1$.

19. From $(1,2,-2)$ to $(2,2,0)$: $x = 1 + t$, $y = 2$, $z = -2 + 2t$, $0 \le t \le 1$.

21. The coefficients are the components of the normal vector:

$3x - 2y - z = d$. To find d, substitute the point into the equation

$d = 3(0) - 2(-2) - (-1) = -3$. $\therefore$ $3x - 2y - z = -3$.

23. Let $\mathbf{A} = (1-2)\mathbf{i} + (1-0)\mathbf{j} + (-1-2)\mathbf{k} = -\mathbf{i} + \mathbf{j} - 3\mathbf{k}$ and

$\mathbf{B} = (1-0)\mathbf{i} + (1+2)\mathbf{j} + (-1-1)\mathbf{k} = \mathbf{i} + 3\mathbf{j} - 2\mathbf{k}$. Then

$$\mathbf{A}\times\mathbf{B} = \begin{vmatrix} \mathbf{i} & \mathbf{j} & \mathbf{k} \\ -1 & 1 & -3 \\ 1 & 3 & -2 \end{vmatrix} = 7\mathbf{i} - 5\mathbf{j} - 4\mathbf{k} \text{ is normal to the plane.}$$

$\therefore$ $7x - 5y - 4z = d$. To find d, substitute a point: $d = 7(2) - 5(0) - 4(2) = 6$

The equation is $7x - 5y - 4z = 6$.

25. Let $\mathbf{A} = \mathbf{i} - \mathbf{j}$ and $\mathbf{B} = \mathbf{j} - \mathbf{k}$ . Then

$$\mathbf{A}\times\mathbf{B} = \begin{vmatrix} \mathbf{i} & \mathbf{j} & \mathbf{k} \\ 1 & -1 & 0 \\ 0 & -1 & 1 \end{vmatrix} = -\mathbf{i} - \mathbf{j} - \mathbf{k} \text{ is normal to the plane.}$$

$\therefore$ $x + y + z = d$. To find d, substitute a point: $d = 0 + 0 + 1$

The equation is $x + y + z = 1$.

27. Using the equation of the line, we find two other points in the plane. Let $t = 0$ gives $P_1(1, -1, 4)$ and letting $t = 1$ gives $P_2(3, 2, 4)$. Using these points and the origin gives two vectors parallel to the plane: $\mathbf{A} = \mathbf{i} - \mathbf{j} + 4\mathbf{k}$ and $\mathbf{B} = 3\mathbf{i} + 2\mathbf{j} + 4\mathbf{k}$. Then

$$\mathbf{N} = \mathbf{A}\times\mathbf{B} = \begin{vmatrix} \mathbf{i} & \mathbf{j} & \mathbf{k} \\ 1 & -1 & 0 \\ 3 & 2 & 4 \end{vmatrix} = -4\mathbf{i} - 4\mathbf{j} + 5\mathbf{k} \text{ and the plane is } 4x + 4y - 5z = 0.$$

29. $\mathbf{N}_1 = 2\mathbf{i} + \mathbf{j} - \mathbf{k}$ is normal to $2x + y - z = 3$ and $\mathbf{N}_2 = \mathbf{i} + 2\mathbf{j} + \mathbf{k}$ is normal to the plane $x + 2y + z = 2$. $\mathbf{N}_1 \times \mathbf{N}_2$ is perpendicular to each normal and hence parallel to the line of intersection of the two planes. $\mathbf{N}_1 \times \mathbf{N}_2$ must then be normal to the required plane.
$\mathbf{N}_1 \times \mathbf{N}_2 = 3\mathbf{i} - 3\mathbf{j} + 3\mathbf{k}$. The plane is $x - y + z = d$. Substituting the point $P_0(2, 1, -1)$ makes $d = 0$. $\therefore x - y + z = 0$.

31. Let $s(t) = (4t)^2 + (-2t)^2 + (2t - 12)^2 = 24t^2 - 48t + 144$.
$s'(t) = 48t - 48 = 0$ if $t = 1$. $s''(t) = 48 > 0 \Rightarrow$ a minimum value.
When $t = 1$, the point is $Q(4, -2, 2)$. The distance
$|PQ| = \sqrt{16 + 4 + 100} = \sqrt{120} = 2\sqrt{30}$.

33. Let $s(t) = (2 + 2t - 2)^2 + (1 + 6t - 1)^2 + (3 - 3)^2$ . $s'(t) = 40t^2 = 0$ if $t = 0$
$s(0) = 0$. This means that the point is on the line.

35. Let $s(t) = (4-2)^2 + (4+2t+1)^2 + (4t+10)^2$ . $s'(t) = 4(2t+5) + 8(4t+10) = 0$
$40t + 100 = 0$ or if $t = -\frac{5}{2}$. $d = \sqrt{4+0+0} = 2$

37. Let $P(13,0,0)$ be a point on the plane. Then $\mathbf{V} = -11\mathbf{i} - 3\mathbf{j} + 4\mathbf{k}$ .

$$\text{Then distance} = \left| \mathbf{V} \cdot \frac{\mathbf{N}}{|\mathbf{N}|} \right| = \left| (-11\mathbf{i} - 3\mathbf{j} + 4\mathbf{k}) \cdot \frac{(\mathbf{i} + 2\mathbf{j} + 2\mathbf{k})}{\sqrt{1+4+4}} \right| = 3.$$

39. Let $P(0,0,-4)$ be a point on the plane. Then $\mathbf{V} = \mathbf{j} + 5\mathbf{k}$.

$$\text{Then distance} = \left| \mathbf{V} \cdot \frac{\mathbf{N}}{|\mathbf{N}|} \right| = \left| (\mathbf{j} + 5\mathbf{k}) \cdot \frac{(4\mathbf{j} + 3\mathbf{k})}{\sqrt{16+9}} \right| = \frac{19}{5}.$$

41. Let $P(2,0,0)$ be a point on the plane. Then $\mathbf{V} = 2\mathbf{i} + \mathbf{j}$.

$$\text{Then distance} = \left| \mathbf{V} \cdot \frac{\mathbf{N}}{|\mathbf{N}|} \right| = \left| (2\mathbf{i} + \mathbf{j}) \cdot \frac{(2\mathbf{i} + \mathbf{j} + 2\mathbf{k})}{\sqrt{4+1+4}} \right| = \frac{5}{3}.$$

43. $2(1-t) - (3t) + 3(1+t) = 6 \Rightarrow -2t + 5 = 6 \Rightarrow t = -\frac{1}{2}$. Then $x = 1 - \left(-\frac{1}{2}\right) = \frac{3}{2}$,
$y = 3\left(-\frac{1}{2}\right) = -\frac{3}{2}$ and $z = 1 - \frac{1}{2} = \frac{1}{2}$. The point is $\left(\frac{3}{2}, -\frac{3}{2}, \frac{1}{2}\right)$.

45. $1 + 2t + 1 + 5t + 3t = 2 \Rightarrow t = 0$. Then $x = 1$,

$y = 1$ and $z = 0$. The point is $(1,1,0)$.

47. $\cos\theta = \dfrac{(2\mathbf{i} + 2\mathbf{j} + 2\mathbf{k}) \cdot (2\mathbf{i} - 2\mathbf{j} - \mathbf{k})}{\sqrt{4+4+4}\sqrt{4+4+1}} = -\dfrac{1}{\sqrt{27}}$. $\theta \approx 78.9°$

49. $\cos\theta = \dfrac{(5\mathbf{i} + \mathbf{j} - \mathbf{k}) \cdot (\mathbf{i} - 2\mathbf{j} + 3\mathbf{k})}{\sqrt{25+1+1}\,\sqrt{1+4+9}} = 0$. $\theta = 90°$.

51. $\mathbf{X} = (\mathbf{i} + \mathbf{j} + \mathbf{k}) \times (\mathbf{i} + \mathbf{j}) = -\mathbf{i} + \mathbf{j}$ is perpendicular to both planes and hence parallel to the required line. We need any point common to both planes. Let $y = 1$. Then $x = 1$ and $z = -1$ is such a point, and the line is $x = 1 - t$, $y = 1 + t$, $z = -1$.

53. $\mathbf{X} = (\mathbf{i} - 2\mathbf{j} + 4\mathbf{k}) \times (\mathbf{i} + \mathbf{j} - 2\mathbf{k}) = 6\mathbf{j} + 3\mathbf{k}$ is perpendicular to to both planes and hence parallel to the required line. We need any point common to both planes. Let $z = 0$. Then $x + y = 5$ and $2x - 2y = 3$. Hence $x = 4$ and $y = 1$, and the line is $x = 4$, $y = 1 + 6t$, $z = 3t$.

55. It meets the xy-plane when $z = 0 \Rightarrow 3t = 0 \Rightarrow t = 0$. The point is $(1,-1,0)$. It meets the xz-plane when $y = 0 \Rightarrow -1-t = 0$ or $t = -1$. The point is $(-1,0,-3)$. It meets the yz-plane when $x = 0 \Rightarrow 1 + 2t = 0 \Rightarrow$ $t = -\frac{1}{2}$. The point is $\left(0, -\frac{1}{2}, -\frac{3}{2}\right)$.

## 13.7 PRODUCTS OF THREE OR MORE VECTORS

1. $V = \mathbf{A} \cdot (\mathbf{B} \times \mathbf{C}) = \begin{vmatrix} 4 & -8 & 1 \\ 2 & 1 & -2 \\ 3 & -4 & 12 \end{vmatrix} = 245$

3. $(\mathbf{A} \times \mathbf{B}) = \begin{vmatrix} \mathbf{i} & \mathbf{j} & \mathbf{k} \\ 4 & -8 & 1 \\ 2 & 1 & -2 \end{vmatrix} = 15\mathbf{i} + 10\mathbf{j} + 20\mathbf{k}$

$(\mathbf{A} \times \mathbf{B}) \times \mathbf{C} = \begin{vmatrix} \mathbf{i} & \mathbf{j} & \mathbf{k} \\ 15 & 10 & 20 \\ 3 & -4 & 12 \end{vmatrix} = 200\mathbf{i} - 120\mathbf{j} - 90\mathbf{k}$

5. $\mathbf{A} = 2\mathbf{i}$, $\mathbf{B} = 2\mathbf{j}$, $\mathbf{C} = 2\mathbf{k}$; $V = \frac{1}{3}(\text{base})(\text{height}) = \frac{1}{6}|\mathbf{A} \cdot (\mathbf{B} \times \mathbf{C})|$.

$V = \frac{1}{6} \begin{vmatrix} 2 & 0 & 0 \\ 0 & 2 & 0 \\ 0 & 0 & 2 \end{vmatrix} = \frac{4}{3}$

7. $\mathbf{A} = 2\mathbf{i} + \mathbf{j}$, $\mathbf{B} = 2\mathbf{i} - \mathbf{j} + \mathbf{k}$, $\mathbf{C} = \mathbf{i} + 2\mathbf{k}$

$V = \frac{1}{6}|\mathbf{A} \cdot (\mathbf{B} \times \mathbf{C})| = \frac{1}{6} \begin{vmatrix} 2 & 1 & 0 \\ 2 & -1 & 1 \\ 1 & 0 & 2 \end{vmatrix} = \frac{|-7|}{6} = \frac{7}{6}$

9. (a) $\overrightarrow{PQ} = 2\mathbf{i} - 3\mathbf{j} + 5\mathbf{k}$; $\overrightarrow{SR} = (2 - x)\mathbf{i} + (6 - y)\mathbf{j} + (2 - z)\mathbf{k}$.

$\therefore\ 2 - x = 2$ or $x = 0$, $6 - y = -3$ or $y = -9$, $2 - z = 5$ or $z = -3$

$S = (0, -9, -3)$.

(b) $\overrightarrow{PQ} \times \overrightarrow{PS} = \begin{vmatrix} \mathbf{i} & \mathbf{j} & \mathbf{k} \\ 2 & -3 & 5 \\ -1 & 7 & -2 \end{vmatrix} = -29\mathbf{i} - \mathbf{j} + 11\mathbf{k}$. Area $= \sqrt{841 + 1 + 121} = \sqrt{963}$

(c) Area of projection in

$yz$-plane: $|(-29\mathbf{i} - \mathbf{j} + 11\mathbf{k}) \cdot \mathbf{i}| = 29$

$xz$-plane: $|(-29\mathbf{i} - \mathbf{j} + 11\mathbf{k}) \cdot \mathbf{j}| = 1$

$xy$-plane: $|(-29\mathbf{i} - \mathbf{j} + 11\mathbf{k}) \cdot \mathbf{k}| = 11$

11. (a) no, $\mathbf{A} \times \mathbf{B} = -(\mathbf{B} \times \mathbf{A})$

(e) no, $\mathbf{A} \cdot \mathbf{B}$ is a scalar, so $(\mathbf{A} \cdot \mathbf{B}) \times \mathbf{C}$ makes no sense

(i) no, not an associative operation

13. $\mathbf{A} = \frac{1}{2}\left[\mathbf{i} \times (\mathbf{A} \times \mathbf{i}) + \mathbf{j} \times (\mathbf{A} \times \mathbf{j}) + \mathbf{k} \times (\mathbf{A} \times \mathbf{k})\right]$

$$= \frac{1}{2}\left(\left[(\mathbf{i} \cdot \mathbf{i})\mathbf{A} - (\mathbf{i} \cdot \mathbf{A})\,\mathbf{i}\right] + \left[(\mathbf{j} \cdot \mathbf{j})\mathbf{A} - (\mathbf{j} \cdot \mathbf{A})\mathbf{j}\right] + \left[(\mathbf{k} \cdot \mathbf{k})\mathbf{A} - (\mathbf{k} \cdot \mathbf{A})\mathbf{k}\right]\right)$$

$$= \frac{1}{2}\left(3\mathbf{A} - \left[(\mathbf{i} \cdot \mathbf{A})\,\mathbf{i} + (\mathbf{j} \cdot \mathbf{A})\mathbf{j} + (\mathbf{k} \cdot \mathbf{A})\mathbf{k}\right]\right) = \frac{1}{2}(3\mathbf{A} - \mathbf{A}) = \mathbf{A}$$

15. (a) $\mathbf{A} \cdot (\mathbf{B} \times \mathbf{C}) = \begin{vmatrix} a_1 & a_2 & a_3 \\ b_1 & b_2 & b_3 \\ c_1 & c_2 & c_3 \end{vmatrix} = -\begin{vmatrix} a_1 & a_2 & a_3 \\ c_1 & c_2 & c_3 \\ b_1 & b_2 & b_3 \end{vmatrix} = -\mathbf{A} \cdot (\mathbf{C} \times \mathbf{B})$

(b) $\mathbf{A} \cdot (\mathbf{A} \times \mathbf{B}) = \begin{vmatrix} a_1 & a_2 & a_3 \\ a_1 & a_2 & a_3 \\ b_1 & b_2 & b_3 \end{vmatrix} = 0$ (two identical rows)

(c) $(\mathbf{A} + \mathbf{D}) \cdot (\mathbf{B} \times \mathbf{C}) = \begin{vmatrix} a_1 + d_1 & a_2 + d_2 & a_3 + d_3 \\ b_1 & b_2 & b_3 \\ c_1 & c_2 & c_3 \end{vmatrix}$

$$= \begin{vmatrix} a_1 & a_2 & a_3 \\ b_1 & b_2 & b_3 \\ c_1 & c_2 & c_3 \end{vmatrix} + \begin{vmatrix} d_1 & d_2 & d_3 \\ b_1 & b_2 & b_3 \\ c_1 & c_2 & c_3 \end{vmatrix} = \mathbf{A} \cdot (\mathbf{B} \times \mathbf{C}) + \mathbf{D} \cdot (\mathbf{B} \times \mathbf{C})$$

## 13.M MISCELLANEOUS

1. Extend $\overrightarrow{CD}$ to $\overrightarrow{CG}$ so that $\overrightarrow{CD} = \overrightarrow{DG}$. Then $\overrightarrow{CG} = \overrightarrow{CA} + \overrightarrow{AG} = \overrightarrow{CA} + \overrightarrow{CB}$. $\overrightarrow{CB} = 3\overrightarrow{CE}$. Let $\overrightarrow{CG} = x\,\overrightarrow{CF}$. Then $x\,\overrightarrow{CF} - 3\,\overrightarrow{CB} - \overrightarrow{CA} = 0$. Since A, E and F are collinear, $x - 3 - 1 = 0$ or $x = 4$. Then $\overrightarrow{CG} = 4\overrightarrow{CF} \Rightarrow \overrightarrow{CD} = 2\overrightarrow{CF}$. $\therefore$ F is the midpoint of $\overrightarrow{CD}$.

3. $x + y = 1 \Rightarrow y = 1 - x$. $\mathbf{P} = \overrightarrow{OP} = x\mathbf{A} + y\mathbf{B} = x\mathbf{A} + (1 - x)\mathbf{B} \Rightarrow$ $\mathbf{P} = \mathbf{B} + x(\mathbf{A} - \mathbf{B})$. $\therefore$ P is on the line AB. Since $x < 1$, P is actually on the segment AB.

5. Let P be the point of intersection of $\overrightarrow{Aa}$, $\overrightarrow{Bb}$ and $\overrightarrow{Cc}$. By Problem 4 if O is any point, then $\overrightarrow{OP} = \frac{1}{3}(\overrightarrow{OA} + \overrightarrow{OB} + \overrightarrow{OC})$. In particular, let O = P. Then $\overrightarrow{PP} = \vec{0} = \frac{1}{3}(\overrightarrow{PA} + \overrightarrow{PB} + \overrightarrow{PC})$. Since $\overrightarrow{PA} = 3\overrightarrow{Aa}$, $\overrightarrow{PB} = 3\overrightarrow{Bb}$ and $\overrightarrow{PC} = 3\overrightarrow{Cc}$, we have that $\overrightarrow{Aa} + \overrightarrow{Bb} + \overrightarrow{Cc} = 0$.

7. Let $\mathbf{A} = a\mathbf{i} + b\mathbf{j}$ and $\mathbf{B} = c\mathbf{i} + d\mathbf{j}$. Then $\mathbf{A} \cdot \mathbf{B} = |\mathbf{A}|\,|\mathbf{B}|\cos\theta \Rightarrow$

$$ac + bd = \sqrt{a^2 + b^2}\sqrt{c^2 + d^2}\cos\theta \Rightarrow (ac + bd)^2 = (a^2 + b^2)(c^2 + d^2)\cos^2\theta$$

or $(ac + bd)^2 \le (a^2 + b^2)(c^2 + d^2)$ since $\cos^2\theta \le 1$.

9. The height of the ball: $y = (v_0 \sin\alpha)t - \frac{1}{2}gt^2$

Let $h$ = height of hill: $h = x\tan\phi = (v_0\cos\alpha)t\cdot\dfrac{\sin\phi}{\cos\phi}$.

When $h = y$, the ball has reached the ground, i.e. when

$$(v_0\cos\alpha)t\cdot\frac{\sin\phi}{\cos\phi} = (v_0\sin\alpha)t - \frac{1}{2}gt^2$$

$$\frac{(v_0\sin\alpha)(\cos\phi)t - \frac{1}{2}gt^2\cos\phi - v_0\cos\alpha\sin\phi}{\cos\phi} = 0$$

$$v_0\sin(\alpha - \phi)\,t - \frac{1}{2}gt^2\cos\phi = 0$$

$$t = \frac{2v_0\sin(\alpha - \phi)}{g\cos\phi}.$$

$$s = \frac{x}{\cos\phi} = \frac{v_0\cos\alpha\, t}{\cos\phi} = \frac{v_0\cos\alpha}{\cos\phi}\cdot\frac{2v_0\sin(\alpha - \phi)}{g\cos\phi} = \frac{2v_0^2\cos\alpha\sin(\alpha - \phi)}{g\cos^2\phi}$$

$$\frac{ds}{d\alpha} = \frac{2v_0^2}{g\cos^2\phi}[-\sin\alpha\sin(\alpha - \phi) + \cos\alpha\cos(\alpha - \phi)] = 0$$

when $\cos(\alpha + \alpha - \phi) = 0 \Rightarrow 2\alpha - \phi = \dfrac{\pi}{2} \Rightarrow \alpha = \dfrac{\phi}{2} + \dfrac{\pi}{4}$.

11. $\text{Proj}_{\mathbf{A}}\mathbf{B} = \left(\dfrac{\mathbf{B}\cdot\mathbf{A}}{\mathbf{A}\cdot\mathbf{A}}\right)\mathbf{A} = \dfrac{(2\mathbf{i} + \mathbf{j} - 2\mathbf{k})\cdot(3\mathbf{i} - \mathbf{j} - 2\mathbf{k})}{\sqrt{9+1+1}\;29+1+1} = \dfrac{3}{11}\mathbf{A} = \dfrac{9}{11}\mathbf{i} - \dfrac{3}{11}\mathbf{j} + \dfrac{3}{11}\mathbf{k}$

13. $\mathbf{C} = \text{proj}_{\mathbf{B}}\mathbf{A} = \left(\dfrac{\mathbf{A}\cdot\mathbf{B}}{\mathbf{B}\cdot\mathbf{B}}\right)\mathbf{B}$ and $\mathbf{D} = \mathbf{A} - \mathbf{C} = \mathbf{A} - \left(\dfrac{\mathbf{A}\cdot\mathbf{B}}{\mathbf{B}\cdot\mathbf{B}}\right)\mathbf{B}$

15. $(a\mathbf{B} + b\mathbf{A})\cdot(b\mathbf{A} - a\mathbf{B}) = a\mathbf{B}\cdot b\mathbf{A} + b\mathbf{A}\cdot b\mathbf{A} - a\mathbf{B}\cdot a\mathbf{B} - b\mathbf{A}\cdot a\mathbf{B}$

$= b\mathbf{A}\cdot a\mathbf{B} + b^2\mathbf{A}\cdot\mathbf{A} - a^2\mathbf{B}\cdot\mathbf{B} - b\mathbf{A}\cdot a\mathbf{B} = b^2a^2 - a^2b^2 = 0.$

17. Let $Q(x,y)$ be a point on the line. Then $\overrightarrow{PQ} = (x_1 - x)\mathbf{i} + (y_1 - y)\mathbf{j}$.

$\mathbf{N} = a\mathbf{i} + b\mathbf{j}$ is normal to the line. The distance is

$$|\text{Proj}_{\mathbf{N}}\overrightarrow{PQ}| = \left|\frac{[(x_1 - x)\mathbf{i} + (y_1 - y)\mathbf{j}]\cdot(a\mathbf{i} + b\mathbf{j})}{|a\mathbf{i} + b\mathbf{j}|}\right| = \frac{|a(x_1 - x) + b(y_1 - y)|}{\sqrt{a^2 + b^2}}$$

$$= \frac{|ax_1 + by_1 - c|}{\sqrt{a^2 + b^2}}, \text{ since } c = ax + by.$$

19. The midpoint of AC is $M\left(\frac{1-1}{2}, \frac{-1+2}{2}, \frac{2-1}{2}\right) = M\left(0, \frac{1}{2}, \frac{1}{2}\right)$.

The line from B to M is: $x = 2 - 2t$, $y = 1 - \frac{1}{2}t$, $z = 3 - \frac{5}{2}t$.

When $t = \frac{2}{3}$, $x = 2 - \frac{4}{3} = \frac{2}{3}$, $y = 1 - \frac{1}{3} = \frac{2}{3}$, and $z = 3 - \frac{5}{3} = \frac{4}{3}$.

The point is $\left(\frac{2}{3}, \frac{2}{3}, \frac{4}{3}\right)$. The vector $\overrightarrow{OP} = \frac{2}{3}\mathbf{i} + \frac{2}{3}\mathbf{j} + \frac{4}{3}\mathbf{k}$.

21. $\mathbf{i} \times (\mathbf{j} \times (\mathbf{i} + \mathbf{j}) = \mathbf{i} \times (\mathbf{j} \times \mathbf{i} + \mathbf{j} \times \mathbf{j}) = \mathbf{i} \times \mathbf{k} = \mathbf{j}$. But

$(\mathbf{i} \times \mathbf{j}) \times (\mathbf{i} \times \mathbf{j}) = \mathbf{k} \times \mathbf{k} = 0$

23. Let $A(3,-1,1)$, $B(1,2,-1)$ and $C(1,1,1)$ be the endpoints. Then $\overrightarrow{AB} = -2\mathbf{i} + 3\mathbf{j} - 2\mathbf{k}$ and $\overrightarrow{AC} = -2\mathbf{i} + 2\mathbf{j}$. A normal to the plane is

$$\overrightarrow{AB} \times \overrightarrow{AC} = \begin{vmatrix} \mathbf{i} & \mathbf{j} & \mathbf{k} \\ -2 & 3 & -2 \\ -2 & 2 & 0 \end{vmatrix} = 4\mathbf{i} + 4\mathbf{j} + 2\mathbf{k}.$$ The plane is $2x + 2y + z = d$.

$d = 2(1) + 2(1) + 1 = 5$, so $2x + 2x + z = 5$.

25. The line through $(0,0,0)$ normal to the plane is $x = 2t$, $y = -t$, $z = -t$. The line intersects the plane $x + y - 2z = 2$ when $2t + (-t) -2(-t) = 2$, or when $t = \frac{2}{3}$. The point is $\left(\frac{4}{3}, -\frac{2}{3}, -\frac{2}{3}\right)$.

27. The required vector is $(2\mathbf{i} - \mathbf{j} - \mathbf{k}) \times (\mathbf{i} + \mathbf{j} + \mathbf{k}) = -3\mathbf{j} + 3\mathbf{k}$.

29. $\mathbf{A} = (2\mathbf{i} + \mathbf{j} - \mathbf{k}) \times (\mathbf{i} + \mathbf{j} + 2\mathbf{k}) = 3\mathbf{i} - 5\mathbf{j} + \mathbf{k}$. $\cos\theta = \frac{\mathbf{A}\cdot\mathbf{i}}{|\mathbf{A}|} = \frac{3}{\sqrt{35}}$. $\theta \approx 59.5°$

31. The intersection occurs when $(3 + 2t) + 3(2t) - t + 4 = 0$, or $t = -1$. The point is $(1,-2,-1)$. The required line must be $\perp$ both to the given line and to the normal and hence is parallel to $(\mathbf{i} + 3\mathbf{j} - \mathbf{k}) \times (2\mathbf{i} + 2\mathbf{j} + \mathbf{k}) = -5\mathbf{i} + 3\mathbf{j} + 4\mathbf{k}$. The line is $x = 1 - 5t$. $y = -2 + 3t$, $z = -1 + 4t$.

33. Let $P(x_1, y_1, z_1)$ be a point on the line of intersection. Then P belongs to both planes, so $x_1 - 2y_1 + z_1 + 3 = 0$ and $2x_1 - y_1 - z_1 + 1 = 0$. Therefore $(x_1 - 2y_1 + z_1 + 3) + k(2x_1 - y_1 - z_1 + 1) = 0$.

35. Let $P(x, y, z)$ be a point in the plane determined by $P_i = (x_i, y_i, z_i)$, $i = 1, 2, 3$. Then the given determinant is $\overrightarrow{PP_1} \cdot (\overrightarrow{PP_2} \times \overrightarrow{PP_3})$, which is also the equation of the plane.

37. Let $L_1 : a_1s + b_1, a_2s + b_2, a_3s + b_3$ and $L_2 : c_1t + d_1, c_2t + d_2, c_3t + d_3$ If $L_1 \parallel L_2$ then for some k, $a_i = kc_i$, $i = 1, 2, 3$. Then

$$\begin{vmatrix} kc_1 & c_1 & b_1 - d_1 \\ kc_2 & c_2 & b_2 - d_2 \\ kc_3 & c_3 & b_3 - d_3 \\ kc_4 & c_4 & b_4 - d_4 \end{vmatrix} = 0.$$

If $L_1$ and $L_2$ intersect then the system $a_is - c_it + (b_i - d_i) = 0$, $i = 1, 2, 3$, has a non-trivial solution so that the coefficient matrix (the given matrix) is non-zero.

39. $(\mathbf{B} \times \mathbf{C}) \times \mathbf{A} = (\mathbf{B} \cdot \mathbf{A})\mathbf{C} - (\mathbf{C} \cdot \mathbf{A})\mathbf{B} = \mathbf{j} + \mathbf{k}$ must be in the plane of **B** and **C** and be orthogonal to **A**. The required unit vector is $\frac{1}{\sqrt{2}}(\mathbf{j} + \mathbf{k})$

41. $\cos\theta = \dfrac{\mathbf{i} \cdot (\mathbf{i} + \mathbf{j} + \sqrt{2}\mathbf{k})}{\sqrt{4}} = \dfrac{1}{2}$; $\theta = 60^\circ$

43. Let $L_1$: $x = 4 + 2t$, $y = 3t$, $z = -\frac{1}{3}t$ and $L_2$ : $x = 18s$, $y = 5 - 6s$, $z = -s$. Then $L_1 \cap L_2$ in the point $\left(6, 3, -\frac{1}{3}\right)$ occuring when $t = 1$. The submarine is then moving along the line $x = 2 + 4t$, $y = -1 + 4t$, $z = -\frac{1}{3}t$ and will be at the point $\left(26, 23, -\frac{1}{3}\right)$ in 20 minutes.

45. Let $S = s^2 = (2 + t)^2 + (2 - t)^2 + (1 + t)^2$. $\dfrac{dS}{dt} = 2(2 + t) + 2(2 - t) + 2(1 + t)$ $= 6t - 2 = 0$ when $t = \dfrac{1}{3}$. $\dfrac{d^2S}{dt^2} = 6 > 0 \Rightarrow$ a minimum distance.

$$s = \sqrt{\left(\frac{7}{3}\right)^2 + \left(\frac{5}{3}\right)^2 + \left(\frac{2}{3}\right)^2} = \frac{\sqrt{78}}{3}.$$

47. $\overrightarrow{AC} = 2\mathbf{i} - \mathbf{j}$ and $\overrightarrow{BC} = 2\mathbf{i} - \mathbf{k}$. $\mathbf{n} = \begin{vmatrix} \mathbf{i} & \mathbf{j} & \mathbf{k} \\ 2 & 0 & -1 \\ 2 & -1 & 0 \end{vmatrix} = -\mathbf{i} - 2\mathbf{j} - 2\mathbf{k}$.

The distance is $d = \dfrac{(\mathbf{i} + 4\mathbf{j}) \cdot (\mathbf{i} + 2\mathbf{j} + 2\mathbf{k})}{\sqrt{1+4+4}} = 3$.

49. (a) Let $(x_1, y_1, z_1)$ be any point on $Ax + By + Cz = D_1$. Then

$$d = \frac{|Ax_1 + By_1 + Cz_1 - D_2|}{\sqrt{A^2 + B^2 + C^2}} = \frac{|D_1 - D_2|}{|A\mathbf{i} + B\mathbf{j} + C\mathbf{k}|} \quad \text{(See Problem 50)}$$

(b) $d = \dfrac{|12 - 6|}{\sqrt{4+9+1}} = \dfrac{6}{\sqrt{14}}$

(c) $\dfrac{|2(3) - 2 + 2(-1) + 4|}{\sqrt{14}} = \dfrac{|2(3) - 2 + 2(-1) + d|}{\sqrt{14}} \Rightarrow d = 4, -8$

$\therefore\ 2x - y + 2z = 8$

(d) Choose the point $(0, 0, 3)$ on the plane. Then $\dfrac{|3 - d|}{\sqrt{6}} = 5$

so the planes are $x - 2y + z = 3 \pm 5\sqrt{6}$.

51. $\overrightarrow{AB} = 2\mathbf{i} - \mathbf{j} - \mathbf{k}$, $\overrightarrow{CD} = \mathbf{i} + 4\mathbf{j} - \mathbf{k}$ and $\overrightarrow{AC} = 2\mathbf{i} + \mathbf{j}$.

$$\mathbf{N} = \begin{vmatrix} \mathbf{i} & \mathbf{j} & \mathbf{k} \\ 2 & -1 & -1 \\ 1 & 4 & -1 \end{vmatrix} = 5\mathbf{i} + \mathbf{j} + 9\mathbf{k}.$$

$$d = \frac{(2\mathbf{i} + \mathbf{j}) \cdot (5\mathbf{i} + \mathbf{j} + 9\mathbf{k})}{\sqrt{25 + 1 + 81}} = \frac{11}{\sqrt{107}}$$

53. (a) $\mathbf{A} \cdot (\mathbf{B} \times \mathbf{C}) = \begin{vmatrix} 1 & 1 & -1 \\ 2 & 1 & 1 \\ -1 & -2 & 3 \end{vmatrix} = 1$

(b) $\mathbf{A} \times (\mathbf{B} \times \mathbf{C}) = (\mathbf{A} \cdot \mathbf{C})\mathbf{B} - (\mathbf{A} \cdot \mathbf{B})\mathbf{C} = -6\mathbf{B} - 2\mathbf{C} = -10\mathbf{i} - 2\mathbf{j} - 12\mathbf{k}$

55. Let $\mathbf{W} = \mathbf{A} \times \mathbf{B}$ and $\mathbf{V} = \mathbf{A} \times \mathbf{W}$. Then $(\mathbf{A} \times \mathbf{V}) \cdot \mathbf{C} = \mathbf{A} \cdot (\mathbf{V} \times \mathbf{C})$

$= \mathbf{A} \cdot \big( (\mathbf{A} \times \mathbf{W}) \times \mathbf{C} \big) = \mathbf{A} \cdot \big[ (\mathbf{A} \cdot \mathbf{C})\mathbf{W} - (\mathbf{W} \cdot \mathbf{C})\mathbf{A} \big]$

$= (\mathbf{A} \cdot \mathbf{C})(\mathbf{A} \cdot \mathbf{W}) - (\mathbf{W} \cdot \mathbf{C})(\mathbf{A} \cdot \mathbf{A})$

$= (\mathbf{A} \cdot \mathbf{C})(\mathbf{A} \cdot \mathbf{A} \times \mathbf{B}) - (\mathbf{A} \times \mathbf{B} \cdot \mathbf{C})|\mathbf{A}|^2$

$= (\mathbf{A} \cdot \mathbf{C})(0) - |\mathbf{A}|^2(\mathbf{A} \times \mathbf{B} \cdot \mathbf{C})$

$= -|\mathbf{A}|^2(\mathbf{A} \times \mathbf{B} \cdot \mathbf{C})$

57. (a) $\mathbf{A}\times(\mathbf{B}\times\mathbf{C})+\mathbf{B}\times(\mathbf{C}\times\mathbf{A})+\mathbf{C}\times(\mathbf{A}\times\mathbf{B})=$

$(\mathbf{A}\cdot\mathbf{C})\mathbf{B}-(\mathbf{A}\cdot\mathbf{B})\mathbf{C}+(\mathbf{B}\cdot\mathbf{A})\mathbf{C}-(\mathbf{B}\cdot\mathbf{C})\mathbf{A}+(\mathbf{C}\cdot\mathbf{B})\mathbf{A}-(\mathbf{C}\cdot\mathbf{A})\mathbf{B}=\mathbf{0}$.

(b) $[\mathbf{A}\cdot(\mathbf{B}\times\mathbf{i})]\mathbf{i}+[\mathbf{A}\cdot(\mathbf{B}\times\mathbf{j})]\mathbf{j}+[\mathbf{A}\cdot(\mathbf{B}\times\mathbf{k})]\mathbf{k}=$

$[(\mathbf{A}\times\mathbf{B})\cdot\mathbf{i}]\mathbf{i}+[(\mathbf{A}\times\mathbf{B})\cdot\mathbf{j}]\mathbf{j}+[(\mathbf{A}\times\mathbf{B})\cdot\mathbf{k}]\mathbf{k}=\mathbf{A}\times\mathbf{B}$

59. $|10\mathbf{i}+11\mathbf{j}-2\mathbf{k}|=\sqrt{100+121+4}=15$

$\cos\alpha=\frac{10}{15}=\frac{2}{3}$ $\cos\beta=\frac{11}{15}$ $\cos\gamma=-\frac{2}{15}$

61. $|\mathbf{j}+\sqrt{3}\,\mathbf{k}|=2$

$\cos\alpha=0$ $\cos\beta=\frac{1}{2}$ $\cos\gamma=\frac{\sqrt{3}}{2}$

63. $|\mathbf{i}|=1$

$\cos\alpha=1$ $\cos\beta=0$ $\cos\gamma=0$

65. $|\mathbf{i}+\mathbf{j}+\mathbf{k}|=\sqrt{3}$

$\cos\alpha=\frac{1}{\sqrt{3}}$ $\cos\beta=\frac{1}{\sqrt{3}}$ $\cos\gamma=\frac{1}{\sqrt{3}}$

67. $\left|\frac{2}{7}\mathbf{i}-\frac{3}{7}\mathbf{j}+\frac{6}{7}\mathbf{k}\right|=\sqrt{\frac{4}{49}+\frac{9}{49}+\frac{36}{49}}=1$

$\cos\alpha=\frac{2}{7}$ $\cos\beta=-\frac{3}{7}$ $\cos\gamma=\frac{6}{7}$

69. Let the line be L: $x=at$, $y=bt$, $z=ct$. Then $\mathbf{A}=a\mathbf{i}+b\mathbf{j}+c\mathbf{k}$ is

parallel to L so $\cos\alpha=\frac{a}{|\mathbf{A}|}$, $\cos\beta=\frac{b}{|\mathbf{A}|}$ and $\cos\gamma=\frac{c}{|\mathbf{A}|}$.

Then $\cos^2\alpha+\cos^2\beta+\cos^2\gamma=\frac{a^2+b^2+c^2}{|\mathbf{A}|^2}=\frac{|\mathbf{A}|^2}{|\mathbf{A}|^2}=1$

# CHAPTER 14

# VECTOR FUNCTIONS AND MOTION

## 14.1 VECTOR FUNCTIONS AND MOTION

1. $\mathbf{R}(t) = (2\cos t)\mathbf{i} + (3\sin t)\mathbf{j}$

   $\mathbf{v}(t) = (-2\sin t)\mathbf{i} + (3\cos t)\mathbf{j}$

   $\mathbf{a}(t) = (-2\cos t)\mathbf{i} + (-3\sin t)\mathbf{j}$

   $\mathbf{v}\left(\frac{\pi}{4}\right) = -\sqrt{2}\,\mathbf{i} + \frac{3\sqrt{2}}{2}\mathbf{j};\ \mathbf{a}\left(\frac{\pi}{4}\right) = -\sqrt{2}\mathbf{i} - \frac{3\sqrt{2}}{2}\mathbf{j};\ \left|\mathbf{v}\left(\frac{\pi}{4}\right)\right| = \frac{\sqrt{26}}{2}$

3. $\mathbf{R}(t) = (\cos 2t)\mathbf{i} + (2\sin t)\mathbf{j}$

   $\mathbf{v}(t) = (-2\sin 2t)\mathbf{i} + (2\cos t)\mathbf{j}$

   $\mathbf{a}(t) = (-4\cos 2t)\mathbf{i} + (-2\sin t)\mathbf{j}$

   $\mathbf{v}(0) = 2\mathbf{j};\ \mathbf{a}(0) = -4\mathbf{i};\ |\mathbf{v}(0)| = 2$

5. $\mathbf{R}(t) = (\sec t)\mathbf{i} + (\tan t)\mathbf{j}$

   $\mathbf{v}(t) = (\sec t\tan t)\mathbf{i} + (\sec^2 t)\mathbf{j}$

   $\mathbf{a}(t) = (\sec^3 t + \tan^2 t\sec t)\mathbf{i} + (2\sec^2 t\tan t)\mathbf{j}$

   $\mathbf{v}\left(\frac{\pi}{6}\right) = \frac{2}{3}\mathbf{i} + \frac{4}{3}\mathbf{j};\ \mathbf{a}\left(\frac{\pi}{6}\right) = \frac{10\sqrt{3}}{9}\mathbf{i} + \frac{8\sqrt{3}}{9}\mathbf{j};\ \left|\mathbf{v}\left(\frac{\pi}{6}\right)\right| = \frac{2\sqrt{5}}{3}$

7. $\mathbf{R}(t) = (a\cos\omega t)\mathbf{i} + (a\sin\omega t)\mathbf{j}$

   $\mathbf{v}(t) = (-a\omega\sin\omega t)\mathbf{i} + (a\omega\cos\omega t)\mathbf{j}$

   $\mathbf{a}(t) = (-a\omega^2\cos\omega t)\mathbf{i} + (-a\omega^2\sin\omega t)\mathbf{j}$

   $\mathbf{v}\left(\frac{\pi}{3\omega}\right) = -\frac{a\omega\sqrt{3}}{2}\mathbf{i} + \frac{a\omega}{2}\mathbf{j};\ \mathbf{a}\left(\frac{\pi}{3\omega}\right) = -\frac{a\omega^2}{2}\mathbf{i} - \frac{a\omega^2\sqrt{3}}{2}\mathbf{j};\ \left|\mathbf{v}\left(\frac{\pi}{3\omega}\right)\right| = a\omega$

9. $\mathbf{R}(t) = (1+t)\mathbf{i} + \frac{t^2}{\sqrt{2}}\mathbf{j} + \frac{t^3}{3}\mathbf{k}$

   $\mathbf{v}(t) = \mathbf{i} + \sqrt{2}t\,\mathbf{j} + t^2\,\mathbf{k}$

   $\mathbf{a}(t) = \sqrt{2}\,\mathbf{j} + 2t\,\mathbf{k}$

   $\mathbf{v}(t) = \mathbf{i} + \sqrt{2}\,\mathbf{j} + \mathbf{k};\ \mathbf{a}(1) = \sqrt{2}\mathbf{j} + 2\mathbf{k};\ |\mathbf{v}(1)| = 2$

11. $\mathbf{R}(t) = \dfrac{\sqrt{2}}{t+1}\mathbf{i} + \dfrac{t^3}{3}\mathbf{j} + (\sqrt{2}\ \ln t)\mathbf{k}$

$\mathbf{v}(t) = -\dfrac{\sqrt{2}}{(t+1)^2}\mathbf{i} + t^2\mathbf{j} + \dfrac{\sqrt{2}}{t}\mathbf{k}$

$\mathbf{a}(t) = \dfrac{2\sqrt{2}}{(t+1)^3}\mathbf{i} + 2t\,\mathbf{j} - \dfrac{\sqrt{2}}{t^2}\mathbf{k}$

$\mathbf{v}(1) = -\dfrac{\sqrt{2}}{4}\mathbf{i} + \mathbf{j} + \sqrt{2}\,\mathbf{k}$ ; $\mathbf{a}(1) = \dfrac{\sqrt{2}}{4}\mathbf{i} + 2\mathbf{j} - \sqrt{2}\mathbf{k}$; $|\mathbf{v}(1)| = \dfrac{5}{2\sqrt{2}}$

13. $\mathbf{R}(t) = (t - \sin t)\mathbf{i} + (1 - \cos t)\mathbf{j}$

$\mathbf{v}(t) = (1 - \cos t)\mathbf{i} + (\sin t)\mathbf{j}$

$\mathbf{a}(t) = (\sin t)\mathbf{i} + (\cos t)\mathbf{j}$

$\mathbf{v} \cdot \mathbf{a} = (1 - \cos t)(\sin t) + \sin t \cos t = 0$ if $\sin t = 0$ or $t = 0, \pi, 2\pi$

15. $\mathbf{R}(t) = \mathbf{i} + (5\cos t)\mathbf{j} + (3\sin t)\mathbf{k}$

$\mathbf{v}(t) = -(5\sin t)\mathbf{j} + (3\cos t)\mathbf{k}$

$\mathbf{a}(t) = -(5\cos t)\mathbf{i} - (3\sin t)\mathbf{k}$

$\mathbf{v} \cdot \mathbf{a} = 25\cos t \sin t - 9\sin t \cos t = 0$ if $t = 0, \dfrac{\pi}{2}, \pi$

17. $\mathbf{R}(t) = e^t\mathbf{i} + (e^t \sin t)\mathbf{j} + (e^t \cos t)\mathbf{k}$

$\mathbf{v}(t) = e^t\mathbf{i} + (e^t \sin t + e^t \cos t)\mathbf{j} + (e^t \cos t - e^t \sin t)\mathbf{k}$

$\mathbf{a}(t) = e^t\mathbf{i} + (2e^t \cos t)\mathbf{j} - (2e^t \sin t)\mathbf{k}$

$\mathbf{v}(0) = \mathbf{i} + \mathbf{j} + \mathbf{k}$; $\mathbf{a}(0) = \mathbf{i} + 2\mathbf{j}$

$\cos\theta = \dfrac{\mathbf{v} \cdot \mathbf{a}}{|\mathbf{v}|\,|\mathbf{a}|} = \dfrac{3}{\sqrt{15}}$. $\theta \approx 39.2^\circ$

19. $\mathbf{R}(t) = \ln(t^2 + 1)\mathbf{i} + (\tan^{-1} t)\mathbf{j} + \sqrt{t^2 + 1}\,\mathbf{k}$

$\mathbf{v}(t) = \dfrac{2t}{t^2 + 1}\mathbf{i} + \dfrac{1}{1 + t^2}\mathbf{j} + \dfrac{t}{\sqrt{t^2 + 1}}\mathbf{k}$

$\mathbf{a}(t) = \dfrac{2 - 2t^2}{(t^2 + 1)^2}\mathbf{i} - \dfrac{2t}{(1 + t^2)^2}\mathbf{j} + (t^2 + 1)^{3/2}\,\mathbf{k}$

$\mathbf{v}(0) = \mathbf{j}$ ; $\mathbf{a}(0) = 2\mathbf{i} + \mathbf{k}$

$\cos\theta = \dfrac{\mathbf{v} \cdot \mathbf{a}}{|\mathbf{v}|\,|\mathbf{a}|} = 0$. $\theta = \dfrac{\pi}{2}$

21. $\mathbf{v}(t) = \int (-3t)\,dt\,\mathbf{i} = \left(-\frac{3}{2}t^2 + C_1\right)\mathbf{i} + C_2\,\mathbf{j}.$

$\mathbf{v}(0) = 2\mathbf{j} \Rightarrow C_1\mathbf{i} + C_2\mathbf{j} = 2\mathbf{j} \Rightarrow C_1 = 0$ and $C_2 = 2$

$\mathbf{R}(t) = \int -\frac{3}{2}t^2\,dt\,\mathbf{i} + \int 2\,dt\,\mathbf{j} = \left(-\frac{1}{2}t^3 + C_3\right)\mathbf{i} + (2t + C_4)\,\mathbf{j}$

$\mathbf{R}(0) = 4\mathbf{i} \Rightarrow C_3\,\mathbf{i} + C_4\,\mathbf{j} = 4\mathbf{i} \Rightarrow C_3 = 4$ and $C_4 = 0$.

$\mathbf{R}(t) = \left(-\frac{1}{2}t^3 + 4\right)\mathbf{i} + (2t)\,\mathbf{j}$

23. $\mathbf{v}(t) = \int (1+t)^{-1/2}\,dt\,\mathbf{i} - \int e^{-t}\,dt\,\mathbf{j} = (2\sqrt{1+t} + C_1)\mathbf{i} + (e^{-t} + C_2)\mathbf{j}.$

$\mathbf{v}(0) = -\mathbf{i} + \mathbf{j} \Rightarrow (2 + C_1)\mathbf{i} + (1 + C_2)\mathbf{j} = -\mathbf{i} + \mathbf{j} \Rightarrow C_1 = -3$ and $C_2 = 0$

$\mathbf{R}(t) = \int (2\sqrt{1+t} - 3)\,dt\,\mathbf{i} + \int e^{-t}\,dt\,\mathbf{j} = \left(\frac{4}{3}(1+t)^{3/2} - 3t + C_3\right)\mathbf{i} - (e^{-t} + C_4)\,\mathbf{j}$

$\mathbf{R}(0) = \frac{1}{3}\mathbf{i} - \mathbf{j} + \mathbf{k} = \left(\frac{4}{3} + C_3\right)\mathbf{i} + (-1 + C_4)\mathbf{j} + C_5\,\mathbf{k} \Rightarrow C_3 = -1, C_4 = 0, C_5 = 1.$

$\mathbf{R}(t) = \left(\frac{4}{3}(1+t)^{3/2} - 3t - 1\right)\mathbf{i} - e^{-t}\,\mathbf{j} + \mathbf{k}$

25. (a) $\mathbf{R}(t) = t\mathbf{i} + t^2\mathbf{j} \Rightarrow \mathbf{v}(t) = \mathbf{i} + 2t\,\mathbf{j}$ and $\mathbf{a}(t) = 2\mathbf{j}$

(b) $\mathbf{v}(2) = \mathbf{i} + 4\mathbf{j}$, $\mathbf{a}(2) = 2\mathbf{j}$

27. (a) $\mathbf{R}(t) = 20t\mathbf{i} + (-4.9t^2 + 100)\mathbf{j} \Rightarrow \mathbf{v}(t) = 20\mathbf{i} - 9.8\mathbf{j}$

(b) $\mathbf{v}(2) = 20\mathbf{i} - 19.6\mathbf{j}$; $|\mathbf{v}(2)| = \sqrt{20^2 + 19.6^2} \approx 28.0$

29. $\mathbf{R}(t) = (3\cos t)\,\mathbf{i} + (2\sin t)\mathbf{j} \Rightarrow \mathbf{v}(t) = (-3\sin t)\mathbf{i} + (2\cos t)\mathbf{j}$ and

$\mathbf{a}(t) = (-3\cos t)\mathbf{i} + (-2\sin t)\,\mathbf{j}$. Let $\mathbf{F}(t) = \sqrt{9\cos^2 t + 4\sin^2 t}$.

$$\mathbf{F}'(t) = \frac{-18\cos t\sin t + 8\sin t\cos t}{2\sqrt{9\cos^2 t + 4\sin^2 t}} = 0 \text{ if } 10\cos t\sin t = 0$$

if $t = 0, \frac{\pi}{2}, \pi$ or $\frac{3\pi}{2}$. $\mathbf{F}(0) = \mathbf{F}(\pi) = 3$ is maximum acceleration

and $\mathbf{F}\left(\frac{\pi}{2}\right) = \mathbf{F}\left(\frac{3\pi}{2}\right) = 2$ is minimum acceleration.

31. Let $f(t) = |\mathbf{v}|^2$. Then $f(t) = \mathbf{v}\cdot\mathbf{v}$ so $f'(t) = 2\,\mathbf{v}\cdot\mathbf{v}' = 0$.

Therefore $f(t)$ is constant.

33. (a) $\frac{d}{dt}(\mathbf{u}\cdot\mathbf{v}\times\mathbf{w}) = \frac{d\mathbf{u}}{dt}\cdot(\mathbf{v}\times\mathbf{w}) + \mathbf{u}\cdot\frac{d}{dt}(\mathbf{v}\times\mathbf{w})$

$$= \frac{d\mathbf{u}}{dt}\cdot(\mathbf{v}\times\mathbf{w}) + \mathbf{u}\cdot\left(\frac{d\mathbf{v}}{dt}\times\mathbf{w} + \mathbf{v}\times\frac{d\mathbf{w}}{dt}\right)$$

$$= \frac{d\mathbf{u}}{dt}\cdot(\mathbf{v}\times\mathbf{w}) + \mathbf{u}\cdot\left(\frac{d\mathbf{v}}{dt}\times\mathbf{w}\right) + \mathbf{u}\cdot\left(\mathbf{v}\times\frac{d\mathbf{w}}{dt}\right)$$

(b) By Equation (3), Section 13.7, each of the determinants is the equivalent of the corresponding triple scalar product in part (a).

35. $$\lim_{\Delta t\to 0}\left(\mathbf{U}\times\frac{\Delta\mathbf{V}}{\Delta t}\right) = \lim_{\Delta t\to 0}\begin{vmatrix} \mathbf{i} & \mathbf{j} & \mathbf{k} \\ u_1 & u_2 & u_3 \\ \frac{\Delta v_1}{\Delta t} & \frac{\Delta v_2}{\Delta t} & \frac{\Delta v_3}{\Delta t}\end{vmatrix}$$

$$= \lim_{\Delta t\to 0}\left(u_2\frac{\Delta v_3}{\Delta t} - u_3\frac{\Delta v_2}{\Delta t}\right)\mathbf{i} - \lim_{\Delta t\to 0}\left(u_1\frac{\Delta v_3}{\Delta t} - u_3\frac{\Delta v_1}{\Delta t}\right)\mathbf{j} + \lim_{\Delta t\to 0}\left(u_1\frac{\Delta v_2}{\Delta t} - u_2\frac{\Delta v_1}{\Delta t}\right)\mathbf{k}$$

$$= \left(u_2\lim_{\Delta t\to 0}\frac{\Delta v_3}{\Delta t} - u_3\lim_{\Delta t\to 0}\frac{\Delta v_2}{\Delta t}\right)\mathbf{i} - \left(u_1\lim_{\Delta t\to 0}\frac{\Delta v_3}{\Delta t} - u_3\lim_{\Delta t\to 0}\frac{\Delta v_1}{\Delta t}\right)\mathbf{j} +$$

$$\left(u_1\lim_{\Delta t\to 0}\frac{\Delta v_2}{\Delta t} - u_2\lim_{\Delta t\to 0}\frac{\Delta v_1}{\Delta t}\right)\mathbf{k}$$

$$= \begin{vmatrix} \mathbf{i} & \mathbf{j} & \mathbf{k} \\ u_1 & u_2 & u_3 \\ \lim_{\Delta t\to 0}\frac{\Delta v_1}{\Delta t} & \lim_{\Delta t\to 0}\frac{\Delta v_2}{\Delta t} & \lim_{\Delta t\to 0}\frac{\Delta v_3}{\Delta t}\end{vmatrix} = \mathbf{U}\times\lim_{\Delta t\to 0}\frac{\Delta\mathbf{V}}{\Delta t}$$

## 14.2 DIRECTED DISTANCE AND THE UNIT TANGENT T

1. $\mathbf{R}(t) = (2\cos t)\mathbf{i} + (2\sin t)\mathbf{j} + \sqrt{5}\,t\,\mathbf{k}$

$\mathbf{v}(t) = (-2\sin t)\,\mathbf{i} + (2\cos t)\,\mathbf{j} + \sqrt{5}\,\mathbf{k}$

$|\mathbf{v}(t)| = \sqrt{4\sin^2 t + 4\cos^2 t + 5} = 3$

$\mathbf{T}(t) = \frac{\mathbf{v}(t)}{|\mathbf{v}(t)|} = -\frac{2}{3}\sin t\,\mathbf{i} + \frac{2}{3}\cos t\,\mathbf{j} + \frac{\sqrt{5}}{3}\mathbf{k}$

$L = \int_0^{\pi} |\mathbf{v}(t)|\,dt = \int_0^{\pi} 3\,dt = 3\pi$

3. $\mathbf{R}(t) = t\mathbf{i} + \frac{2}{3}t^{3/2}\mathbf{j}$; $\mathbf{v}(t) = \mathbf{i} + \sqrt{t}\,\mathbf{j}$

$|\mathbf{v}(t)| = \sqrt{1+t}$

$$\mathbf{T}(t) = \frac{\mathbf{v}(t)}{|\mathbf{v}(t)|} = \frac{1}{\sqrt{1+t}}\mathbf{i} \; |+ \sqrt{\frac{t}{1+t}}\,\mathbf{j}$$

$$L = \int_0^8 |\mathbf{v}(t)|\,dt = \int_0^8 \sqrt{1+t}\,dt = \frac{2}{3}(1+t)^{3/2}\Big]_0^8 = \frac{52}{3}$$

5. $\mathbf{R}(t) = t^3(6\mathbf{i} - 2\mathbf{j} - 3\mathbf{k})$; $\mathbf{v}(t) = 3t^2\,(6\mathbf{i} - 2\mathbf{j} - 3\mathbf{k})$ $|\mathbf{v}(t)| = 21t^2$

$$\mathbf{T}(t) = \frac{\mathbf{v}(t)}{|\mathbf{v}(t)|} = \frac{6}{7}\mathbf{i} - \frac{2}{7}\mathbf{j} - \frac{3}{7}\mathbf{k}$$

$$L = \int_{-1}^{1} |\mathbf{v}(t)|\,dt = \int_{-1}^{1} 21t^2\,dt = 7t^3\Big]_{-1}^{1} = 14$$

7. $\mathbf{R}(t) = (t\cos t)\mathbf{i} + (t\sin t)\mathbf{j} + \frac{2\sqrt{2}}{3}t^{3/2}\,\mathbf{k}$

$\mathbf{v}(t) = (\cos t - t\sin t)\mathbf{i} + (\sin t + t\cos t)\mathbf{j} + \sqrt{2}t^{1/2}\,\mathbf{k}$

$|\mathbf{v}(t)| = |1+t|$

$$\mathbf{T}(t) = \frac{\mathbf{v}(t)}{|\mathbf{v}(t)|} = \frac{\cos t - t\sin t}{|1+t|}\mathbf{i} + \frac{\sin t + t\cos t}{|1+t|}\mathbf{j} + \frac{\sqrt{2t}}{|1+t|}\mathbf{k}$$

$$L = \int_0^{\pi} |\mathbf{v}(t)|\,dt = \int_0^{\pi} (1+t)\,dt = \pi + \frac{1}{2}\pi^2$$

9. $\mathbf{R}(t) = (a\cos\omega t)\mathbf{i} + (a\sin\omega t)\mathbf{j} + b\mathbf{k}$ $a > 0$, $\omega > 0$

$\mathbf{v}(t) = (-a\omega\sin\omega t)\mathbf{i} + (a\omega\cos\omega t)\mathbf{j}$; $|\mathbf{v}| = |a\omega| = a\omega$

$$\mathbf{T}(t) = \frac{\mathbf{v}(t)}{|\mathbf{v}(t)|} = (-\sin\omega t)\,\mathbf{i} + (\cos\omega t)\,\mathbf{j}$$

$$L = \int_0^{\frac{2\pi}{\omega}} |\mathbf{v}(t)|\,dt = \int_0^{\frac{2\pi}{\omega}} a\omega\,dt = 2\pi a$$

11. $\mathbf{R}(t) = (e^t\cos t)\mathbf{i} + (e^t\sin t)\mathbf{j} + e^t\,\mathbf{k}$

$\mathbf{v}(t) = (-e^t\sin t + e^t\cos t)\mathbf{i} + (e^t\cos t + e^t\sin t)\mathbf{j} + e^t\,\mathbf{k}$;

$$|\mathbf{v}| = \sqrt{e^{2t}(\sin^2 t - 2\sin t\cos t + \cos^2 t + \cos^2 t + 2\sin t\cos t + \sin^2 t + 1)}$$

$$= \sqrt{3}\,e^t;\quad s(t) = \int_0^t \sqrt{3}\,e^{\tau}\,d\tau = \sqrt{3}\,(e^t - 1).\quad L = \sqrt{3}e^t\Big]_{-\pi}^{\pi} = \sqrt{3}\,(e^{\pi} - e^{-\pi})$$

13. $\mathbf{R}(t) = 3t^2\mathbf{i} + (6t+7)\mathbf{j} + 2t^4\,\mathbf{k}$

$\mathbf{v}(t) = 6t\mathbf{i} + 6\mathbf{j} + 8t^3\,\mathbf{k}$; $\mathbf{v}(0) = 6\mathbf{j}$; $|\mathbf{v}(0)| = 6$

$\mathbf{T}(0) = \mathbf{j}$; $\mathbf{a}(t) = 6\mathbf{i} + 24t^2\,\mathbf{k}$; $\mathbf{a}(o) = 6\mathbf{i}$

15. Cut the cylinder vertically and open it into the desired square. The helix lies along the diagonal.

## 14.3 CURVATURE, TORSION, AND THE TNB FRAME

1. $\mathbf{R}(t) = t\,\mathbf{i} + (\ln \cos t)\mathbf{j},\ -\frac{\pi}{2} < t < \frac{\pi}{2};\ \mathbf{v}(t) = \mathbf{i} - (\tan t)\,\mathbf{j}$

$|\mathbf{v}(t)| = \sqrt{1+\tan^2 t} = \sec t$

$\mathbf{T}(t) = \frac{\mathbf{v}(t)}{|\mathbf{v}(t)|} = (\cos t)\,\mathbf{i} - (\sin t)\mathbf{j};\ \mathbf{a}(t) = (-\sec^2 t)\,\mathbf{j}$

$\mathbf{v} \times \mathbf{a} = (-\sec^2 t)\,\mathbf{k};\ \kappa = \frac{|\mathbf{v} \times \mathbf{a}|}{|\mathbf{v}|^3} = \cos t$

$\frac{d\mathbf{T}}{dt} = (-\sin t)\mathbf{i} - (\cos t)\mathbf{j};\ \left|\frac{d\mathbf{T}}{dt}\right| = 1;\ \mathbf{N} = (-\sin t)\mathbf{i} - (\cos t)\mathbf{j}$

3. $\mathbf{R}(t) = (\ln \sec t)\,\mathbf{i} + t\,\mathbf{j},\ -\frac{\pi}{2} < t < \frac{\pi}{2};\ \mathbf{v}(t) = (\tan t)\,\mathbf{i} + \mathbf{j}$

$|\mathbf{v}(t)| = \sqrt{1+\tan^2 t} = \sec t$

$\mathbf{T}(t) = \frac{\mathbf{v}(t)}{|\mathbf{v}(t)|} = (\sin t)\,\mathbf{i} + (\cos t)\mathbf{j};\ \mathbf{a}(t) = (\sec^2 t)\,\mathbf{i}$

$\mathbf{v} \times \mathbf{a} = (-\sec^2 t)\,\mathbf{k};\ \kappa = \frac{|\mathbf{v} \times \mathbf{a}|}{|\mathbf{v}|^3} = \cos t$

$\frac{d\mathbf{T}}{dt} = (\cos t)\mathbf{i} - (\sin t)\mathbf{j};\ \left|\frac{d\mathbf{T}}{dt}\right| = 1;\ \mathbf{N} = (\cos t)\mathbf{i} - (\sin t)\mathbf{j}$

5. $\mathbf{R}(t) = \frac{t^3}{3}\mathbf{i} + \frac{t^2}{2}\mathbf{j};\ \mathbf{v}(t) = t^2\,\mathbf{i} + t\,\mathbf{j};\ |\mathbf{v}(t)| = t\sqrt{1+t^2}$

$\mathbf{T}(t) = \frac{\mathbf{v}(t)}{|\mathbf{v}(t)|} = \frac{t}{\sqrt{1+t^2}}\mathbf{i} + \frac{1}{\sqrt{1+t^2}}\mathbf{j};\ \mathbf{a}(t) = 2t\,\mathbf{i} + \mathbf{j}$

$\mathbf{v} \times \mathbf{a} = -t^2\,\mathbf{k};\ \kappa = \frac{|\mathbf{v} \times \mathbf{a}|}{|\mathbf{v}|^3} = t^{-1}(1+t^2)^{-3/2}$

$\frac{d\mathbf{T}}{dt} = (1+t^2)^{-3/2}(\mathbf{i} - t\mathbf{j});\ \left|\frac{d\mathbf{T}}{dt}\right| = \frac{1}{1+t^2}$

$\mathbf{N} = \frac{1}{\sqrt{1+t^2}}\mathbf{i} - \frac{t}{\sqrt{1+t^2}}\mathbf{j}$

7. $\mathbf{R}(t) = (\cos^3 t)\mathbf{i} + (\sin^3 t)\mathbf{j}$

$\mathbf{v}(t) = (-3\cos^2 t \sin t)\,\mathbf{i} + (3\sin^2 t \cos t)\,\mathbf{j};\ |\mathbf{v}(t)| = 3 \cos t \sin t$

$$\mathbf{T}(t) = \frac{\mathbf{v}(t)}{|\mathbf{v}(t)|} = (-\cos t)\,\mathbf{i} + (\sin t)\mathbf{j}$$

$\mathbf{a}(t) = 3\cos t(2\sin^2 t - \cos^2 t)\,\mathbf{i} + 3\sin t(2\cos^2 t - \sin^2 t)\mathbf{j}$

$$\mathbf{v}\times\mathbf{a} = -9\sin^2 t \cos^2 t\ \mathbf{k};\ \kappa = \frac{|\mathbf{v}\times\mathbf{a}|}{|\mathbf{v}|^3} = -\frac{1}{3}\sec t \csc t$$

$$\frac{d\mathbf{T}}{dt} = (\sin t)\,\mathbf{i} + (\cos t)\mathbf{j});\ \left|\frac{d\mathbf{T}}{dt}\right| = 1;\ \mathbf{N} = (\sin t)\,\mathbf{i} + (\cos t)\mathbf{j}$$

9. $\mathbf{R}(t) = (3\sin t)\,\mathbf{i} + (3\cos t)\mathbf{j} + 4t\,\mathbf{k};\ \mathbf{v}(t) = (3\cos t)\mathbf{i} - (3\sin t)\mathbf{j} + 4\mathbf{k}$

$$|\mathbf{v}(t)| = 5;\ \mathbf{T}(t) = \frac{\mathbf{v}(t)}{|\mathbf{v}(t)|} = \left(\frac{3}{5}\cos t\right)\mathbf{i} - \left(\frac{3}{5}\sin t\right)\mathbf{j} + \frac{4}{5}\mathbf{k}$$

$\mathbf{a}(t) = (-3\sin t)\,\mathbf{i} - (3\cos t)\mathbf{j}$

$$\mathbf{v}\times\mathbf{a} = (12\cos t)\mathbf{i} - (12\sin t)\mathbf{j} - 9\,\mathbf{k};\ |\,\mathbf{v}\times\mathbf{a}|;\ \kappa = \frac{|\mathbf{v}\times\mathbf{a}|}{|\mathbf{v}|^3} = \frac{3}{25}$$

$$\frac{d\mathbf{T}}{dt} = \left(-\frac{3}{5}\sin t\right)\mathbf{i} + \left(-\frac{3}{5}\cos t\right)\mathbf{j});\ \left|\frac{d\mathbf{T}}{dt}\right| = \frac{3}{5};\ \mathbf{N} = (-\sin t)\,\mathbf{i} + (-\cos t)\mathbf{j}$$

$$\mathbf{B} = |\mathbf{T}\times\mathbf{N}| = \left(\frac{4}{5}\cos t\right)\mathbf{i} - \left(\frac{4}{5}\sin t\right)\mathbf{j} - \frac{3}{5}\mathbf{k}$$

$$\tau = \frac{1}{225}\begin{vmatrix} 3\cos t & -3\sin t & 4 \\ -3\sin t & -3\cos t & 0 \\ -3\cos t & 3\sin t & 0 \end{vmatrix} = \frac{4}{225}(-9\sin^2 t - 9\cos^2 t) = -\frac{4}{25}$$

11. $\mathbf{R}(t) = (e^t \cos t)\mathbf{i} + (e^t \sin t)\mathbf{j} + 2\,\mathbf{k}$

$\mathbf{v}(t) = (e^t \cos t - e^t \sin t)\,\mathbf{i} + (e^t \sin t + e^t \cos t)\,\mathbf{j};\ |\mathbf{v}(t)| = \sqrt{2}e^t$

$$\mathbf{T}(t) = \frac{\mathbf{v}(t)}{|\mathbf{v}(t)|} = \frac{1}{\sqrt{2}}(\cos t - \sin t)\,\mathbf{i} + \frac{1}{\sqrt{2}}(\sin t + \cos t)\mathbf{j}$$

$\mathbf{a}(t) = (-2e^t \sin t)\,\mathbf{i} + (2e^t \cos t)\mathbf{j};\ \tau = 0$

$$\mathbf{v}\times\mathbf{a} = 2e^{2t};\ \kappa = \frac{|\mathbf{v}\times\mathbf{a}|}{|\mathbf{v}|^3} = \frac{1}{\sqrt{2}e^t}$$

$$\frac{d\mathbf{T}}{dt} = \frac{1}{\sqrt{2}}(-\sin t - \cos t)\,\mathbf{i} + \frac{1}{\sqrt{2}}(\cos t - \sin t)\mathbf{j}$$

$$\left|\frac{d\mathbf{T}}{dt}\right| = 1;\ \mathbf{N} = \frac{1}{\sqrt{2}}(-\sin t - \cos t)\,\mathbf{i} + \frac{1}{\sqrt{2}}(\cos t - \sin t)\mathbf{j};\ \mathbf{B} = |\mathbf{T}\times\mathbf{N}| = \mathbf{k}$$

13. $\mathbf{R}(t) = \left(\frac{4}{9}(1+t)^{3/2}\right)\mathbf{i} + \left(\frac{4}{9}(1-t)^{3/2}\right)\mathbf{j} + \frac{1}{3}t\,\mathbf{k}$

$\mathbf{v}(t) = \left(\frac{2}{3}(1+t)^{1/2}\right)\mathbf{i} - \left(\frac{2}{3}(1-t)^{1/2}\right)\mathbf{j} + \frac{1}{3}\mathbf{k};\ |\mathbf{v}(t)| = 1;\ \mathbf{T}(t) = \mathbf{v}(t)$

$\frac{d\mathbf{T}}{dt} = \left(\frac{1}{3}(1+t)^{-1/2}\right)\mathbf{i} + \left(\frac{1}{3}(1-t)^{-1/2}\right)\mathbf{j}$

$\left|\frac{d\mathbf{T}}{dt}\right| = \frac{\sqrt{2}}{3}(1-t^2)^{-1/2};\ \mathbf{N} = \sqrt{\frac{1-t}{2}}\,\mathbf{i} + \sqrt{\frac{1+t}{2}}\,\mathbf{j}$

$$\mathbf{v}\times\mathbf{a} = \begin{vmatrix} \mathbf{i} & \mathbf{j} & \mathbf{k} \\ \frac{2}{3}(1+t)^{1/2} & -\frac{2}{3}(1-t)^{1/2} & \frac{1}{3} \\ \frac{1}{3}(1+t)^{-1/2} & \frac{1}{3}(1-t)^{-1/2} & 0 \end{vmatrix} = -\frac{1}{9\sqrt{1+t}}\mathbf{i} + \frac{1}{9\sqrt{1-t}}\mathbf{j} + \frac{4}{9\sqrt{1-t^2}}\mathbf{k}$$

$$\kappa = |\mathbf{v}\times\mathbf{a}| = \left[\frac{1}{81(1+t)} + \frac{1}{81(1-t)} + \frac{16}{81(1-t^2)}\right]^{1/2} = \frac{2}{3\sqrt{1-t^2}}$$

15. $\mathbf{R}(t) = (2t+3)\,\mathbf{i} + (t^2-1)\mathbf{j}\ ;\ \mathbf{v}(t) = 2\mathbf{i} + 2\mathbf{j};\ \mathbf{a}(t) = 2\mathbf{j}$

$|\mathbf{v}(t)| = 2\sqrt{1+t^2};\ \mathbf{a_T} = \frac{d}{dt}|\mathbf{v}(t)| = \frac{2t}{\sqrt{1+t^2}}$

$\mathbf{a_N} = \sqrt{|\mathbf{a}|^2 - \mathbf{a}_T^2} = \sqrt{4 - \frac{4t^2}{1+t^2}} = \frac{2}{\sqrt{1+t^2}}$

$\mathbf{a} = \frac{2t}{\sqrt{1+t^2}}\mathbf{T} + \frac{2}{\sqrt{1+t^2}}\mathbf{N}$

17. $\mathbf{R}(t) = (2\cos t)\,\mathbf{i} + (2\sin t)\mathbf{j}\ ;\ \mathbf{v}(t) = (-2\sin t)\mathbf{i} + (2\cos t)\mathbf{j}$

$\mathbf{a}(t) = (-2\cos t)\mathbf{i} - (2\cos t)\mathbf{j};\ |\mathbf{v}(t)| = 2;\ \mathbf{a_T} = \frac{d}{dt}|\mathbf{v}(t)| = 0$

$\mathbf{a_N} = \sqrt{|\mathbf{a}|^2 - \mathbf{a}_T^2} = 2 \quad \mathbf{a} = 2\,\mathbf{N}$

19. $\mathbf{R}(t) = (a\cos\omega t)\mathbf{i} + (a\sin\omega t)\mathbf{j} + bt\mathbf{k};\ \mathbf{v}(t) = (-a\omega\sin\omega t)\mathbf{i} + (a\omega\cos\omega t)\mathbf{j} + b\mathbf{k}$

$\mathbf{a}(t) = (-a\omega^2\cos\omega t)\mathbf{i} - (a\omega^2\sin\omega t)\mathbf{j};\ |\mathbf{v}(t)| = \sqrt{a^2\omega^2 + b^2}$

$\mathbf{a_T} = \frac{d}{dt}|\mathbf{v}(t)| = 0;\ \mathbf{a_N} = \sqrt{|\mathbf{a}|^2 - \mathbf{a}_T^2} = a\omega^2;\quad \mathbf{a} = a\omega^2\,\mathbf{N}$

21. $\mathbf{R}(t) = (t+1)\mathbf{i} + 2t\mathbf{j} + t^2\mathbf{k}$; $\mathbf{v}(t) = \mathbf{i} + 2\mathbf{j} + 2t\mathbf{k}$; $\mathbf{a}(t) = 2\mathbf{k}$

$$|\mathbf{v}(t)| = \sqrt{5+4t^2};\ \mathbf{a_T} = \frac{d}{dt}|\mathbf{v}(t)| = \left.\frac{4t}{\sqrt{5+4t^2}}\right]_{t=1} = \frac{4}{3}$$

$$\mathbf{a_N} = \sqrt{|\mathbf{a}|^2 - \mathbf{a}_T^2} = \sqrt{4 - \frac{16}{9}} = \frac{2\sqrt{5}}{3};\ \mathbf{a} = \frac{4}{3}\mathbf{T} + \frac{2\sqrt{5}}{3}\mathbf{N}$$

23. $\mathbf{R}(t) = t^2\mathbf{i} + \left(t + \frac{1}{3}t^3\right)\mathbf{j} + \left(t - \frac{1}{3}t^3\right)\mathbf{k}$

$$\mathbf{v}(t) = 2t\mathbf{i} + (1+t^2)\mathbf{j} + (1-t^2)\mathbf{k};\ \mathbf{a}(t) = 2\mathbf{i} + 2t\mathbf{j} - 2t\mathbf{k}$$

$$|\mathbf{v}(t)| = \sqrt{2}(t^2+1);\ \mathbf{a_T} = \frac{d}{dt}|\mathbf{v}(t)| = \left.2\sqrt{2}t\right]_{t=0} = 0$$

$$\mathbf{a_N} = \sqrt{|\mathbf{a}|^2 - \mathbf{a}_T^2} = 2;\ \mathbf{a} = 2\mathbf{N}$$

25. $\mathbf{R}(t) = (2 + 3t + 3t^2)\mathbf{i} + (4t + 4t^2)\mathbf{j} - (6\cos t)\mathbf{k}$

$$\mathbf{v}(t) = (3+6t)\mathbf{i} + (4+8t)\mathbf{j} + (6\sin t)\mathbf{k}$$

$$\mathbf{a}(t) = 6\mathbf{i} + 8\mathbf{j} + (6\cos t)\mathbf{k};\ |\mathbf{a}| = \sqrt{100 + 36\cos^2 t}$$

$$|\mathbf{v}(t)| == \sqrt{25 + 100t + 100t^2 + 36\sin^2 t}$$

$$\mathbf{a_T} = \frac{d}{dt}|\mathbf{v}(t)| = \left.\frac{50 + 100t\ \ 36\sin t\cos t}{\sqrt{25 + 100t + 100t^2 + 36\sin^2 t}}\right]_{t=0} = 10$$

At $t = 0$, $\mathbf{a_N} = \sqrt{|\mathbf{a}|^2 - \mathbf{a}_T^2} = 6$; $\mathbf{a} = 10\mathbf{T} + 6\mathbf{N}$

27. $\mathbf{R}(t) = (\cos t)\mathbf{i} + (\sin t)\mathbf{j}$; $\mathbf{R}\left(\frac{\pi}{4}\right) = \frac{1}{\sqrt{2}}\mathbf{i} + \frac{1}{\sqrt{2}}\mathbf{j}$

$$\mathbf{v}(t) = (-\sin t)\mathbf{i} + (\cos t)\mathbf{j}\ |\mathbf{v}(t)| = 1;\ \mathbf{T}(t) = \frac{\mathbf{v}(t)}{|\mathbf{v}(t)|} = \mathbf{v}(t)$$

$$\mathbf{T}\left(\frac{\pi}{4}\right) = -\frac{1}{\sqrt{2}}\mathbf{i} + \frac{1}{\sqrt{2}}\mathbf{j};\ \frac{d\mathbf{T}}{dt} = (-\cos t)\mathbf{i} + (-\sin t)\mathbf{j})$$

$$\left|\frac{d\mathbf{T}}{dt}\right| = 1;\ \mathbf{N} = (-\cos t)\mathbf{i} + (-\sin t)\mathbf{j};\ \mathbf{N}\left(\frac{\pi}{4}\right) = -\frac{1}{\sqrt{2}}\mathbf{i} - \frac{1}{\sqrt{2}}\mathbf{j};\ \mathbf{B} = |\mathbf{T}\times\mathbf{N}| = \mathbf{k}$$

normal: $-\frac{1}{\sqrt{2}}x + \frac{1}{\sqrt{2}}y = 0$; rectifying: $\frac{1}{\sqrt{2}}x + \frac{1}{\sqrt{2}}y = 1$

osculating: $z = 0$

29. $\mathbf{R}(t) = (2\cos t)\,\mathbf{i} + (2\sin t)\mathbf{j} + t\mathbf{k}$; $\mathbf{R}(0) = 2\mathbf{i}$

$\mathbf{v}(t) = (-2\sin t)\mathbf{i} + (2\cos t)\mathbf{j} + \mathbf{k}$; $|\mathbf{v}(t)| = \sqrt{5}$

$$\mathbf{T}(t) = \frac{\mathbf{v}(t)}{|\mathbf{v}(t)|} = \left(-\frac{2}{\sqrt{5}}\sin t\right)\mathbf{i} + \left(\frac{2}{\sqrt{5}}\cos t\right)\mathbf{j} + \frac{1}{\sqrt{5}}\mathbf{k}$$

$$\mathbf{T}(0) = \frac{2}{\sqrt{5}}\mathbf{j} + \frac{1}{\sqrt{5}}\mathbf{k};\ \frac{d\mathbf{T}}{dt} = \left(-\frac{2}{\sqrt{5}}\cos t\right)\mathbf{i} - \left(\frac{2}{\sqrt{5}}\sin t\right)\mathbf{j}$$

$$\left|\frac{d\mathbf{T}}{dt}\right| = \frac{2}{\sqrt{5}};\ \mathbf{N} = (-\cos t)\,\mathbf{i} + (-\sin t)\mathbf{j};\ \mathbf{N}(0) = -\mathbf{i};\ \mathbf{B}(0) = -\frac{1}{\sqrt{5}}\mathbf{j} + \frac{2}{\sqrt{5}}\mathbf{k}$$

Normal: $\frac{2}{\sqrt{5}}y + \frac{1}{\sqrt{5}}z = 0$; rectifying: $x = 2$; osculating: $-\frac{1}{\sqrt{5}}y + \frac{2}{\sqrt{5}}z = 0$

31. $\mathbf{R}(t) = (x_0 + At)\mathbf{i} + (y_0 + Bt)\mathbf{j} + (z_0 + Ct)\,\mathbf{k}$

$\mathbf{v}(t) = A\mathbf{i} + B\mathbf{j} + C\mathbf{k}$; $\mathbf{a}(t) = 0 \Rightarrow \mathbf{v} \times \mathbf{a} = \mathbf{O}$ so $\kappa = 0$.

$\tau = \frac{d\mathbf{B}}{ds} = 0$ since $\mathbf{B} = \mathbf{0}$.

33. If $a_N\mathbf{N} = 0$, then $\mathbf{a} = a_T\,\mathbf{T} = a_T\frac{\mathbf{v}}{|\mathbf{v}|}$. Therefore, $\mathbf{v} \times \mathbf{a} = \mathbf{v} \times\ a_T\frac{\mathbf{v}}{|\mathbf{v}|} = 0$.

Then $\kappa = 0$ so the particle moves in a straight line.

35. $\mathbf{F} = m\mathbf{a} = m\,(a_T\mathbf{T} + a_N\ a_T\ \mathbf{N}) = m\left(\mathbf{T}\frac{d^2s}{dt^2} + \mathbf{N}\left(\frac{ds}{dt}\right)^2\right)$. If $\frac{ds}{dt}$ is not constant, then $\frac{d^2s}{dt^2} \neq 0$. Then $\mathbf{F}$ cannot be $\perp \mathbf{v}$, a contradiction.

37. $x = \ln(\sec t) \Rightarrow \dot{x} = \tan t$ and $\ddot{x} = \sec^2 t$; $y = t \Rightarrow y = 1$ and $\ddot{y} = 0$

$$\kappa = \frac{|\dot{x}\ddot{y} - \dot{y}\ddot{x}|}{(\dot{x}^2 + \dot{y}^2)^{3/2}} = \frac{|(\tan t)(0) - (1)(\sec^2 t)|}{(\tan^2 t + 1)^{3/2}} = \frac{\sec^2 t}{|\sec^3 t|} = |\cos t| = \cos t$$

39. $\kappa = \dfrac{|f''|}{(1 + (f')^2)^{3/2}} = \dfrac{|-\sin x|}{(1 + \cos^2 x)^{3/2}}$. At $x = \frac{\pi}{2}$, $\kappa = 1$ so $\rho = \frac{1}{\kappa} = 1$

$y'\left(\frac{\pi}{2}\right) = 0 \Rightarrow$ tangent line is horizontal. Therefore, the normal is vertical $\Rightarrow$ center is $\left(\frac{\pi}{2}, 0\right)$, radius $= 1$ and the equation is:

$$\left(x - \frac{\pi}{2}\right)^2 + y^2 = 1.$$

41. $\phi = \tan^{-1}\left(\frac{\dot{y}}{\dot{x}}\right) \Rightarrow \frac{d\phi}{ds} = \frac{1}{1+\left(\frac{\dot{y}}{\dot{x}}\right)^2}\frac{d}{dx}\left(\frac{\dot{y}}{\dot{x}}\right) = \frac{\dot{x}^2}{\dot{x}^2+\dot{y}^2}\left(\frac{\dot{x}\frac{d\dot{y}}{ds} - \dot{y}\frac{d\dot{x}}{ds}}{\dot{x}^2}\right)$

$$= \frac{\dot{x}\frac{d\dot{y}}{dt}\frac{dt}{ds} - \dot{y}\frac{d\dot{x}}{dt}\frac{dt}{ds}}{\dot{x}^2+\dot{y}^2} = \frac{1}{\left(\frac{ds}{dt}\right)(\dot{x}^2+\dot{y}^2)}(\dot{x}\ddot{y} - \ddot{x}\dot{y}) = 0 \text{ if } (\dot{x}\ddot{y} - \ddot{x}\dot{y}) = 0$$

If $y = f(x)$ then $\dot{y} = \frac{dy}{dt} = \frac{dy}{dx}\frac{dx}{dt} = y'\dot{x}$.

$$\ddot{y} = \frac{d}{dt}(y'\dot{x}) = \dot{x}\frac{dy'}{dt} + y'\ddot{x} = \dot{x}\left(\frac{dy'}{dx}\frac{dx}{dt}\right) + y'\ddot{x} = y''(\dot{x})^2 + y'\ddot{x}.$$

$0 = \dot{x}\ddot{y} - \ddot{x}\dot{y} = \dot{x}[y''(\dot{x})^2 + y'\ddot{x}] - \ddot{x}(y'\dot{x}) = y''(\dot{x})^3$. If $\dot{x} = 0$ then $x$ is constant $\Rightarrow y = f(x)$ is a point. If $y'' = 0$ Then $y = C_1x + C_2$.

43. $\mathbf{v} = \mathbf{T}\frac{ds}{dt}$ (Eq. 17) and $\mathbf{a} = \frac{d^2s}{dt^2}\mathbf{T} + \kappa\left(\frac{ds}{dt}\right)^2\mathbf{N}$ (Eq. 19)

$$|\mathbf{v}\times\mathbf{a}| = \left|\left(\mathbf{T}\frac{ds}{dt}\right)\times\left(\frac{d^2s}{dt^2}\mathbf{T} + \kappa\left(\frac{ds}{dt}\right)^2\mathbf{N}\right)\right| = \left|\kappa\left(\frac{ds}{dt}\right)^3\mathbf{T}\times\mathbf{N}\right|$$

$$= \kappa\,|\mathbf{v}|^3\,|\mathbf{B}| = \kappa\,|\mathbf{v}|^3$$

45. $\kappa = \frac{a\omega^2}{a^2\omega^2+b^2} \Rightarrow \frac{d\kappa}{da} = \frac{(a^2\omega^2+b^2)(\omega^2) - (a\omega^2)(2a\omega^2)}{(a^2\omega^2+b^2)^2} = \frac{\omega^2(b^2 - a^2\omega^2)}{(a^2\omega^2+b^2)^2} = 0$

if $a = \frac{b}{\omega}$ (if $b, \omega > 0$). $\frac{d\kappa}{da} > 0$ if $a < \frac{b}{\omega}$ and $\frac{d\kappa}{da} < 0$ if $a > \frac{b}{\omega} \Rightarrow$ $\kappa(a) = \frac{\omega}{2b}$ is a maximum.

47. $\mathbf{v}(t) = \dot{x}(t)\mathbf{i} + \dot{y}(t)\mathbf{j} + \dot{z}(t)\mathbf{k}$; $\mathbf{v}\cdot\mathbf{k} = 0 \Rightarrow \dot{z}(t) = 0 \Rightarrow z(t) = C$. $\mathbf{R}(0) = \mathbf{0} \Rightarrow \dot{z}(t) = 0 \Rightarrow z(t) = 0$.

## 14.4 PLANETARY MOTION AND SATELLITES

1. $\frac{T^2}{a^3} = \frac{4\pi^2}{GM} \Rightarrow T = \sqrt{\frac{4\pi^2a^3}{GM}}$

$$= 2\pi(6.808\times10^6)\sqrt{\frac{6.808\times10^6}{(6.6720\times10^{-11})(5.976\times10^{24})}}$$

$= 5{,}589.5376$ sec $= 93.1590$ min. Table has 93.11 min.

3. $a = \left(\frac{T^2 GM}{4\pi^2}\right)^{1/3} = \left[\frac{(5535)^2(6.6720\times10^{-11})(5.976\times10^{24})}{4\pi^2}\right]^{1/3}$

$= 6,763,643.563$ m. By comparison, $\frac{1}{2}(\text{apogee}+\text{perigee}+d)$

$= \frac{1}{2}[589+183+2(6378.533)]\times10^3 = 6,764,533.000$ m.

5. $\frac{T^2}{a^3} = \frac{4\pi^2}{GM} \Rightarrow T = \sqrt{\frac{4\pi^2 a^3}{GM}}$

$= 2\pi(2.2030\times10^7)\sqrt{\frac{2.2030\times10^7}{(6.6720\times10^{-11})(6.418\times10^{23})}}$

$= 99,282.737$ sec $= 1,654.71$ min.

7. $a = \left(\frac{T^2 GM}{4\pi^2}\right)^{1/3} = \left[\frac{(8.8644\times10^4)^2(6.6720\times10^{-11})(6.418\times10^{23})}{4\pi^2}\right]^{1/3}$

$= 2.0426701\times10^7$ m.

9. $e = \frac{r_0 v_0^2}{GM} - 1 \Rightarrow v_0 = \sqrt{(e+1)\frac{GM}{r_0}}$. Hence, we have:

Circle: $e = 0 \Rightarrow v_0 = \sqrt{\frac{GM}{r_0}}$

Ellipe: $0 < e < 1 \Rightarrow \sqrt{\frac{GM}{r_0}} < v_0 < \sqrt{\frac{2GM}{r_0}}$

Parabola: $e = 1 \Rightarrow v_0 = \sqrt{\frac{2GM}{r_0}}$

Hyperbola: $e > 1 \Rightarrow v_0 > \sqrt{\frac{2GM}{r_0}}$

11. (a) For planets: $\frac{T^2}{a^3} = \frac{4\pi^2}{(6.6720\times10^{-11})(1.99\times10^{30})} = 2.973\times10^{-19}$

(b) For earth satellites:

$$\frac{T^2}{a^3} = \frac{4\pi^2}{(6.6720\times10^{-11})(5.975\times10^{24})} = 9.9013\times10^{-14}$$

(c) For moon satellites:

$$\frac{T^2}{a^3} = \frac{4\pi^2}{(6.6720\times10^{-11})(7.354\times10^{22})} = 8.046\times10^{-12}$$

13. From Equation (17) we have $r^2 \dfrac{d\theta}{dt} = r_0 v_0$. Also

$\mathbf{v} = \dfrac{dr}{dt}\mathbf{u}_r + r\dfrac{d\theta}{dt}\mathbf{u}_\theta$ . Since r a constant, $\dfrac{dr}{dt} = 0$.

Also, $r = r_0$ since the path is a circle. Hence

$$\mathbf{v} = r_0\frac{d\theta}{dt}\mathbf{u}_\theta = r_0\left(\frac{r_0 v_0}{r_0^2}\right)\mathbf{u}_\theta = v_0\mathbf{u}_\theta \Rightarrow |\mathbf{v}| = v_0 \text{ which is constant.}$$

15. $r = a(1-\cos\theta)$, $\dfrac{d\theta}{dt} = 3$; $\dfrac{dr}{dt} = a\sin\theta\dfrac{d\theta}{dt} = 3a\sin\theta$

$$\mathbf{v} = \frac{dr}{dt}\mathbf{u}_r + r\frac{d\theta}{dt}\mathbf{u}_\theta = (3a\sin\theta)\mathbf{u}_r + 3a(1-\cos\theta)\mathbf{u}_\theta$$

$$\mathbf{a} = \left(\frac{d^2r}{dt^2} - r\left(\frac{d\theta}{dt}\right)^2\right)\mathbf{u}_r + \left(r\frac{d^2\theta}{dt^2} + 2\frac{dr}{dt}\frac{d\theta}{dt}\right)\mathbf{u}_\theta$$

$\dfrac{d^2r}{dt^2} = 3a\cos\theta\dfrac{d\theta}{dt} = 9a\cos\theta$. Therefore,

$$\mathbf{a} = (9a\cos\theta - 9a(1-\cos\theta))\mathbf{u}_r + (0 + 6(3a\sin\theta))\mathbf{u}_\theta$$

$$= (18a\cos\theta - 9a)\mathbf{u}_r + (18a\sin\theta)\mathbf{u}_\theta$$

17. $r = e^{a\theta}$, $\dfrac{d\theta}{dt} = 2$; $\dfrac{dr}{dt} = ae^{a\theta}\dfrac{d\theta}{dt} = 2e^{a\theta}$

$$\mathbf{v} = \frac{dr}{dt}\mathbf{u}_r + r\frac{d\theta}{dt}\mathbf{u}_\theta = (2ae^{a\theta})\mathbf{u}_r + (2e^{a\theta})\mathbf{u}_\theta$$

$$\mathbf{a} = \left(\frac{d^2r}{dt^2} - r\left(\frac{d\theta}{dt}\right)^2\right)\mathbf{u}_r + \left(r\frac{d^2\theta}{dt^2} + 2\frac{dr}{dt}\frac{d\theta}{dt}\right)\mathbf{u}_\theta$$

$\dfrac{d^2r}{dt^2} = a^2e^{a\theta}\dfrac{d\theta}{dt} = 2a^2e^{a\theta}$. Therefore,

$$\mathbf{a} = (4a^2e^{a\theta} - 4e^{a\theta})\mathbf{u}_r + (8ae^{a\theta})\mathbf{u}_\theta$$

19. $r = 2\cos 4t, \theta = 2t \Rightarrow \frac{d\theta}{dt} = 2;\ \frac{dr}{dt} = -8\sin 4t$

$$\mathbf{v} = \frac{dr}{dt}\mathbf{u}_r + r\frac{d\theta}{dt}\mathbf{u}_\theta = (-8\sin 4t)\mathbf{u}_r + (4\cos 4t)\mathbf{u}_\theta$$

$$\mathbf{a} = \left(\frac{d^2r}{dt^2} - r\left(\frac{d\theta}{dt}\right)^2\right)\mathbf{u}_r + \left(r\frac{d^2\theta}{dt^2} + 2\frac{dr}{dt}\frac{d\theta}{dt}\right)\mathbf{u}_\theta$$

$\frac{d^2r}{dt^2} = -32\cos 4t$ . Therefore,

$$\mathbf{a} = (-40\cos 4t)\,\mathbf{u}_r + (-32\sin 4t)\,\mathbf{u}_\theta$$

## 14.M MISCELLANEOUS

1. $x(t) = (1+t^2)^{-1/2} \Rightarrow x'(t) = -t(1+t^2)^{-3/2}$

$y(t) = t(1+t^2)^{-1/2} \Rightarrow y'(t) = (1+t^2)^{-3/2}$

$$\mathbf{v}(t) = \left[-t(1+t^2)^{-3/2}\right]\mathbf{i} + \left[(1+t^2)^{-3/2}\right]\mathbf{j}$$

$s(t) = |\mathbf{v}(t)| = (1+t^2)^{-1};\ s'(t) = -2t(1+t^2)^{-2} = 0$ if $t = 0$.

$s''(t) = (6t^2-2)(1+t^2)^{-3};\ s''(0) = -2 \Rightarrow s(0) = 1$ is maximum.

3. $\mathbf{R}(t) = e^t\mathbf{i} + (\sin t)\mathbf{j} + \ln(1-t)\mathbf{k};\ \mathbf{R}(0) = \mathbf{i} \Rightarrow (1,0,0)$ is a point on the line. $\mathbf{v}(t) = e^t\mathbf{i} + (\cos t)\mathbf{j} - \frac{1}{1-t}\mathbf{k};\ \mathbf{v}(0) = \mathbf{i} + \mathbf{j} - \mathbf{k}$ is parallel to the line. The equation of the line is : $x = 1+t,\ y = t,\ z = -t$

5. Let $\mathbf{a} = \mathbf{i}+\mathbf{j}+\mathbf{k}$ and $\mathbf{b} = \mathbf{i}+3\mathbf{j}+2\mathbf{k}$

$\mathbf{V} = (\mathbf{i}+\mathbf{j}+\mathbf{k})\times(\mathbf{i}+3\mathbf{j}+2\mathbf{k}) = \mathbf{i}+\mathbf{j}-2\mathbf{k}$ is parallel to $\mathbf{v}$.

$\text{Proj}_{\mathbf{a}}\mathbf{b} = 2\mathbf{i}+2\mathbf{j}+2\mathbf{k}$ so $r = \sqrt{1^2+1^2+0^2} = \sqrt{2}$. Then $|\mathbf{v}| = 6\sqrt{2}$

and $\mathbf{v} = 6\sqrt{2}\left(\frac{1}{\sqrt{6}}\mathbf{i} + \frac{1}{\sqrt{6}}\mathbf{j} - \frac{2}{\sqrt{6}}\mathbf{k}\right) = 2\sqrt{3}(\mathbf{i}+\mathbf{j}-2\mathbf{k})$

7. $\mathbf{v}\cdot\mathbf{i} = \frac{dx}{dt} = 4;\ \mathbf{v}\cdot\mathbf{j} = \frac{dy}{dt} = \frac{1}{3}x^2\frac{dx}{dt} = \frac{1}{3}(3)^2(4) = 12$

$$\mathbf{a}\cdot\mathbf{i} = \frac{d^2x}{dt^2} = -2;\ \mathbf{a}\cdot\mathbf{j} = \frac{d^2y}{dt^2} = \frac{2}{3}x\left(\frac{dx}{dt}\right)^2 + \frac{1}{3}x^2\frac{d^2x}{dt^2} = 26$$

9. $\mathbf{R}(t) = (e^t \cos t)\mathbf{i} + (e^t \sin t)\mathbf{j}$; $\mathbf{v}(t) = e^t(\cos t - \sin t)\mathbf{i} + e^t(\cos t + \sin t)\mathbf{j}$

$\mathbf{a}(t) = (-2e^t \sin t)\mathbf{i} + (2e^t \cos t)\mathbf{j}$

(a) $2\mathbf{v} - 2\mathbf{R} = 2\left[e^t(\cos t - \sin t)\mathbf{i} + e^t(\cos t + \sin t)\mathbf{j}\right]$

$$+2\left[(e^t \cos t2)\mathbf{i} + (e^t \sin t)\mathbf{j}\right.$$

$$= (-2e^t \sin t)\mathbf{i} + (2e^t \cos t)\mathbf{j}$$

(b) $\mathbf{R} \bullet \mathbf{a} = -2e^{2t} \sin t \cos t + 2e^{2t} \sin t \cos t = 0$

$$\therefore \cos\theta = \frac{\mathbf{R} \bullet \mathbf{a}}{|\mathbf{R}|\,|\mathbf{a}|} = 0$$

(c) $\theta = \dfrac{\pi}{2}$

11. $\dfrac{d\mathbf{R}}{dt} \perp \mathbf{R} \Rightarrow \dfrac{d\mathbf{R}}{dt} \bullet \mathbf{R} = \dfrac{d}{dt}\left(\dfrac{1}{2}\mathbf{R} \bullet \mathbf{R}\right) = 0$. Then $\dfrac{1}{2}\mathbf{R} \bullet \mathbf{R} = k$, a constant.

$\therefore\ \mathbf{R} \bullet \mathbf{R} = \mathbf{R}^2 \Rightarrow [x(t)]^2 + [y(t)]^2 = K^2$

13. $\kappa = \dfrac{|y''|}{(1 + (y')^2)^{3/2}} = \dfrac{e^x}{(1 + e^{2x})^{3/2}}$. $\rho = \dfrac{1}{\kappa} = e^{-x}(1 + e^{2x})^{3/2}$

$\rho' = -e^{-x}(1 + e^{2x})^{3/2} + 3e^x(1 + e^{2x})^{1/2}$

$$= e^{-x}(1 + e^{2x})^{1/2}\left[-(1 + e^{2x}) + 3e^{2x}\right] = e^{-x}(1 + e^{2x})^{1/2}(2e^{2x} - 1)$$

$\rho' = 0$ if $2e^{2x} - 1 = 0$ or if $x = -\ln\sqrt{2}$, $y = \dfrac{1}{\sqrt{2}}$. $\rho' < 0$ if $x < -\ln\sqrt{2}$ and

$\rho' > 0$ if $x > -\ln\sqrt{2} \Rightarrow$ a minimum value occurs at $\left(-\ln\sqrt{2}, \dfrac{1}{\sqrt{2}}\right)$.

15. $\kappa = \dfrac{|\dot{x}\ddot{y} - \dot{y}\ddot{x}|}{(\dot{x}^2 + \dot{y}^2)^{3/2}} \Rightarrow \rho = \dfrac{(\dot{x}^2 + \dot{y}^2)^{3/2}}{|\dot{x}\ddot{y} - \dot{y}\ddot{x}|} = \dfrac{(\dot{x}^2 + \dot{y}^2)^{3/2}}{|\dot{x}\ddot{y} - \dot{y}\ddot{x}|} \cdot \dfrac{(\ddot{x}^2 + \ddot{y}^2 - \ddot{s}^2)^{1/2}}{(\ddot{x}^2 + \ddot{y}^2 - \ddot{s}^2)^{1/2}}$

$= \dfrac{(\dot{x}^2 + \dot{y}^2)}{(\ddot{x}^2 + \ddot{y}^2 - \ddot{s}^2)^{1/2}} \cdot \dfrac{(\dot{x}^2 + \dot{y}^2)^{1/2}(\ddot{x}^2 + \ddot{y}^2 - \ddot{s}^2)^{1/2}}{|\dot{x}\ddot{y} - \dot{y}\ddot{x}|}$. Now it suffices to show

that $(\ddot{x}^2 + \ddot{y}^2 - \ddot{s}^2)^{1/2} = \dfrac{|\dot{x}\ddot{y} - \dot{y}\ddot{x}|}{(\dot{x}^2 + \dot{y}^2)^{1/2}}$. Consider

$$(\ddot{x}^2 + \ddot{y}^2 - \ddot{s}^2)^{1/2} = \left[(\ddot{x}^2 + \ddot{y}^2)\cdot\frac{\dot{s}^2}{\dot{s}^2} - \left(\frac{\dot{x}\ddot{y} - \dot{y}\ddot{x}}{\dot{s}}\right)^2\right]^{1/2}$$

$$= \left[\frac{(\ddot{x}^2 + \ddot{y}^2)(\dot{x}^2 + \dot{y}^2)\ (\dot{x}\ddot{y} - \dot{y}\ddot{x})^2}{\dot{s}^2}\right]^{1/2} = \frac{|\dot{x}\ddot{y} - \dot{y}\ddot{x}|}{(\dot{x}^2 + \dot{y}^2)^{1/2}}.$$

17. $\mathbf{R}(t) = (e^t \sin 2t)\mathbf{i} + (e^t \cos 2t)\mathbf{j} + (2e^t)\mathbf{k}$

$\mathbf{v}(t) = e^t(\sin 2t + 2\cos 2t)\,\mathbf{i} + e^t(\cos 2t - 2\sin 2t)\,\mathbf{j} + (2e^t)\mathbf{k}$

$\mathbf{v}(0) = 2\mathbf{i} + \mathbf{j} + 2\mathbf{k}$; $|\mathbf{v}(0)| = 3$; $\mathbf{T}(t) = \dfrac{\mathbf{v}(t)}{|\mathbf{v}(t)|} = \dfrac{2}{3}\mathbf{i} + \dfrac{1}{3}\mathbf{j} + \dfrac{2}{3}\mathbf{k}$

$\mathbf{a}(t) = e^t(4\cos 2t - 3\sin 2t)\,\mathbf{i} + e^t(-4\sin 2t - 3\cos 2t)\mathbf{j} + (2e^t)\mathbf{k}$

$\mathbf{a}(0) = 4\mathbf{i} - 3\mathbf{j} + 2\mathbf{k}$; $\mathbf{v}\times\mathbf{a} = 8\mathbf{i} + 4\mathbf{j} - 10\mathbf{k}$; $\kappa = \dfrac{|\mathbf{v}\times\mathbf{a}|}{|\mathbf{v}|^3} = \dfrac{2\sqrt{5}}{9}$

$|\mathbf{v}| = \dfrac{ds}{dt} = 3e^t$; $\dfrac{d^2s}{dt^2} = 3e^t \Big|_{t=0} = 3$

$\mathbf{a} = \mathbf{T}\dfrac{d^2s}{dt^2} + \mathbf{N}\kappa\left(\dfrac{ds}{dt}\right)^2$ so $4\mathbf{i} - 3\mathbf{j} + 2\mathbf{k} = 3\,\mathbf{T} + (2\mathbf{i} - 4\,\mathbf{j})$

$2\mathbf{i} - 4\,\mathbf{j} = \dfrac{2\sqrt{5}}{9}(3)^2\,\mathbf{N} \Rightarrow \mathbf{N} = \dfrac{1}{\sqrt{5}}\mathbf{i} - \dfrac{2}{\sqrt{5}}\mathbf{j}$

$\mathbf{B} = \mathbf{T}\times\mathbf{N} = \dfrac{4}{3\sqrt{5}}\mathbf{i} + \dfrac{2}{3\sqrt{5}}\mathbf{j} - \dfrac{5}{3\sqrt{5}}\mathbf{k}$

$\dot{\mathbf{a}}(t) = e^t(-2\cos 2t - 11\sin 2t)\mathbf{i} + e^t(-8\cos 2t + 6\sin 2t)\mathbf{j} + (2e^t)\mathbf{k}$

$$\begin{vmatrix} 2 & 1 & 2 \\ 4 & -3 & 2 \\ -2 & -11 & 2 \end{vmatrix} = -80. \quad \tau = \frac{|-80|}{|\mathbf{v}|^2} = \frac{80}{180} = \frac{4}{9}$$

19. $\phi = \theta + \dfrac{\pi}{2} = \dfrac{s}{a} + \dfrac{\pi}{2}$. $\kappa = \left|\dfrac{d\phi}{ds}\right| = \dfrac{1}{a}$

21. $$\kappa = \frac{r^2 + 2\left(\dfrac{dr}{d\theta}\right)^2 - r\dfrac{d^2t}{d\theta^2}}{\left[r^2 + \left(\dfrac{dr}{d\theta}\right)^2\right]^{3/2}} = \frac{f^2 + 2(f')^2 - f\,f''}{[f^2 + (f')^2]^{3/2}}$$

23. (a) $r = 2 - t,\ \theta = 3t \Rightarrow \frac{dr}{dt} = -1, \frac{d\theta}{dt} = 3$ and $\frac{d^2r}{dt^2} = \frac{d^2\theta}{dt^2} = 0$

$\mathbf{v}(1) = -\mathbf{u}_r + 3\,\mathbf{u}_\theta;$

$$\mathbf{a}(1) = \left[\frac{d^2r}{dt^2} - r\left(\frac{d\theta}{dt}\right)^2\right]\mathbf{u}_r + \left[r\frac{d^2\theta}{dt^2} + 2\,\frac{dr}{dt}\,\frac{d\theta}{dt}\right]\mathbf{u}_\theta = -9\mathbf{u}_r - 6\mathbf{u}_\theta$$

(b) $$L = \int_0^6 \sqrt{[f(\theta)]^2 + [f'(\theta]^2}\,d\theta = \int_0^6 \sqrt{\left(2 - \frac{\theta}{3}\right)^2 + \left(-\frac{1}{3}\right)^2}\,d\theta$$

$$= \frac{1}{3}\int_0^6 \sqrt{37 - 12\theta + \theta^2}\,d\theta \qquad (\text{Let } u = 6 - \theta,\ dy = -\,d\theta)$$

$$= -\frac{1}{2}\int_0^6 \sqrt{u^2 + 1}\,du = -\frac{1}{6}\left[u\sqrt{u^2+1} + \ln\left(u + \sqrt{u^2+1}\right)\right]_0^6$$

$$= \ln(6 + \sqrt{37}) + \sqrt{37}$$

25. (a) $\mathbf{u}_r = \mathbf{i}\cos\theta + \mathbf{j}\sin\theta;\ \mathbf{u}_\theta = -\mathbf{i}\sin\theta + \mathbf{j}\cos\theta$

$$\frac{dx}{dt} = \mathbf{v}\cdot\mathbf{i} = \left(\frac{dr}{dt}\mathbf{u}_r + r\frac{d\theta}{dt}\mathbf{u}_\theta\right)\cdot\mathbf{i} = \frac{dr}{dt}\mathbf{u}_r\cdot\mathbf{i} + r\frac{d\theta}{dt}\mathbf{u}_\theta\cdot\mathbf{i} = \cos\theta\frac{dr}{dt} - r\sin\theta\,\frac{d\theta}{dt}$$

$$\frac{dy}{dt} = \mathbf{v}\cdot\mathbf{j} = \left(\frac{dr}{dt}\mathbf{u}_r + r\frac{d\theta}{dt}\mathbf{u}_\theta\right)\cdot\mathbf{j} = \sin\theta\,\frac{dr}{dt} + r\cos\theta\,\frac{d\theta}{dt}$$

(b) $$\frac{dr}{dt} = \mathbf{v}\cdot\mathbf{u}_r = \left(\frac{dx}{dt}\mathbf{i} + \frac{dy}{dt}\mathbf{j}\right)\cdot\mathbf{u}_r = \cos\theta\,\frac{dx}{dt} + \sin\theta\frac{dy}{dt}$$

$$r\frac{d\theta}{dt} = \mathbf{v}\cdot\mathbf{u}_\theta = \left(\frac{dx}{dt}\mathbf{i} + \frac{dy}{dt}\mathbf{j}\right)\cdot\mathbf{u}_\theta = -\sin\theta\,\frac{dx}{dt} + \cos\theta\frac{dy}{dt}$$

27. $\frac{OA}{OT} = \frac{OT}{OS} \Rightarrow \frac{a}{R} = \frac{R}{R+h} \Rightarrow a = \frac{R^2}{R+h}$

$$L(TR) = 2\pi\int_a^{R+h} y\,ds = 2\pi\int_a^{R+h} \sqrt{R^2 - x^2}\cdot\frac{R}{\sqrt{R^2 - x^2}}\,dx = 2\pi[Rx]_a^{R+h}$$

$$= 2\pi\left(R^2 + Rh - R\left(\frac{R^2}{R+h}\right)\right) = \frac{2\pi\,(R(R+h)^2 - R^3)}{R+h} = \frac{2\pi\,(2R^2h)}{R+h}$$

$$\frac{\frac{2\pi\,(2R^2h)}{R+h}}{4\pi R^2} = \frac{h}{R+h} = \frac{437}{6356.9 + 437} = 6.0\%$$

# CHAPTER 15

## SURFACES, COORDINATE SYSTEMS AND DRAWING

### 15.1 CYLINDERS

1. $x^2 + y^2 = 4$

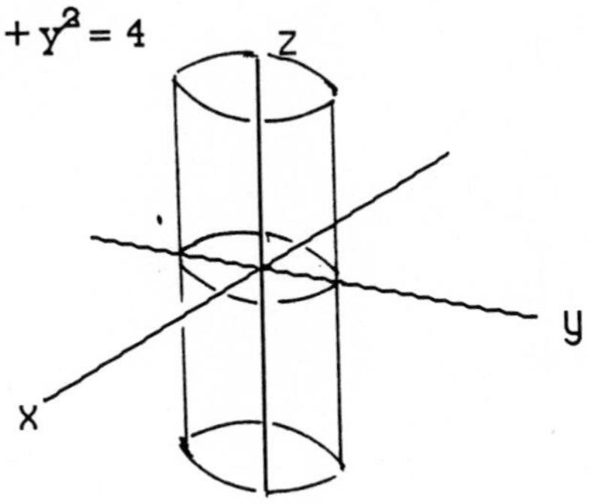


3. $y^2 + z^2 = 1$

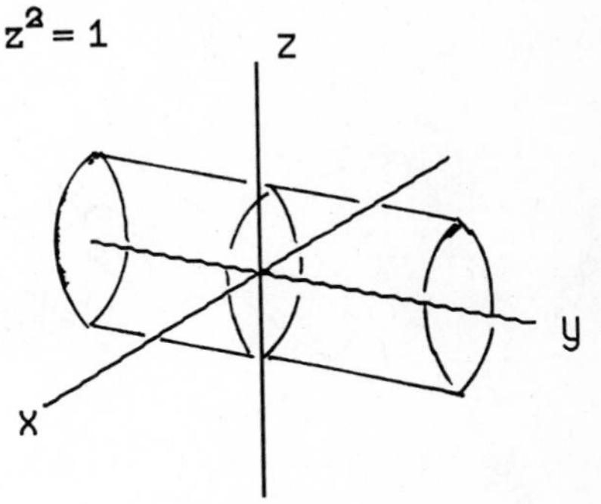


5. $z = y^2 - 1$

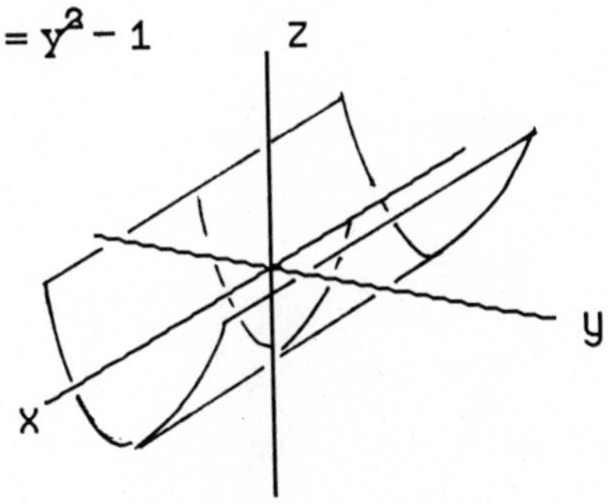


7. $z = 4 - x^2$

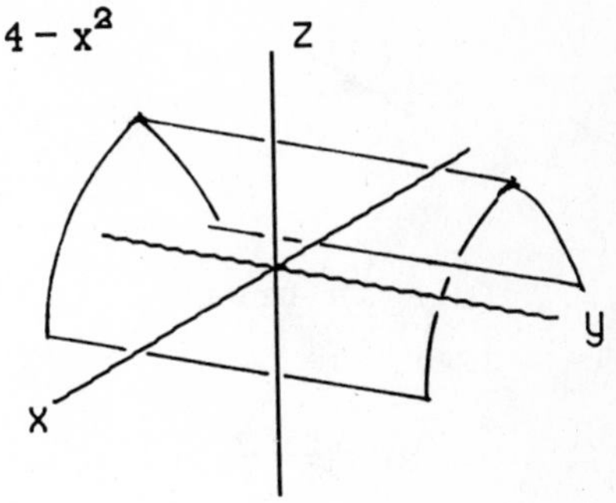


9. $y = x^2$

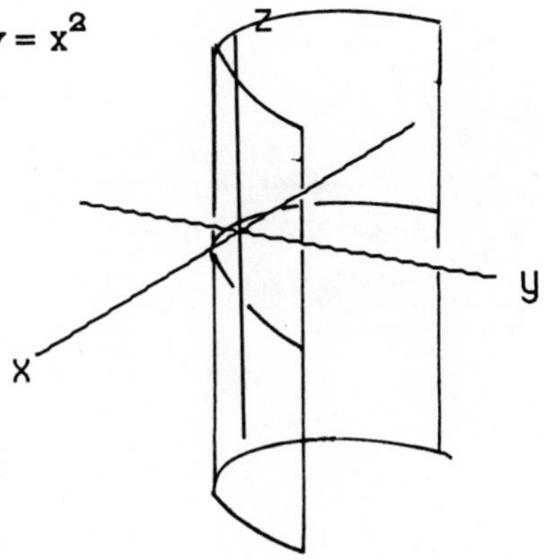


11. $y = -x$

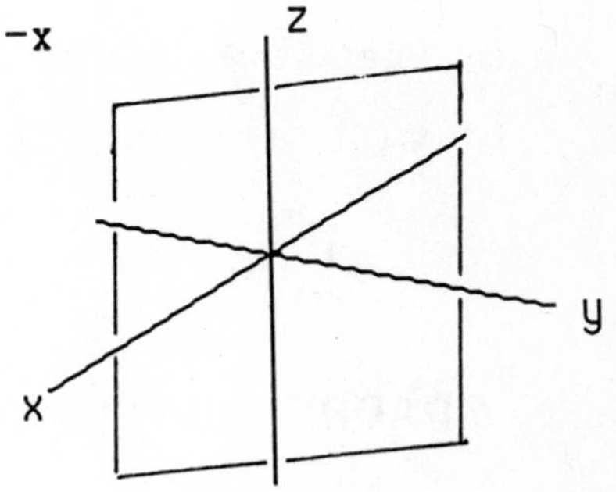

13. $y^2 + 4z^2 = 16$

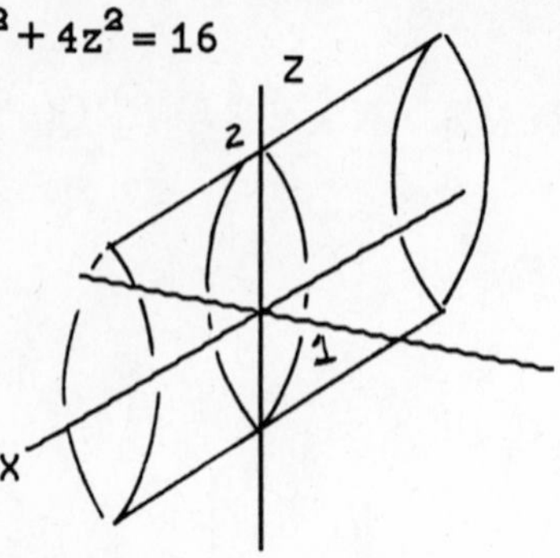


15. $z^2 + 4y^2 = 9$

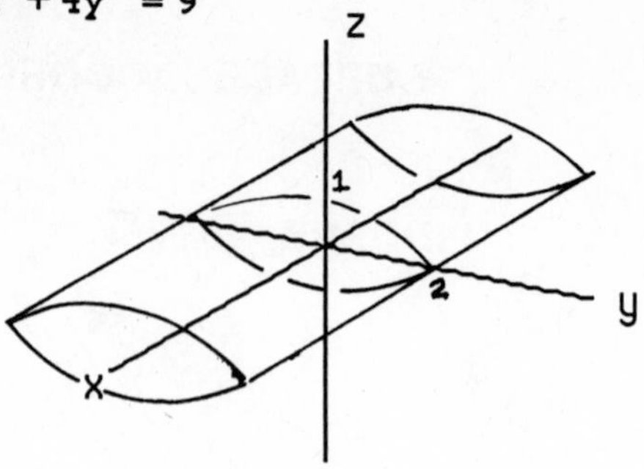


17. $z^2 - y^2 = 1$

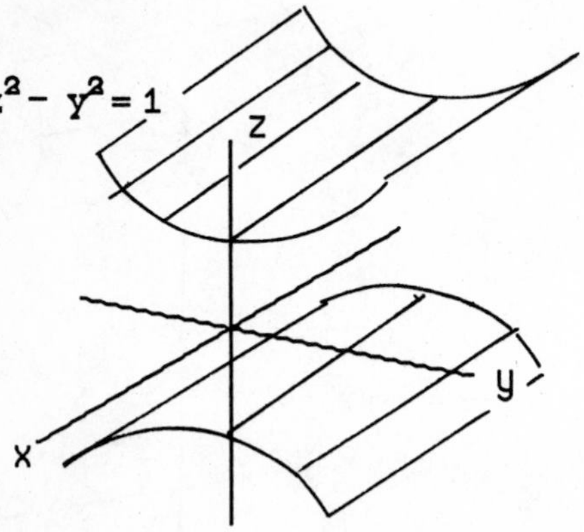


19. This is true; the generating plane is a line. See, for example, Exercise 11.

21. (a) $\mathbf{R}(t) = (\cos t)\mathbf{i} + (\sin t)\mathbf{j} + (1 - \cos t)\mathbf{k}$

$x = \cos t$ and $y = \sin t \Rightarrow x^2 + y^2 = 1$; $z = 1 - \cos t = 1 - x \Rightarrow x + z = 1$

(b) See Answer section of the text.

(c) $\mathbf{v}(t) = (-\sin t)\mathbf{i} + (\cos t)\mathbf{j} + (\sin t)\mathbf{k}$.

$$s = \int_0^{2\pi} \sqrt{\sin^2 t + \cos^2 t + \sin^2 t}\, dt = \int_0^{2\pi} \sqrt{2 - \cos^2 t}\, dt$$

## 15.2 QUADRIC SURFACES

1. $9x^2 + y^2 + z^2 = 9$

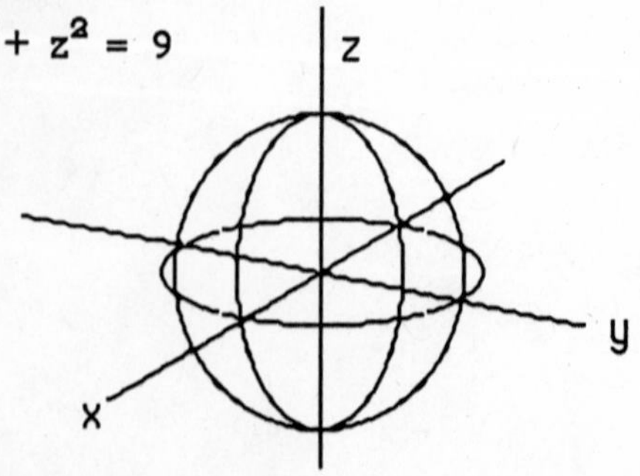

3. $x^2 + y^2 + z^2 = 1$

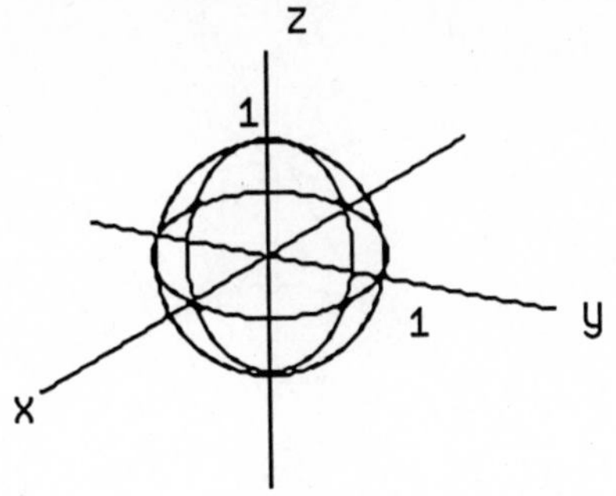


5. $4x^2 + 9y^2 + 4z^2 = 36$

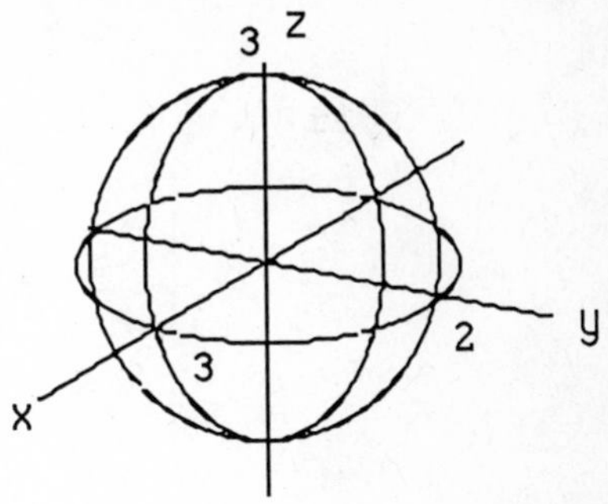


7. $x^2 + y^2 = z$

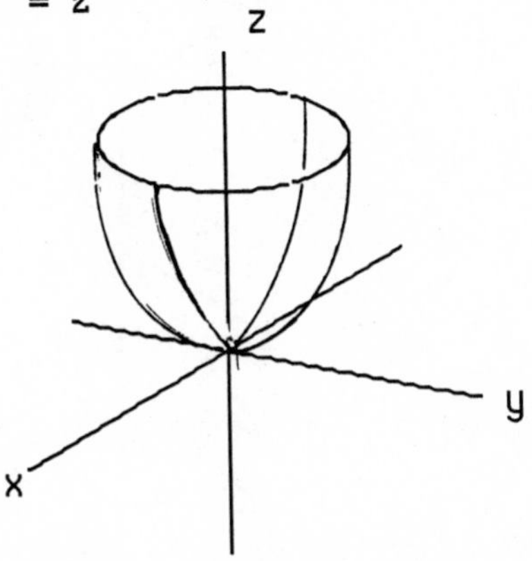


9. $x^2 + 3y^2 = z$

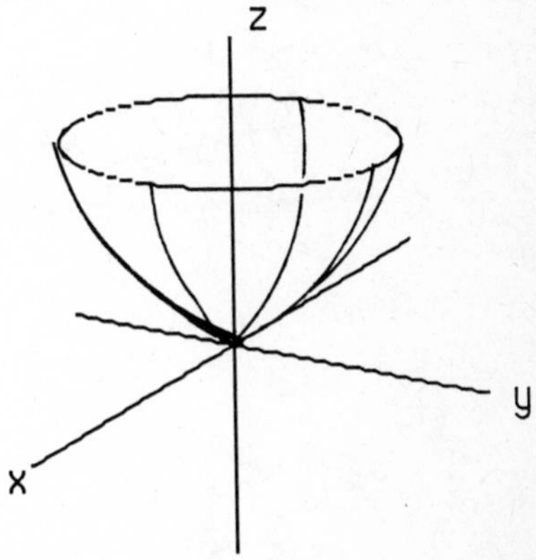


11. $z = 8 - x^2 - y^2$

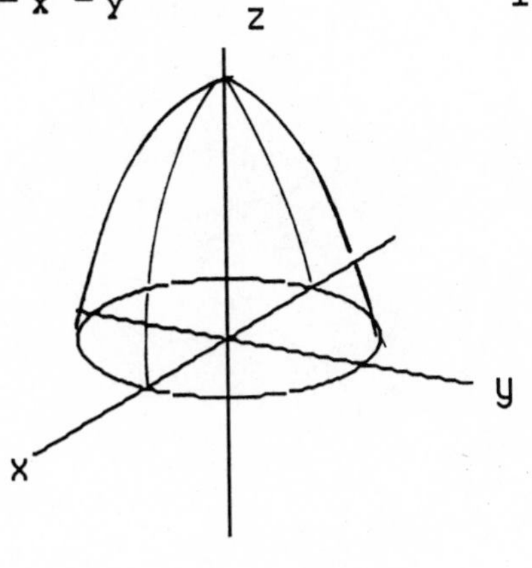


13. $x = y^2 + 4z^2 + 1$

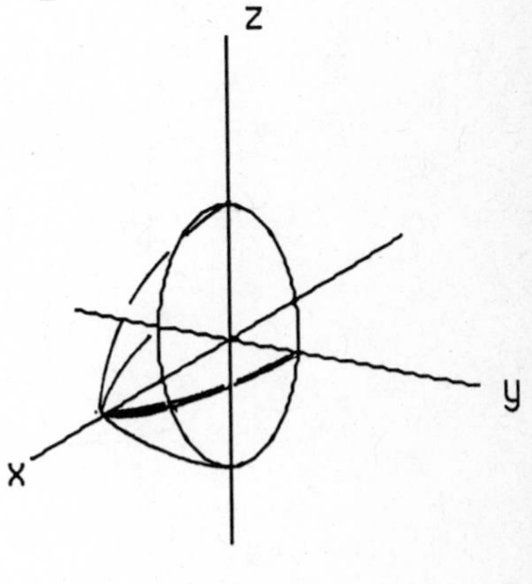

15. $z = x^2 + y^2 + 1$

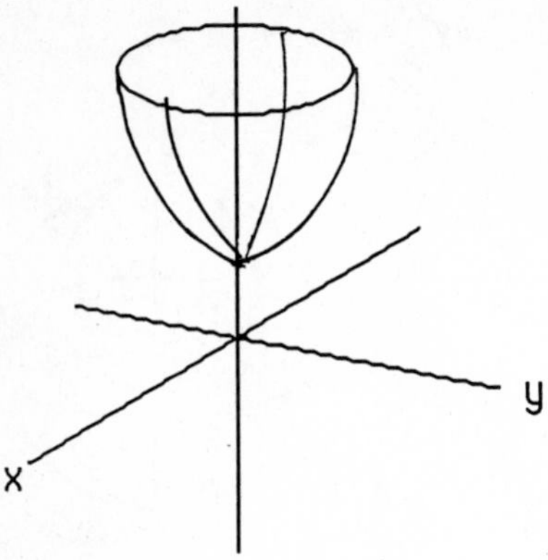


17. $x^2 + y^2 = z^2$

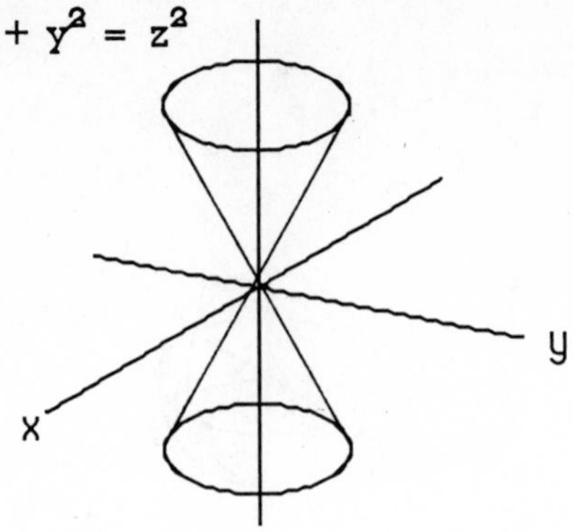


19. $x^2 + z^2 = y^2$

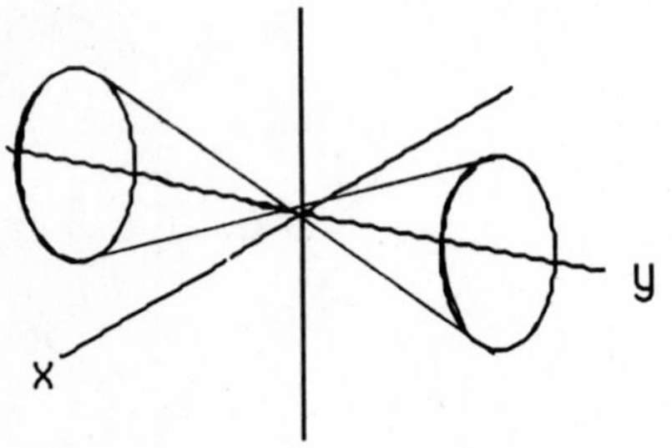


21. $4x^2 + 4y^2 = 36z^2$

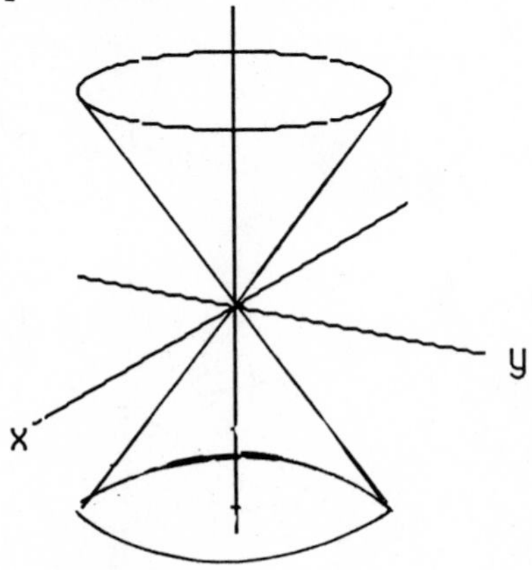


23. $x^2 + y^2 - z^2 = 1$

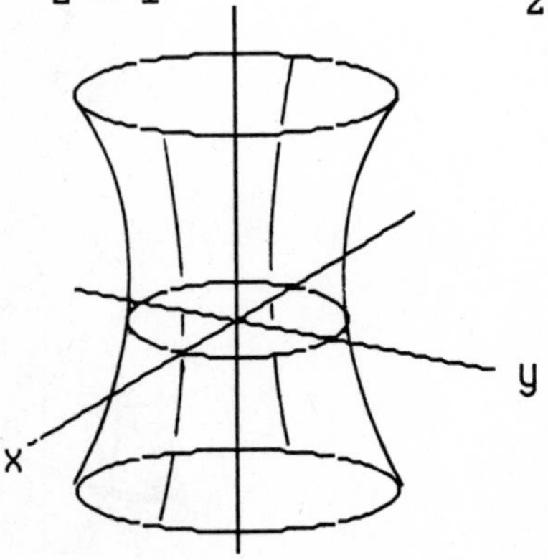


25. $\frac{y^2}{4} + \frac{z^2}{9} - \frac{x^2}{4} = 1$

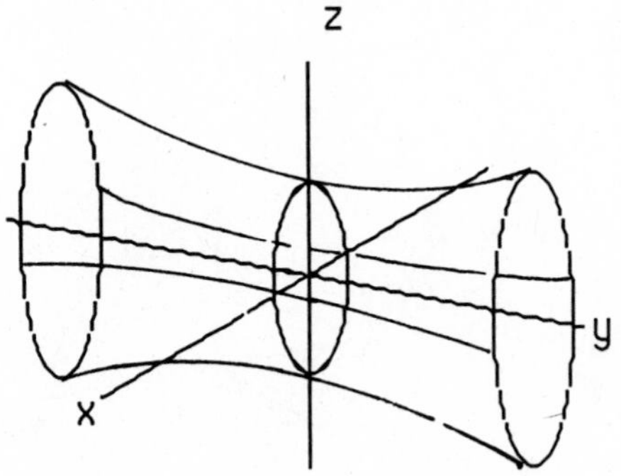

27. $\frac{x^2}{9} + \frac{y^2}{4} - z^2 = 1$

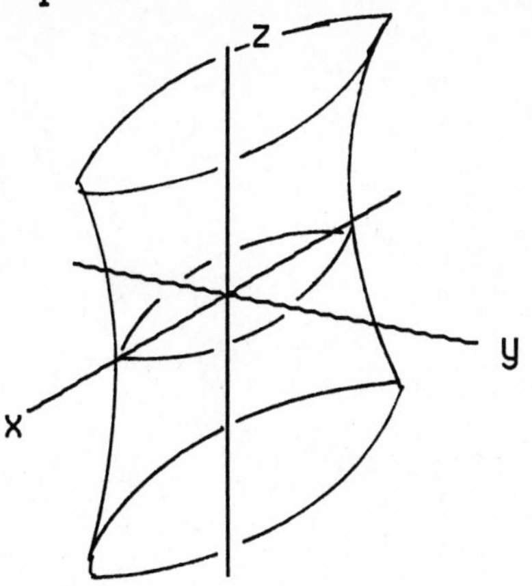


29. $z^2 - \frac{x^2}{4} - y^2 = 1$

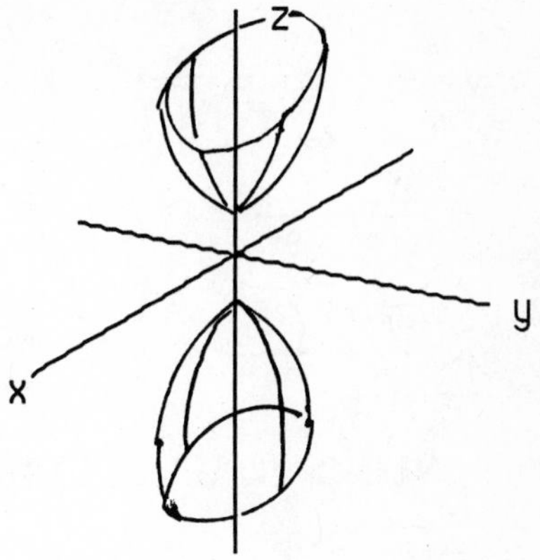


31. $\frac{x^2}{4} - \frac{y^2}{9} - z^2 = 1$

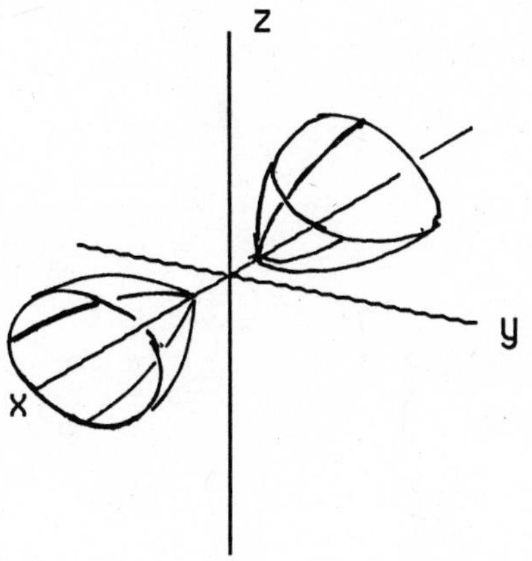


33. $y^2 - x^2 = z$

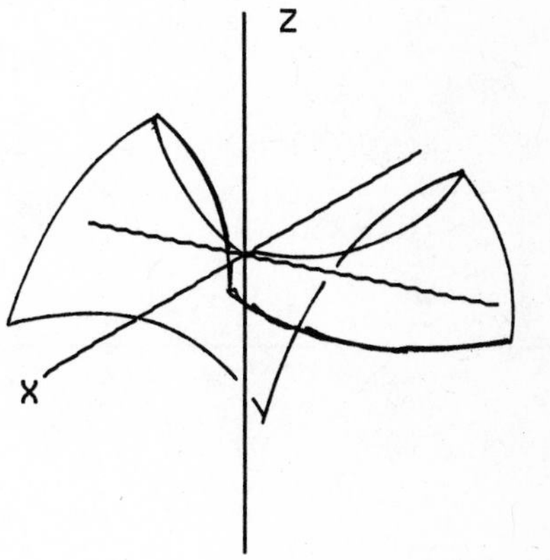


35. $z = x^2 + y$

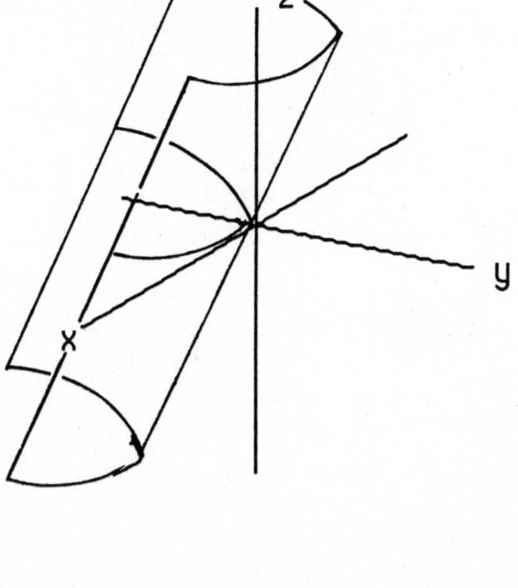


37. $y = x^2 + z$

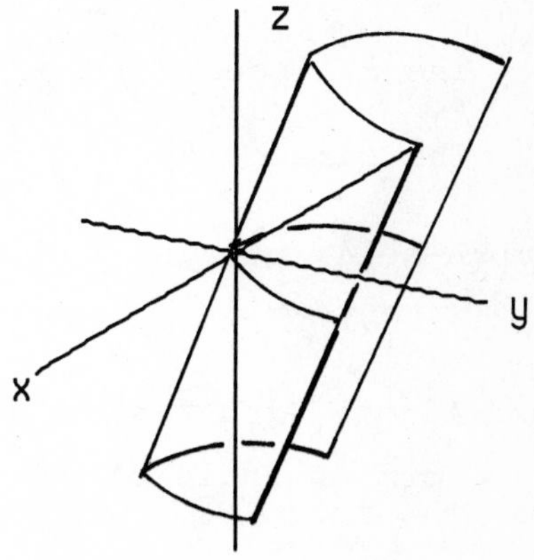

39. $x = 2\sqrt{t}\cos t \Rightarrow x^2 = 4t\cos^2 t \Rightarrow \dfrac{x^2}{4t} = \cos^2 t$

$y = 3\sqrt{t}\sin t \Rightarrow y^2 = 9t\sin^2 t \Rightarrow \dfrac{y^2}{9t} = \sin^2 t$

$\therefore \dfrac{x^2}{4t} + \dfrac{y^2}{9t} = 1.$ $z = \sqrt{1-t} \Rightarrow t = 1 - z^2$

$\therefore \dfrac{x^2}{4} + \dfrac{y^2}{9} + z^2 = 1;$ an ellipsoid

## 15.3 CYLINDRICAL COORDINATES AND SPHERICAL COORDINATES

| | Cartesian $(x,y,z)$ | Cylindrical $(r,\theta,z)$ | Spherical $(\rho,\phi,\theta)$ |
|---|---|---|---|
| 1. | $(0,0,0)$ | $(0,0,0)$ | $(0,0,0)$ |
| 3. | $(0,1,0)$ | $(1,\frac{\pi}{2},0)$ | $(1,\frac{\pi}{2},\frac{\pi}{2})$ |
| 5. | $(1,0,0)$ | $(1,0,0)$ | $(1,\frac{\pi}{2},0)$ |
| 7. | $(0,1,1)$ | $(1,\frac{\pi}{2},1)$ | $(\sqrt{2},\frac{\pi}{4},\frac{\pi}{2})$ |
| 9. | $(0,-2\sqrt{2},0)$ | $(2\sqrt{2},\frac{3\pi}{2},0)$ | $(2\sqrt{2},\frac{\pi}{2},\frac{3\pi}{2})$ |

| | Cartesian | Cylindrical | Spherical | Graph |
|---|---|---|---|---|
| 11. | $x=y=0$ | $r = 0$ | $\rho\sin\phi = 0$ | z - axis |
| 13. | $z = 0$ | $z = 0$ | $\phi = \frac{\pi}{2}$ | xy - plane |
| 15. | $z = 3$ | $z = 3$ | $\rho\cos\phi = 3$ | plane |
| 17. | $x = 0$ | $r\cos\theta = 0$ | $\rho\sin\phi\cos\theta = 0$ | yz - plane |
| 19. | $x^2 + y^2 + z^2 = 4$ | $r^2 + z^2 = 4$ | $\rho = 2$ | sphere |

21. The cylinder $x^2 + y^2 = 16$.

23. The cylinder $r = 1 - \cos\theta$ (see answer section of text)

25. The circle in the plane $z = 3$ with center $(0,0,3)$ and radius 2.

27. A helix passing through $(3,0,0)$ and spiraling up the cylinder $x^2 + y^2 = 9$ (see answer section of text).

29. A cone with vertex at origin, z-axis as axis, whose elements form an angle of $\frac{\pi}{6}$ with the z-axis.

31. A semicircle on the surface of the sphere $x^2 + y^2 + z^2 = 25$. The semicircle passes through the points $(0,0,5)$, $(5/\sqrt{2},5/\sqrt{2},0)$ and $(0,0,-5)$. (See answer section of text.)

33. A semicircle formed by cutting the hemisphere $x^2 + y^2 + (z - 2)^2 = 4$, $y \geq 0$, by the yz-plane.

## 15.M MISCELLANEOUS

1. A line; a plane

3. A circle; a cylinder

5. A parabola; a cylinder

7. A four-leaf petal curve; a cylinder

9. A circle; a cylinder

11. A four-leaf petal curve; a cylinder

13. The region between two concentric spheres.

15. The wedge-shaped region cut from the cone $\phi = \frac{\pi}{4}$ by the planes $y = 0$ and $y = x$.

17. $x = \rho \sin\phi \cos\theta = \sin\theta \cos\theta$ and $y = \rho \sin\phi \sin\theta = \sin^2\theta \Rightarrow$ $x^2 + y^2 = \sin^2\theta(\cos^2\theta + \sin^2\theta) = \sin^2\theta = y$. The set is the intersection of the sphere $\rho = 1$ and the cylinder $x^2 + y^2 - y = 0$.

19. Symmetry to the z-axis.

21. $r^2 + z^2 = 4r\cos\theta + 6r\sin\theta + 2z$

$x^2 + y^2 + z^2 = 4x + 6y + 2z$

$(x^2 - 4x + 4) + (y^2 - 6y + 9) + (z^2 - 2z + 1) = 14$

$(x - 2)^2 + (y - 3)^2 + (z - 1)^2 = 14$. Center $(2,3,1)$

23. Let $\frac{x^2}{R^2}+\frac{y^2}{R^2}+\frac{z^2}{c^2}=1$ be the ellipsoid. The point (0, r, h) lies on the surface $\Rightarrow \frac{y^2}{R^2}+\frac{h^2}{c^2}=1 \Rightarrow c^2=\frac{h^2R^2}{R^2-r^2}$. Substituting, we find $y=R\sqrt{1-\frac{z^2(R^2-r^2)}{h^2R^2}}$. Then the volume is:

$$V=\pi\int_{-hr/\sqrt{R^2-r^2}}^{hr/\sqrt{R^2-r^2}} y^2\,dz = 2\pi R^2\int_0^{hr/\sqrt{R^2-r^2}}\left[1-\left(\frac{R^2-r^2}{h^2R^2}\right)z^2\right]dz =$$

$$= 2\pi R^2\left[z-\frac{1}{3}z^3\left(\frac{R^2-r^2}{h^2R^2}\right)\right]_0^{hr/\sqrt{R^2-r^2}} = 2\pi R^2 h\left[1-\frac{R^2-r^2}{3R^2}\right].$$

No for the cylinder, yes for the sphere.

25. (a) For $z=z_0$, $\frac{x^2}{a^2}+\frac{y^2}{b^2}=1+\frac{z_0^2}{c^2} \Rightarrow \frac{x^2}{\frac{a^2(c^2+z_0^2)}{c^2}}+\frac{y^2}{\frac{b^2(c^2+z_0^2)}{c^2}}=1$. The area of a cross-section $=\pi ab=\pi\left(\frac{a}{c}\sqrt{c^2+z_0^2}\right)\left(\frac{b}{c}\sqrt{c^2+z_0^2}\right)=\frac{\pi ab}{c^2}(c^2+z_0^2)$.

$$\therefore\quad V=\int_0^h \frac{\pi ab}{c^2}(c^2+z^2)\,dz=\frac{\pi abh}{3c^2}(3c^2+h^2).$$

(b) $A_0=\pi ab$ and $A_h=\frac{\pi ab}{c^2}(c^2+h^2) \Rightarrow V=\frac{\pi abh}{3}\left(2+1+\frac{h^2}{c^2}\right)=\frac{h}{3}(2A_0+A_h)$

(c) $A_m=\frac{\pi ab}{c^2}(c^2+h^2)$.

$$V=\frac{\pi h}{6}\left[ab+\frac{4ab}{c^2}\left(c^2+\frac{h^2}{4}\right)+\frac{ab}{c^2}(c^2+h^2)\right]=\frac{\pi ab}{3c^2}(3c^2+h^2)$$

27. (a) $\mathbf{R}(\theta) = (a\theta \cos \theta)\mathbf{i} + (a\theta \sin \theta)\mathbf{j} + (b\theta)\mathbf{k}$

$$\mathbf{v} = [a(\cos \theta - \theta \sin \theta)\mathbf{i} + a(\sin \theta + \theta \cos\theta)\mathbf{j} + b\mathbf{k}]\frac{d\theta}{dt}$$

$$|\mathbf{v}| = (a^2 + a^2\theta^2 + b^2)^{1/2}\frac{d\theta}{dt}$$

$$\frac{d\theta}{dt} = \frac{\sqrt{2gb\,\theta}}{\sqrt{a^2(1+\theta^2) + b^2}}$$

(b) $$s = \int_0^t (a^2 + a^2\theta^2 + b^2)^{1/2}\frac{d\theta}{dt}dt = \int_0^\theta (a^2 + a^2u^2 + b^2)^{1/2}\,du$$

$$= a\int_0^\theta \sqrt{c^2 + u^2}\,du, \quad c^2 = \frac{a^2 + b^2}{a^2}$$

$$s = \frac{a}{2}\left[u\sqrt{c^2+u^2} + c^2 \ln\left(u + \sqrt{c^2+u^2}\right)\right]_0^\theta$$

$$= \frac{a}{2}\left[\theta\sqrt{c^2+\theta^2} + c^2 \ln\left(\theta + \sqrt{c^2+\theta^2}\right) - c^2 \ln c\right]$$

29. (a) $\mathbf{u}_\rho = (\sin\phi \cos\theta)\mathbf{i} + (\sin\phi \sin\theta)\mathbf{j} + (\cos\phi)\mathbf{k}$

$\mathbf{u}_\phi = (\cos\theta \cos\phi)\mathbf{i} + (\sin\theta \cos\phi)\mathbf{j} - (\sin\phi)\mathbf{k}$

$\mathbf{u}_\theta = (\sin\theta)\mathbf{i} + (\cos\theta)\mathbf{j}$

(b) $$\mathbf{u}_\rho \cdot \mathbf{u}_\phi = \sin\phi\cos\phi\cos^2\theta + \sin\phi\cos\phi\sin^2\theta - \sin\phi\cos\phi$$

$$= \sin\phi\cos\phi(\sin^2\theta + \cos^2\theta) - \sin\phi\cos\phi = 0$$

(c) $$\mathbf{u}_\rho \times \mathbf{u}_\phi = \begin{vmatrix} \mathbf{i} & \mathbf{j} & \mathbf{k} \\ \sin\phi\cos\theta & \sin\phi\sin\theta & \cos\phi \\ \cos\phi\cos\theta & \cos\phi\sin\theta & -\sin\phi \end{vmatrix}$$

$$= (-\sin^2\phi\sin\theta - \cos^2\phi\sin\theta)\mathbf{i} - (-\sin^2\phi\cos\theta - \cos^2\phi\cos\theta)\mathbf{j} + 0\mathbf{k}$$

$$= (-\sin\theta)\mathbf{i} + (\cos\theta)\mathbf{j} = \mathbf{u}_\theta$$

31. (a) $x = r\cos\theta \Rightarrow dx = \cos\theta\,dr - r\sin\theta\,d\theta$

$y = r\sin\theta \Rightarrow dy = \sin\theta\,dr + r\cos\theta\,d\theta$

$dx^2 = \cos^2\theta\,dr^2 - 2r\cos\theta\sin\theta\,dr\,d\theta + r^2\sin^2\theta\,d\theta^2$

$dy^2 = \sin^2\theta\,dr^2 + 2r\cos\theta\sin\theta\,dr\,d\theta + r^2\cos^2\theta\,d\theta^2$

$\therefore \quad dx^2 + dy^2 + dz^2 = dr^2 + r^2d\theta^2 + dz^2$

(b) $x = \rho \sin\phi \cos\theta \;\Rightarrow$

$$dx = \sin\phi \cos\theta \, d\rho - \rho \sin\phi \sin\theta \, d\theta + \rho \cos\theta \cos\phi \, d\phi$$

$y = \rho \sin\phi \sin\theta \;\Rightarrow$

$$dy = \sin\phi \sin\theta \, d\rho + \rho \sin\phi \cos\theta \, d\theta + \rho \cos\phi \sin\theta \, d\phi$$

$z = \rho \cos\phi \;\Rightarrow\; dz = \cos\phi \, d\rho - \rho \sin\phi \, d\phi$

$$\begin{aligned} dx^2 = {} & \sin^2\phi \cos^2\theta \, d\rho^2 - 2 \sin^2\phi \sin\theta \cos\theta \, d\rho \, d\theta + \rho^2 \sin^2\phi \sin^2\theta \, d\theta^2 \\ & + 2\rho \cos^2\theta \sin\phi \cos\phi \, d\phi \, d\rho - 2\rho^2 \sin\phi \sin\theta \cos\theta \cos\phi \, d\phi d\theta \\ & + \rho^2 \cos^2\theta \cos^2\phi \, d\phi^2 \end{aligned}$$

$$\begin{aligned} dy^2 = {} & \sin^2\phi \sin^2\theta \, d\rho^2 + 2\rho \sin^2\phi \sin\theta \cos\theta \, d\theta \, d\rho + \rho^2 \cos^2\phi \sin^2\theta \, d\phi^2 \\ & + 2\rho \cos\phi \sin\phi \sin^2\theta \, d\rho \, d\phi + 2\rho^2 \sin\phi \cos\phi \sin\theta \cos\theta \, d\phi \, d \\ & + \rho^2 \cos^2\phi \sin^2\theta \, d\phi^2 \end{aligned}$$

$$dz^2 = \cos^2\phi \, d\rho^2 - 2\rho \cos\phi \sin\phi \, d\phi \, d\rho + \rho^2 \sin^2\phi \, d\phi^2$$

$$dx^2 + dy^2 = \sin^2\phi \, d\rho^2 + \rho^2 \cos^2\phi \, d\phi^2 + \rho^2 \sin^2\phi \, d\theta^2 + 2\rho \sin\phi \cos\phi \, d\phi \, d\rho$$

$$\therefore \quad dx^2 + dy^2 + dz^2 = d\rho^2 + \rho^2 \, d\phi^2 + \rho^2 \sin^2\phi \, d\theta^2$$

# CHAPTER 16

# FUNCTIONS OF TWO OR MORE VARIABLES AND THEIR DERIVATIVES

## 16.1 FUNCTIONS OF TWO OR MORE INDEPENDENT VARIABLES

1. $f(x, y) = x + y$

   Domain: $(-\infty, \infty)$ Range: $(-\infty, \infty)$

   Level Curves: lines $x + y = k$

3. $f(x, y) = \ln(x + y)$

   Domain: $x + y > 0 \Rightarrow y > -x \quad \therefore \{(x, y): y > -x\}$ Range: $(-\infty, \infty)$

   Level Curves: lines $x + y = e^k$

5. $f(x, y) = \tan^{-1} \frac{y}{x}$

   Domain: $\{(x, y): x \neq 0\}$ Range: $\left(-\frac{\pi}{2}, \frac{\pi}{2}\right)$

   Level Curves: lines $y = mx, m \neq 0$

7. $f(x, y) = \frac{\sqrt{y}}{x}$

   Domain: $\{(x, y): x \neq 0, y \geq 0\}$ Range: $(-\infty, \infty)$

   Level Curves: parabolas $y = kx^2, x \neq 0, k \geq 0$

9. Spheres centered at the origin.
11. Spheres centered at the origin.
13. Planes parallel to the yz-plane.
15. Planes of the form x + y + z = k
17. Cylinders with axes along the x-axis.

19. (a) $f(x,y) = 4 - y^2$

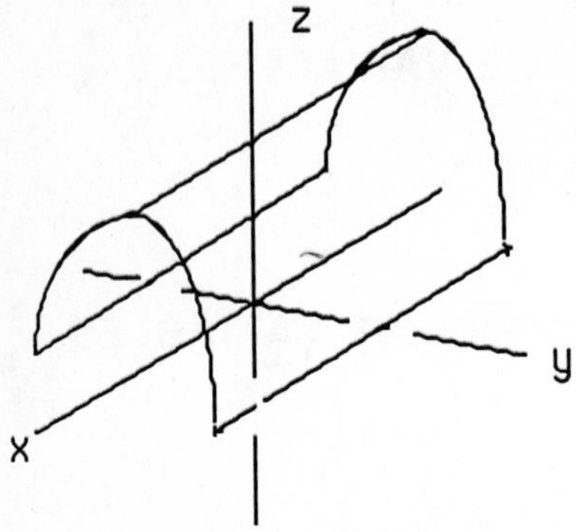


(b)

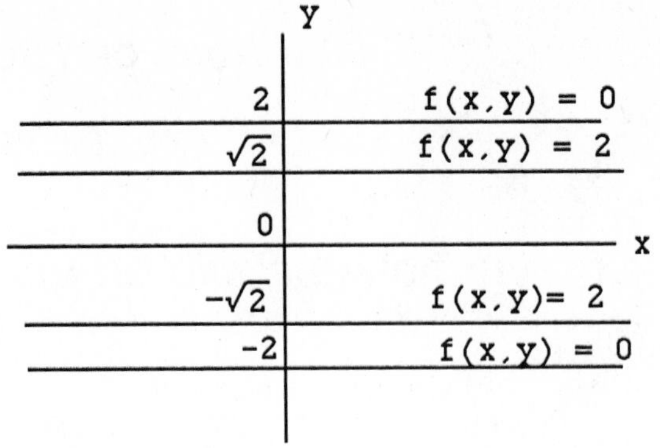


21. (a) $f(x,y) = 4x^2 + y^2$

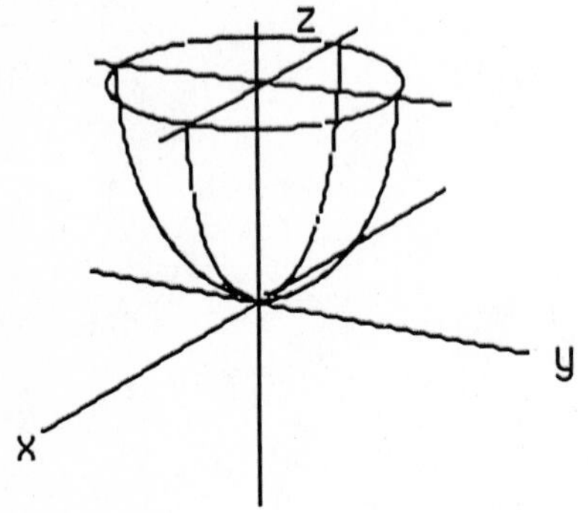


(b)

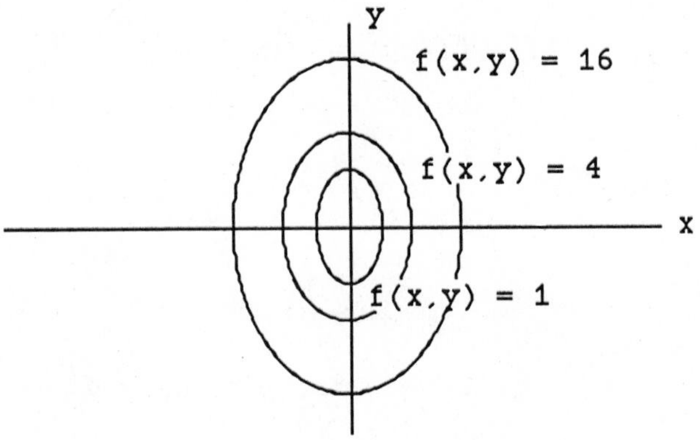


23. (a) $f(x,y) = \sqrt{4 - x^2 - y^2}$

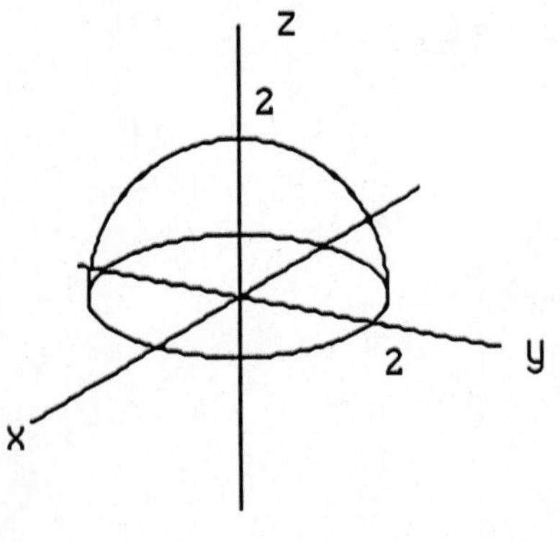


(b)

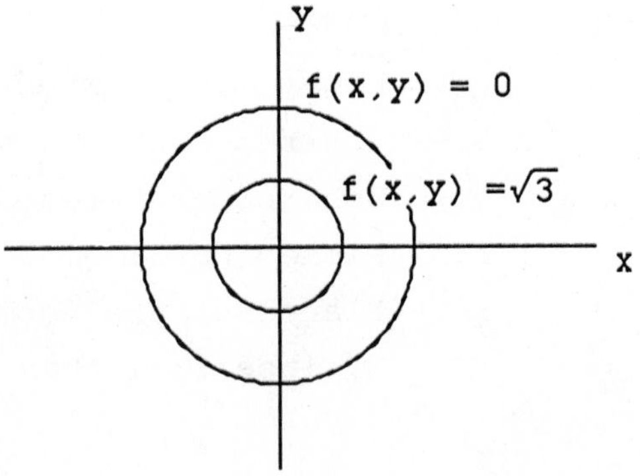


25. See answer section of text.

27. $f(x,y) = 16 - x^2 - y^2$; $f(2\sqrt{2}, \sqrt{2}) = 16 - 8 - 2 = 6$

$\therefore$ $16 - x^2 - y^2 = 6$ or $x^2 + y^2 = 10$.

29. $w = 4\left(\frac{Th}{d}\right)^{1/2} = 4\left(\frac{290 \cdot 16.8}{5}\right)^{1/2} \approx 124.86$. $\therefore$ 62.43 miles south

## 16.2 LIMITS AND CONTINUITY

1. $\lim_{(x,y)\to(0,0)} \dfrac{3x^2 - y^2 + 5}{x^2 + y^2 + 2} = \dfrac{5}{2}$

3. $\lim_{(x,y)\to(0,\ln 2)} e^{x-y} = e^{-\ln 2} = \dfrac{1}{2}$

5. $\lim_{P\to(1,3,4)} \sqrt{x^2 + y^2 + z^2 - 1} = \sqrt{25} = 5$

7. $\lim_{(x,y)\to(0,0)} \dfrac{e^y \sin x}{x} = 1$

9. $\lim_{(x,y)\to(-2,2)} \dfrac{xy + y - 2x - 2}{x + 1} = \lim_{(x,y)\to(-2,2)} (y - 2) = 0$

11. $\lim_{(x,y)\to(1,1)} \cos \sqrt[3]{|xy| - 1} = 1$

13. $\lim_{(x,y)\to(1,1)} \dfrac{x^2 - 2xy + y^2}{x - y} = \lim_{(x,y)\to(1,1)} (x - y) = 0$

15. $\lim_{(x,y)\to(0,0)} \tan^{-1} \dfrac{1}{\sqrt{x^2 + y^2}} = \dfrac{\pi}{2}$

17. $\lim_{(x,y)\to(0,0)} \dfrac{x + y}{x - y}$ does not exist. Let $(x,y) \to (0,0)$ along the line $y = mx$.

Then $f(x,mx) = \dfrac{x + mx}{x - mx} = \dfrac{1 + m}{1 - m}$, which is dependent on m.

19. $\lim_{(x,y)\to(0,0)} \dfrac{x^2 - y^2}{x^2 + y^2}$ does not exist. Let $(x,y) \to (0,0)$ along the line $y = mx$.

Then $f(x,mx) = \dfrac{x^2 - m^2 x^2}{x^2 + m^2 x^2} = \dfrac{1 - m^2}{1 + m^2}$, which is dependent on m.

21. $\lim_{(x,y)\to(0,0)} \dfrac{x^2 + y^2}{xy}$ does not exist. Let $(x,y) \to (0,0)$ along the line $y = mx$.

Then $f(x,mx) = \dfrac{x^2 + m^2 x^2}{mx^2} = \dfrac{1 + m^2}{m}$, which is dependent on m.

23. Let $\delta = 0.1$. Then $\sqrt{x^2 + y^2} < \delta \Rightarrow |f(x,y) - f(0,0)| = x^2 + y^2 < \delta^2 = 0.01$

25. Let $\delta = 0.005$. Then $\left|\dfrac{x + y}{x^2 + 1}\right| \le |x + y| \le |x| + |y| < 0.005 + 0.005 = 0.01.$

27. Let $\delta = 0.1$. Then $\sqrt{x^2 + y^2 + z^2} < 0.1 \Rightarrow x^2 + y^2 + z^2 < 0.01$

29. Let $\delta = 0.005$. Then $\left|\dfrac{x + y + z}{x^2 + y^2 + z^2 + 1}\right| \le |x + y + z|$

$\le |x| + |y| + |z| = 0.005 + 0.005 + 0.005 = 0.015$

31. $f(x,y,z)=\sqrt{x^2+y^2+z^2}$ is continuous at (0,0,0)

because $\lim_{(x,y,z)\to(0,0,0)} \sqrt{x^2+y^2+z^2} = f(0,0,0)=0$

33. See answer section of text.

## 16.3 PARTIAL DERIVATIVES

1. $f(x,y)=2x$ $\quad \frac{\partial f}{\partial x}=2$ $\quad \frac{\partial f}{\partial y}=0$

3. $f(x,y)=-4$ $\quad \frac{\partial f}{\partial x}=0$ $\quad \frac{\partial f}{\partial y}=0$

5. $f(x,y)=x(y-1)$ $\quad \frac{\partial f}{\partial x}=y-1$ $\quad \frac{\partial f}{\partial y}=x$

7. $f(x,y)=x^2-xy+y^2$ $\quad \frac{\partial f}{\partial x}=2x-y$ $\quad \frac{\partial f}{\partial y}=2y-x$

9. $f(x,y)=5xy-7x^2-y^2+3x-6y+2$

$\frac{\partial f}{\partial x}=5y-14x+3$ $\quad \frac{\partial f}{\partial y}=5x-2y-6$

11. $f(x,y)=\sqrt{x^2+y^2}$ $\quad \frac{\partial f}{\partial x}=\frac{x}{\sqrt{x^2+y^2}}$ $\quad \frac{\partial f}{\partial y}=\frac{y}{\sqrt{x^2+y^2}}$

13. $f(x,y)=\frac{x+y}{xy-1}$

$$\frac{\partial f}{\partial x}=\frac{(xy-1)-y(x+y)}{(xy-1)^2}=-\frac{y^2+1}{(xy-1)^2}$$

$$\frac{\partial f}{\partial y}=\frac{(xy-1)-x(x+y)}{(xy-1)^2}=-\frac{x^2+1}{(xy-1)^2}$$

15. $f(x,y)=e^x \ln y$ $\quad \frac{\partial f}{\partial x}=e^x \ln y$ $\quad \frac{\partial f}{\partial y}=\frac{e^x}{y}$

17. $f(x,y)=e^x \sin(y+1)$ $\quad \frac{\partial f}{\partial x}=e^x \sin(y+1)$ $\quad \frac{\partial f}{\partial y}=e^x \cos(y+1)$

19. $f(x,y)=\tanh(2x+5y)$

$\frac{\partial f}{\partial x}=2\,\text{sech}^2(2x+5y)$ $\quad \frac{\partial f}{\partial y}=5\,\text{sech}^2(2x+5y)$

21. $f(x,y,z)=xy+yz+zx$

$\frac{\partial f}{\partial x}=y+z$ $\quad \frac{\partial f}{\partial y}=x+z$ $\quad \frac{\partial f}{\partial z}=y+x$

23. $f(x,y,z) = 1 + y^2 + 2z^2$

$$\frac{\partial f}{\partial x} = 0 \qquad \frac{\partial f}{\partial y} = 2y \qquad \frac{\partial f}{\partial z} = 4z$$

25. $f(P,Q,R) = \frac{1}{PQR} = (PQR)^{-1}$

$$\frac{\partial f}{\partial P} = -\frac{1}{QRP^2} \qquad \frac{\partial f}{\partial Q} = -\frac{1}{PRQ^2} \qquad \frac{\partial f}{\partial R} = -\frac{1}{PQR^2}$$

27. $f(\rho,\phi,\theta) = \rho \sin\phi \cos\theta$

$$f_\rho = \sin\phi\cos\theta \qquad f_\phi = \rho\cos\phi\cos\theta \qquad f_\theta = -\rho\sin\phi\sin\theta$$

29. $xy + z^3x - 2yz = 0$ $\qquad y\frac{\partial x}{\partial x} + x\frac{\partial y}{\partial x} + z^3\frac{\partial x}{\partial x} + 3z^2x\frac{\partial z}{\partial x} - 2y\frac{\partial z}{\partial x} - 2z\frac{\partial y}{\partial x} = 0$

$$y + z^3 + 3z^2x\frac{\partial z}{\partial x} - 2y\frac{\partial z}{\partial x} = 0 \Rightarrow \frac{\partial z}{\partial x} = \left.\frac{-y - z^3}{3z^2x - 2y}\right|_{(1,1,1)} = -2$$

31. $x\sin(y+z) - xy + z^2 = 0$

$$x\cos(y+z) + \sin(y+z)\frac{\partial x}{\partial y} - x - y\frac{\partial x}{\partial y} = 0$$

$$\frac{\partial x}{\partial y} = \left.\frac{x - x\cos(y+z)}{\sin(y+z) - y}\right|_{(1,-1,1)} = 0$$

$$x\cos(y+z) + \sin(y+z)\frac{\partial x}{\partial z} - y\frac{\partial x}{\partial z} + 2z = 0$$

$$\frac{\partial x}{\partial z} = \left.\frac{-2z - x\cos(y+z)}{\sin(y+z) - y}\right|_{(1,-1,1)} = -3$$

33. $a^2 = b^2 + c^2 - 2bc\cos A$

$$2a = 2bc\sin A\frac{\partial A}{\partial a} \Rightarrow \frac{\partial A}{\partial a} = \frac{a}{bc\sin A}$$

$$0 = 2b - 2c\cos A + 2bc\sin A\frac{\partial A}{\partial b} \Rightarrow \frac{\partial A}{\partial b} = \frac{c\cos A - b}{bc\sin A}$$

35. $\rho = (x^2 + y^2 + z^2)^{1/2} \Rightarrow \frac{\partial \rho}{\partial x} = \frac{x}{\sqrt{x^2 + y^2 + z^2}}$

37. $\theta = \tan^{-1}\frac{y}{x} \Rightarrow \frac{\partial \theta}{\partial y} = \frac{\frac{1}{x}}{1 + \frac{y^2}{x^2}} = \frac{x}{x^2 + y^2}$

39. $\cos\phi = \frac{z}{\rho} \Rightarrow \phi = \cos^{-1}\frac{z}{\rho} = \cos^{-1}\frac{z}{(x^2+y^2+z^2)^{1/2}}$

$$\frac{\partial\phi}{\partial x} = \frac{-1}{\sqrt{1-\frac{z^2}{x^2+y^2+z^2}}} \cdot -\frac{xz}{(x^2+y^2+z^2)^{3/2}} = \frac{xz}{(x^2+y^2+z^2)\sqrt{x^2+y^2}}$$

41. $\mathbf{R}(x,y,z) = x\mathbf{i} + y\mathbf{j} + z\mathbf{k}$

$$= (\rho\sin\phi\cos\theta)\mathbf{i} + (\rho\sin\phi\sin\theta)\mathbf{j} + (\rho\cos\phi)\,\mathbf{j}$$

$$\frac{\partial\mathbf{R}}{\partial\rho} = (\sin\phi\cos\theta)\mathbf{i} + (\sin\phi\sin\theta)\mathbf{j} + (\cos\phi)\,\mathbf{j} = \mathbf{u}_\rho$$

$$\frac{\partial\mathbf{R}}{\partial\phi} = (\rho\cos\phi\cos\theta)\mathbf{i} + (\rho\cos\phi\sin\theta)\mathbf{j} + (-\rho\sin\phi)\,\mathbf{j} = \rho\mathbf{u}_\phi$$

$$\frac{\partial\mathbf{R}}{\partial\theta} = (-\rho\sin\phi\sin\theta)\mathbf{i} + (\rho\sin\phi\cos\theta)\mathbf{j} = (\rho\sin\phi)\mathbf{u}_\theta$$

## 16.4 THE CHAIN RULE

1. $f(x,y,z) = \ln(x+y+z)$, $x = \cos^2 t$, $y = \sin^2 t$, $z = t$ at $t = \pi$

$$\frac{df}{dt} = \frac{\partial f}{\partial x}\frac{dx}{dt} + \frac{\partial f}{\partial y}\frac{dy}{dt} + \frac{\partial f}{\partial z}\frac{dz}{dt}$$

$$= \frac{1}{x+y+z}(2\cos t\sin t + 2\sin t\cos t + 1) = \frac{1}{1+\pi}$$

3. $f(x,y) = x^2 + y^2$, $x = \cos^2 t$, $y = \sin t$ at $t = \pi$

$$\frac{df}{dt} = \frac{\partial f}{\partial x}\frac{dx}{dt} + \frac{\partial f}{\partial y}\frac{dy}{dt} = -2x\sin t + 2y\cos t$$

$$= -2\sin t\cos t + 2\sin t\cos t = 0$$

5. $f(x,y,z) = \sqrt{x^2+y^2+z^2}$, $x = 2+t$, $y = -1-t$, $z = t$ at $t = -2$

$$\frac{df}{dt} = \frac{\partial f}{\partial x}\frac{dx}{dt} + \frac{\partial f}{\partial y}\frac{dy}{dt} + \frac{\partial f}{\partial z}\frac{dz}{dt}$$

$$= \frac{x}{x^2+y^2+z^2}(1) + \frac{y}{x^2+y^2+z^2}(-1) + \frac{z}{x^2+y^2+z^2}(1) = -\frac{3}{\sqrt{5}}$$

7. $f(x, y, z) = \sqrt{x^2 + y^2 + z^2}$, $x = y = z = t$ at $t = 1$

$$\frac{df}{dt} = \frac{\partial f}{\partial x}\frac{dx}{dt} + \frac{\partial f}{\partial y}\frac{dy}{dt} + \frac{\partial f}{\partial z}\frac{dz}{dt}$$

$$= \frac{-x}{(x^2+y^2+z^2)^{3/2}}(1) + \frac{-y}{(x^2+y^2+z^2)^{3/2}}(1) + \frac{-z}{(x^2+y^2+z^2)^{3/2}}(1) = -\frac{1}{\sqrt{3}}$$

9.

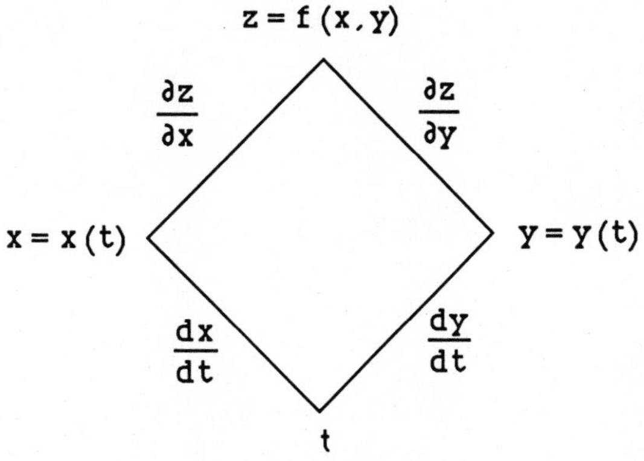


$$\frac{\partial z}{\partial t} = \frac{\partial z}{\partial x}\cdot\frac{dx}{dt} + \frac{\partial z}{\partial y}\cdot\frac{dy}{dt}$$

11.

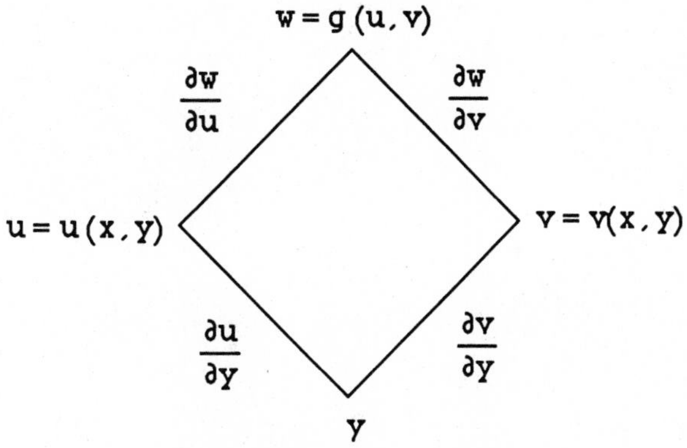


$$\frac{\partial w}{\partial y} = \frac{\partial w}{\partial u}\frac{\partial u}{\partial y} + \frac{\partial w}{\partial v}\frac{\partial v}{\partial y}$$

13.

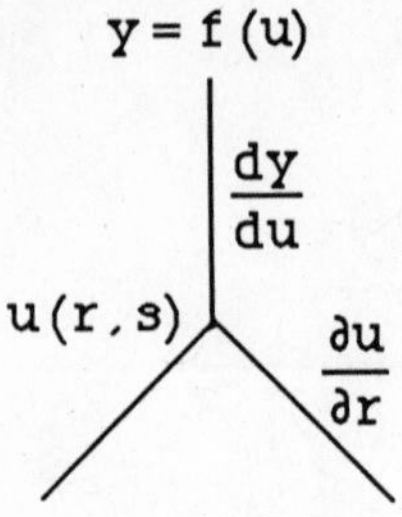


$$\frac{\partial y}{\partial r} = \frac{dy}{du} \cdot \frac{\partial u}{\partial r}$$

15.

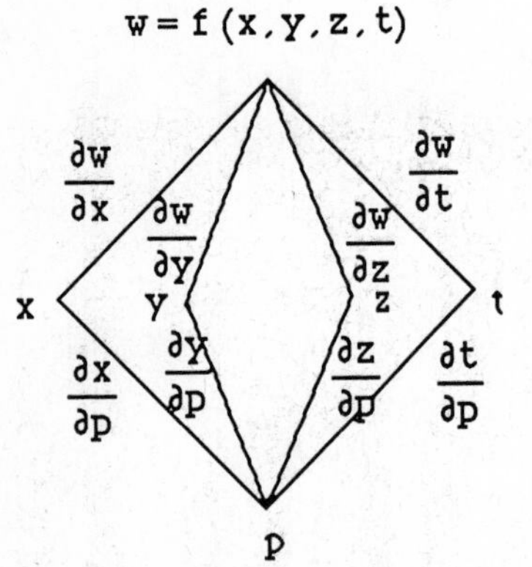


$$\frac{\partial w}{\partial p} = \frac{\partial w}{\partial x} \cdot \frac{\partial x}{\partial p} + \frac{\partial w}{\partial y} \cdot \frac{\partial y}{\partial p} + \frac{\partial w}{\partial z} \cdot \frac{\partial z}{\partial p} + \frac{\partial w}{\partial t} \cdot \frac{\partial t}{\partial p}$$

17. $u = x^2 + e^{(y^2)}$, $x = \sin 2t$, $y = \cos (t^2)$

$$\frac{\partial u}{\partial t} = \frac{\partial u}{\partial x}\frac{dx}{dt} + \frac{\partial u}{\partial y}\frac{dy}{dt} = 2x(2 \cos 2t) + 2y\, e^{(y^2)}(-\sin (t^2)) \cdot 2t$$

$$= 4x \cos 2t - 4ye^{(y^2)} t \sin (t^2)$$

(a) yes (b) yes (c) no

19. $$\frac{\partial f}{\partial y} = \frac{\partial f}{\partial u}\frac{\partial u}{\partial y} + \frac{\partial f}{\partial v}\frac{\partial v}{\partial y} + \frac{\partial f}{\partial w}\frac{\partial w}{\partial y} = \frac{\partial f}{\partial u}(-1) + \frac{\partial f}{\partial v}(1) + \frac{\partial f}{\partial w}(0) = -\frac{\partial f}{\partial u} + \frac{\partial f}{\partial v}$$

$$\frac{\partial f}{\partial z} = \frac{\partial f}{\partial u}\frac{\partial u}{\partial z} + \frac{\partial f}{\partial v}\frac{\partial v}{\partial z} + \frac{\partial f}{\partial w}\frac{\partial w}{\partial z} = \frac{\partial f}{\partial u}(0) + \frac{\partial f}{\partial v}(-1) + \frac{\partial f}{\partial w}(1) = -\frac{\partial f}{\partial v} + \frac{\partial f}{\partial w}$$

21. $w = uv + \ln v$, $u = x + y^2$, $v = e^x \cos y$

$$\frac{\partial w}{\partial x} = \frac{dw}{\partial u}\frac{\partial u}{\partial x} + \frac{\partial w}{\partial v}\frac{\partial v}{\partial x} = (v)(1) + \left(u + \frac{1}{v}\right)(e^x \cos y)$$

$$= v + \left(u + \frac{1}{v}\right)v = v + uv + 1$$

23. $w = x^2 + y^2$, $x = u - v$, $y = ve^{2u}$

$$\frac{\partial w}{\partial u} = \frac{\partial w}{\partial x}\frac{\partial x}{\partial u} + \frac{\partial w}{\partial y}\frac{\partial y}{\partial u} = 2x(1) + 2y(2ve^{2u}) = 2x + 4y^2$$

25. $w = (x^2 + y - 2)^4 + (x - y + 2)^3$, $x = u - 2v + 1$, $y = 2u + v - 2$

$$\frac{\partial w}{\partial v} = \frac{\partial w}{\partial x}\frac{\partial x}{\partial v} + \frac{\partial w}{\partial y}\frac{\partial y}{\partial v} \qquad u = 0,\ v = 0 \Rightarrow x = 1,\ y = -2$$

$$= \left[8x(x^2 + y - 2)^3 + 3(x - y + 2)^2\right](-2) + \left[4(x^2 + y - 2)^3 - 3(x - y + 2)^2\right]$$

$$= -2\left[(8)(-3)^3 + 3(5)^2\right] + \left[4(-3)^3 - 3(5)^2\right] = 282 - 183 = 99$$

27. $F(x, y) = \int_0^{x^2 y} \cos\sqrt{t}\, dt \Rightarrow \frac{\partial F}{\partial x} = \cos\sqrt{x^2 y} \cdot \frac{\partial}{\partial x}(x^2 y)$

$$= 2xy \cos\sqrt{x^2 y}\,\Big|_{(\pi, 1)} = -2\pi$$

29. $\frac{\partial w}{\partial y} = \frac{dw}{du}\frac{\partial u}{\partial y} = b\frac{dw}{du}$ $\qquad \frac{\partial w}{\partial x} = \frac{dw}{du}\frac{\partial u}{\partial x} = a\frac{dw}{du}$

Then $\quad a\frac{\partial w}{\partial y} = ab\frac{dw}{du} = b\left(a\frac{dw}{du}\right) = b\frac{\partial w}{\partial x}$

31. $\frac{\partial w}{\partial x}\frac{\partial w}{\partial y} = \left(\frac{\partial w}{\partial u}\frac{\partial u}{\partial x} + \frac{\partial w}{\partial v}\frac{\partial v}{\partial x}\right)\left(\frac{\partial w}{\partial u}\frac{\partial u}{\partial y} + \frac{\partial w}{\partial v}\frac{\partial v}{\partial y}\right)$

$$= \left(\frac{\partial w}{\partial u} + \frac{\partial w}{\partial v}\right)\left(\frac{\partial w}{\partial u} - \frac{\partial w}{\partial v}\right) = \left(\frac{\partial w}{\partial u}\right)^2 - \left(\frac{\partial w}{\partial v}\right)^2$$

33. $\frac{dw}{dt} = \frac{\partial w}{\partial x}\frac{dx}{dt} + \frac{\partial w}{\partial y}\frac{dy}{dt} + \frac{\partial w}{\partial z}\frac{dz}{dt}$

$$= (\cos t)(-\sin t) + (\sin t)(\cos t) + (t^2 + t - 2)(1)$$

$$= t^2 + t - 2 = 0 \text{ if } t = -2 \text{ or } 1.$$

35. (a) $\frac{df}{dt} = \frac{\partial f}{\partial x}\frac{dx}{dt} + \frac{\partial f}{\partial y}\frac{dy}{dt}$

$$= (8\cos t - 4\sin t)(-\sin t) + (8\sin t - 4\cos t)(\cos t) = -4\cos 2t$$

$-4\cos 2t = 0$ if $t = \frac{\pi}{4}, \frac{3\pi}{4}, \frac{5\pi}{4}, \frac{7\pi}{4}$. $\quad \frac{d^2 f}{dt^2} = 8\sin 2t > 0$ if $t = \frac{\pi}{4}$ or $\frac{5\pi}{4}$ =

a minimum value of 2. $\frac{d^2 f}{dt^2} < 0$ if $t = \frac{3\pi}{4}$ or $\frac{7\pi}{4}$ $\Rightarrow$ a maximum value of 6.

(b) If $f(x,y) = 4x^2 - 4xy + 4y^2$ then $\frac{\partial f}{\partial x} = 8x - 4y$ and $\frac{\partial f}{\partial y} = 8y - 4x$

$f\left(\frac{1}{\sqrt{2}}, \frac{1}{\sqrt{2}}\right) = f\left(-\frac{1}{\sqrt{2}}, -\frac{1}{\sqrt{2}}\right) = 2$ is minimum temperature

$f\left(-\frac{1}{\sqrt{2}}, \frac{1}{\sqrt{2}}\right) = f\left(\frac{1}{\sqrt{2}}, -\frac{1}{\sqrt{2}}\right) = 6$ is maximum temperature.

37. $\Delta = \begin{vmatrix} \cos\theta & \sin\theta \\ -\sin\theta & \cos\theta \end{vmatrix} = \cos^2\theta + \sin^2\theta = 1$

$$f_y = \begin{vmatrix} \cos\theta & \frac{\partial w}{\partial r} \\ -\sin\theta & \frac{1}{r}\frac{\partial w}{\partial \theta} \end{vmatrix} = \frac{\cos\theta}{r}\frac{\partial w}{\partial \theta} + \sin\theta\,\frac{\partial w}{\partial r}$$

$$f_x = \begin{vmatrix} \frac{\partial w}{\partial r} & \sin\theta \\ \frac{1}{r}\frac{\partial w}{\partial \theta} & \cos\theta \end{vmatrix} = \cos\theta\frac{\partial w}{\partial r} - \frac{\sin\theta}{r}\frac{\partial w}{\partial \theta}$$

## 16.5 PARTIAL DERIVATIVES WITH CONSTRAINED VARIABLES

1. $w = x^2 + y^2 + z^2$ and $z = x^2 + y^2$

(a) $\begin{pmatrix} w \\ z \end{pmatrix} \to \begin{pmatrix} x = x(y,z) \\ y = y \\ z = z \end{pmatrix} \to w$

$$\left(\frac{\partial w}{\partial y}\right)_z = \frac{\partial w}{\partial x}\frac{\partial x}{\partial y} + \frac{\partial w}{\partial y}\frac{\partial y}{\partial y} + \frac{\partial w}{\partial z}\frac{\partial z}{\partial y}$$

$$\frac{\partial z}{\partial y} = 2x\frac{\partial x}{\partial y} + 2y\frac{\partial y}{\partial y} \Rightarrow \frac{\partial x}{\partial y} = -\frac{y}{x}$$

$$\therefore \left(\frac{\partial w}{\partial y}\right)_z = (2x)\left(-\frac{y}{x}\right) + (2y)(1) + (2z)(0) = 0$$

(b) $\begin{pmatrix} w \\ x \end{pmatrix} \to \begin{pmatrix} x = x \\ y = y(x,z) \\ z = z \end{pmatrix} \to w$

$$\left(\frac{\partial w}{\partial z}\right)_x = \frac{\partial w}{\partial x}\frac{\partial x}{\partial z} + \frac{\partial w}{\partial y}\frac{\partial y}{\partial z} + \frac{\partial w}{\partial z}\frac{\partial z}{\partial z}$$

$$\frac{\partial z}{\partial z} = 2x\frac{\partial x}{\partial z} + 2y\frac{\partial y}{\partial z} \Rightarrow \frac{\partial y}{\partial z} = \frac{1}{2y}$$

$$\therefore \left(\frac{\partial w}{\partial z}\right)_x = (2x)(0) + (2y)\left(\frac{1}{2y}\right) + (2z)(1) = 1 + 2z$$

(c) $\begin{pmatrix} w \\ y \end{pmatrix} \to \begin{pmatrix} x = x(y,z) \\ y = y \\ z = z \end{pmatrix} \to w$

$$\left(\frac{\partial w}{\partial z}\right)_y = \frac{\partial w}{\partial x}\frac{\partial x}{\partial z} + \frac{\partial w}{\partial y}\frac{\partial y}{\partial z} + \frac{\partial w}{\partial z}\frac{\partial z}{\partial z}$$

$$\frac{\partial z}{\partial z} = 2x\frac{\partial x}{\partial z} + 2y\frac{\partial y}{\partial z} \Rightarrow \frac{\partial x}{\partial z} = \frac{1}{2x}$$

$$\therefore \left(\frac{\partial w}{\partial z}\right)_y = (2x)\left(\frac{1}{2x}\right) + (2y)(0) + (2z)(1) = 1 + 2z$$

3. $U = f(p, v, T)$ and $pv = nRT$ (n and R constant)

(a) $\begin{pmatrix} p \\ v \end{pmatrix} \to \begin{pmatrix} p \\ v \\ T = T(p,v) \end{pmatrix} \to U$

$$\left(\frac{\partial U}{\partial p}\right)_v = \frac{\partial U}{\partial p}\frac{\partial p}{\partial p} + \frac{\partial U}{\partial v}\frac{\partial v}{\partial p} + \frac{\partial U}{\partial T}\frac{\partial T}{\partial p}$$

$$T = \frac{v}{nR}p \Rightarrow \frac{\partial T}{\partial p} = \frac{v}{nR}$$

$$\left(\frac{\partial U}{\partial p}\right)_v = \frac{\partial U}{\partial p}(1) + \frac{\partial U}{\partial v}(0) + \frac{\partial U}{\partial T}\left(\frac{v}{nR}\right) = \frac{\partial U}{\partial p} + \frac{v}{nR}\frac{\partial U}{\partial T}$$

(b) $\begin{pmatrix} p \\ v \end{pmatrix} \to \begin{pmatrix} p = p(v,T) \\ v \\ T = T \end{pmatrix} \to U$

$$\left(\frac{\partial U}{\partial T}\right)_v = \frac{\partial U}{\partial p}\frac{\partial p}{\partial T} + \frac{\partial U}{\partial v}\frac{\partial v}{\partial T} + \frac{\partial U}{\partial T}\frac{\partial T}{\partial T}$$

$$p = nRTv^{-1} \Rightarrow \frac{\partial p}{\partial T} = \frac{nR}{v}$$

$$\left(\frac{\partial U}{\partial T}\right)_v = \frac{\partial U}{\partial p}\left(\frac{nR}{v}\right) + \frac{\partial U}{\partial v}(0) + \frac{\partial U}{\partial T}(1) = \frac{nR}{v}\frac{\partial U}{\partial p} + \frac{\partial U}{\partial T}$$

5. $w = x^2y^2 + yz - z^3$ and $x^2 + y^2 + z^2 = 6$, $(x,y,z,w) = (4,2,1,-1)$

(a) $\begin{pmatrix} x \\ y \end{pmatrix} \to \begin{pmatrix} x \\ y \\ z = z(x,y) \end{pmatrix} \to w$

$$\left(\frac{\partial w}{\partial y}\right)_x = \frac{\partial w}{\partial x}\frac{\partial x}{\partial y} + \frac{\partial w}{\partial y}\frac{\partial y}{\partial y} + \frac{\partial w}{\partial z}\frac{\partial z}{\partial y}$$

$$2x\frac{\partial x}{\partial y} + 2y\frac{\partial y}{\partial y} + 2z\frac{\partial z}{\partial y} = 0 \Rightarrow \frac{\partial z}{\partial y} = -\frac{y}{z}$$

$$\left(\frac{\partial w}{\partial y}\right)_x = (2xy^2)(0) + (2x^2y + z)(1) + (y - 3z^2)\left(-\frac{y}{z}\right)$$

$$= 2x^2y + z - \frac{y^2}{z} + 3yz\Big|_{(4,2,1,-1)} = 5$$

(b) $\begin{pmatrix} y \\ z \end{pmatrix} \to \begin{pmatrix} x = x(y,z) \\ y \\ z \end{pmatrix} \to w$

$$\left(\frac{\partial w}{\partial y}\right)_z = \frac{\partial w}{\partial x}\frac{\partial x}{\partial y} + \frac{\partial w}{\partial y}\frac{\partial y}{\partial y} + \frac{\partial w}{\partial z}\frac{\partial z}{\partial y}$$

$$2x\frac{\partial x}{\partial y} + 2y\frac{\partial y}{\partial y} + 2z\frac{\partial z}{\partial y} = 0 \Rightarrow \frac{\partial x}{\partial y} = -\frac{y}{x}$$

$$\left(\frac{\partial w}{\partial y}\right)_x = (2xy^2)\left(-\frac{y}{x}\right) + (2x^2y + z)(1) + (y - 3z^2)(0)$$

$$= -2y^3 + 2x^2y + z\Big|_{(4,2,1,-1)} = 5$$

7. $x^2 + y^2 = r^2$ and $x = r\cos\theta$

(a) $\left(\frac{\partial x}{\partial r}\right)_\theta = \cos\theta$

(b) $2x = 2r\frac{\partial r}{\partial x} \Rightarrow \left(\frac{\partial r}{\partial x}\right)_y = \frac{x}{r} = \cos\theta$

9. $f(x,y,z) = 0 \Rightarrow \left(\frac{\partial f}{\partial y}\right)_z = 0$. Hence

$$\left(\frac{\partial f}{\partial y}\right)_z = \frac{\partial f}{\partial x}\frac{\partial x}{\partial y} + \frac{\partial f}{\partial y}\frac{\partial y}{\partial y} + \frac{\partial f}{\partial z}\frac{\partial z}{\partial y} = \frac{\partial f}{\partial x}\frac{\partial x}{\partial y} + \frac{\partial f}{\partial y} = 0 \Rightarrow \left(\frac{\partial x}{\partial y}\right)_z = -\frac{\partial f/\partial y}{\partial f/\partial x}$$

Similarly, $\left(\frac{\partial y}{\partial z}\right)_x = -\frac{\partial f/\partial z}{\partial f/\partial y}$ and $\left(\frac{\partial z}{\partial x}\right)_y = -\frac{\partial f/\partial x}{\partial f/\partial z}$

$$\therefore \left(\frac{\partial x}{\partial y}\right)_z\left(\frac{\partial y}{\partial z}\right)_x\left(\frac{\partial z}{\partial x}\right)_y = \left(-\frac{\partial f/\partial y}{\partial f/\partial x}\right)\left(-\frac{\partial f/\partial z}{\partial f/\partial y}\right)\left(-\frac{\partial f/\partial x}{\partial f/\partial z}\right) = -1$$

11. $x = x^2 - y^2 + 4z + t$ and $x + 2z + t = 25$

If x, y and z are independent:

$$1 + \frac{\partial t}{\partial x} = 0 \Rightarrow \frac{\partial t}{\partial x} = -1 . \therefore \left(\frac{\partial w}{\partial x}\right)_{y,z} = 2x + \frac{\partial t}{\partial x} = 2x - 1.$$

If x, y and t are independent:

$$1 + 2\frac{\partial z}{\partial x} = 0 \Rightarrow \frac{\partial z}{\partial x} = -\frac{1}{2}. \therefore \left(\frac{\partial w}{\partial x}\right)_{y,t} = 2x + 4\frac{\partial z}{\partial x} = 2x - 2$$

## 16.6 GRADIENTS AND DIRECTIONAL DERIVATIVES

1. $f(x, y, z) = x^2 + y^2 - 2z^2$ at (1, 1, 1)

$$\frac{\partial f}{\partial x} = 2x \qquad \frac{\partial f}{\partial y} = 2y \qquad \frac{\partial f}{\partial z} = -4z$$

$$\nabla f = 2x\,\mathbf{i} + 2y\,\mathbf{j} - 4z\,\mathbf{k} \qquad \nabla f\Big|_{(1,1,1)} = 2\mathbf{i} + 2\mathbf{j} - 4\mathbf{k}$$

3. $f(x, y, z) = e^{-2y}\cos 2x$ at $\left(\frac{\pi}{4}, 0, 0\right)$

$$\frac{\partial f}{\partial x} = -2e^{-2y}\sin 2x \qquad \frac{\partial f}{\partial y} = -2e^{-2y}\cos 2x$$

$$\nabla f\,\Big|_{(\pi/4,0,0)} = -2\mathbf{i}$$

5. $f(x, y, z) = (x^2 + y^2 + z^2)^{-1/2}$ at (1, 2, −2)

$$f_x = -x\,(x^2 + y^2 + z^2)^{-3/2} \qquad f_y = -y\,(x^2 + y^2 + z^2)^{-3/2}$$

$$f_z = -z(x^2 + y^2 + z^2)^{-3/2}$$

$$\nabla f\Big|_{(1,2,-2)} = -\frac{1}{27}\mathbf{i} - \frac{2}{27}\mathbf{j} + \frac{2}{27}\mathbf{k}$$

7. $f(x, y, z) = \cos x \cos y \sinh z$ at $\left(0, \frac{\pi}{4}, 0\right)$

$$\frac{\partial f}{\partial x} = -\sin x \cos y \sinh z \qquad \frac{\partial f}{\partial y} = -\cos x \sin y \sinh z$$

$$\frac{\partial f}{\partial z} = \cos x \cos y \cosh z$$

$$\nabla f\,\Big|_{(0,\pi/4,0)} = \frac{1}{\sqrt{2}}\mathbf{k}$$

9. $f(x,y) = x^2 + y^2$ at $(1,0)$ in direction of $\mathbf{A} = \mathbf{i} - \mathbf{j}$

$\mathbf{u} = \frac{1}{\sqrt{2}}\mathbf{i} - \frac{1}{\sqrt{2}}\mathbf{j}$. $f_x = 2x\Big|_{(1,0)} = 2$. $f_y = 2y\Big|_{(1,0)} = 0$

$\nabla f\Big|_{(1,0)} = 2\mathbf{i}$. $(D_{\mathbf{u}}f)\Big|_{(1,0)} = \nabla f \cdot \mathbf{u} = 2\mathbf{i} \cdot \left(\frac{1}{\sqrt{2}}\mathbf{i} - \frac{1}{\sqrt{2}}\mathbf{j}\right) = \sqrt{2}$

11. $f(x,y) = \cos xy$ at $\left(2, \frac{\pi}{4}\right)$ in direction of $\mathbf{A} = 4\mathbf{i} - \mathbf{j} \Rightarrow \mathbf{u} = \frac{4}{\sqrt{17}}\mathbf{i} - \frac{1}{\sqrt{17}}\mathbf{j}$

$f_x = -y \sin xy\Big|_{(2,\pi/4)} = -\frac{\pi}{4}$. $f_y = -x \sin xy\Big|_{(2,\pi/4)} = -2$

$\nabla f\Big|_{(2,\pi/4)} = -\frac{\pi}{4}\mathbf{i} - 2\mathbf{j}$.

$(D_{\mathbf{u}}f)\Big|_{(2,\pi/4)} = \nabla f \cdot \mathbf{u} = \left(-\frac{\pi}{4}\mathbf{i} - 2\mathbf{j}\right) \cdot \left(\frac{4}{\sqrt{17}}\mathbf{i} - \frac{1}{\sqrt{17}}\mathbf{j}\right) = \frac{2 - \pi}{\sqrt{17}}$

13. $f(x,y) = x^2 + 2xy - 3y^2$ at $\left(\frac{1}{2}, \frac{1}{2}\right)$ in direction of $\mathbf{A} = \sqrt{3}\mathbf{i} + \mathbf{j}$

$\mathbf{u} = \frac{\sqrt{3}}{2}\mathbf{i} + \frac{1}{2}\mathbf{j}$. $f_x = 2x + 2y\,|_{(1/2,1/2)} = 2$

$f_y = 2x - 6y\Big|_{(1/2,1/2)} = -2$. $\nabla f\Big|_{(1/2,1/2)} = 2\mathbf{i} - 2\mathbf{j}$.

$(D_{\mathbf{u}}f)\Big|_{(1/2,1/2)} = \nabla f \cdot \mathbf{u} = (2\mathbf{i} - 2\mathbf{j}) \cdot \left(\frac{\sqrt{3}}{2}\mathbf{i} + \frac{1}{2}\mathbf{j}\right) = \sqrt{3} - 1$

15. $f(x,y,z) = xy + yz + zx$ at $(1,-1,2)$ in direction of $\mathbf{A} = 10\mathbf{i} + 11\mathbf{j} - 2\mathbf{k}$

$\mathbf{u} = \frac{2}{3}\mathbf{i} + \frac{11}{15}\mathbf{j} - \frac{2}{15}\mathbf{k}$. $f_x = y + z\Big|_{(1,-1,2)} = 1$

$f_y = x + z\Big|_{(1,-1,2)} = 3$. $f_z = y + x\Big|_{(1,-1,2)} = 0$

$\nabla f\Big|_{(1,-1,2)} = \mathbf{i} + 3\mathbf{j}$.

$(D_{\mathbf{u}}f)\Big|_{(1,-1,2)} = \nabla f \cdot \mathbf{u} = (\mathbf{i} + 3\mathbf{j}) \cdot \left(\frac{2}{3}\mathbf{i} + \frac{11}{15}\mathbf{j} - \frac{2}{15}\mathbf{k}\right) = \frac{43}{15}$

17. $f(x,y,z) = e^x \cos yz$ at $(0,0,0)$ in direction of $\mathbf{A} = 2\mathbf{i} + \mathbf{j} - 2\mathbf{k}$

$$\mathbf{u} = \frac{2}{3}\mathbf{i} + \frac{1}{3}\mathbf{j} - \frac{2}{3}\mathbf{k}. \quad f_x = e^x \cos yz\Big|_{(0,0,0)} = 1$$

$$f_y = -ze^x \sin yz\Big|_{(0,0,0)} = 0. \quad f_z = -ye^x \sin yz\Big|_{(0,0,0)} = 0$$

$$\nabla f\Big|_{(0,0,0)} = \mathbf{i}$$

$$(D_{\mathbf{u}}f)\Big|_{(0,0,0)} = \nabla f \cdot \mathbf{u} = (\mathbf{i}) \cdot \left(\frac{2}{3}\mathbf{i} + \frac{1}{3}\mathbf{j} - \frac{2}{3}\mathbf{k}\right) = \frac{2}{3}$$

19. $f(x,y) = x^2 + \cos xy$ at $(1,0)$

$$f_x = 2x - y \sin xy\Big|_{(1,0)} = 2 \quad f_y = -x \sin xy\Big|_{(1,0)} = 0$$

$$\nabla f\Big|_{(1,0)} = 2\mathbf{i} \qquad |\nabla f| = 2$$

Most rapid increase in direction of $\mathbf{i}$ at rate $= 2$.

Most rapid decrease in direction of $-\mathbf{i}$ at rate $= -2$.

21. $f(x,y,z) = (x + y - 2)^2 + (3x - y - 6)^2$ at $(1,1,0)$

$$f_x = 20x - 4y - 40\Big|_{(1,1,0)} = -24 \quad f_y = -4x + 4y + 8\Big|_{(1,1,0)} = 8 \quad f_z = 0$$

$$\nabla f\Big|_{(1,1,0)} = -24\mathbf{i} + 8\mathbf{k} \quad |\nabla f| = 8\sqrt{10}$$

Most rapid increase in direction of $-\frac{3}{\sqrt{10}}\mathbf{i} + \frac{1}{\sqrt{10}}\mathbf{k}$ at rate $8\sqrt{10}$

Most rapid decrease in direction of $\frac{3}{\sqrt{10}}\mathbf{i} - \frac{1}{\sqrt{10}}\mathbf{k}$ at rate $-8\sqrt{10}$

23. $f(x,y,z) = (x + y)^2 + (y + z)^2 + (z + x)^2$ at $(2,-1,2)$

$$f_x = 4x + 2y + 2z\Big|_{(2,-1,2)} = 10 \quad f_y = 2x + 4y + 2z\Big|_{(2,-1,2)} = 4$$

$$f_z = 2x + 2y + 4z\Big|_{(2,-1,2)} = 10 \quad \nabla f\Big|_{(2,-1,2)} = 10\mathbf{i} + 4\mathbf{j} + 10\mathbf{k} \quad |\nabla f| = 6\sqrt{6}$$

Most rapid increase in direction of $\frac{1}{6\sqrt{6}}(10\mathbf{i} + 4\mathbf{j} + 10\mathbf{k})$ at rate $= 6\sqrt{6}$.

Most rapid decrease in direction of $-\frac{1}{6\sqrt{6}}(10\mathbf{i} + 4\mathbf{j} + 10\mathbf{k})$ at rate $= -6\sqrt{6}$

25. $f(x,y) = \cos \pi xy + xy^2$ from $(-1,-1)$ along $\mathbf{A} = \mathbf{i} + \mathbf{j}$, $ds = 0.1$

$f_x = -\pi y \sin \pi xy + y^2 \qquad f_y = -\pi x \sin \pi xy + 2xy$

At $(-1,-1)$, $\nabla f = \mathbf{i} + 2\mathbf{j}$. $\mathbf{u} = \frac{1}{\sqrt{2}}\mathbf{i} + \frac{1}{\sqrt{2}}\mathbf{j}$

$df = (\nabla f \cdot \mathbf{u})\,ds = (0.1)(\mathbf{i} + 2\mathbf{j}) \cdot \left(\frac{1}{\sqrt{2}}\mathbf{i} + \frac{1}{\sqrt{2}}\mathbf{j}\right) = \frac{3\sqrt{2}}{20}$

27. $df = (\nabla f \cdot \mathbf{u})\,ds = \frac{1}{10}(\mathbf{i}) \cdot \left(\frac{2}{3}\mathbf{i} + \frac{1}{3}\mathbf{j} + \frac{2}{3}\mathbf{k}\right) = \frac{1}{15}$ (See Problem 17)

29. $f(x,y) = xy + y^2$ at $(2,5)$

$f_x = y$ and $f_y = x + 2y \Rightarrow \nabla f = 5\mathbf{i} + 12\mathbf{j}$ so $\mathbf{u} = \frac{5}{13}\mathbf{i} + \frac{12}{13}\mathbf{j}$.

We need $\mathbf{a}$ so that $\mathbf{u} \cdot \mathbf{a} = 0$. The vectors $\frac{12}{13}\mathbf{i} - \frac{5}{13}\mathbf{j}$ and $-\frac{12}{13}\mathbf{i} + \frac{5}{13}\mathbf{j}$ satisfy this requirement.

31. $(f_x\mathbf{i} + f_y\mathbf{j}) \cdot \left(\frac{1}{\sqrt{2}}\mathbf{i} + \frac{1}{\sqrt{2}}\mathbf{j}\right) = \frac{1}{\sqrt{2}}f_x + \frac{1}{\sqrt{2}}f_y = 2\sqrt{2} \Rightarrow f_x + f_y = 4$

$(f_x\mathbf{i} + f_y\mathbf{j}) \cdot (-\mathbf{j}) = -f_y = -3 \Rightarrow f_y = 3$. $\therefore f_x = 1$

Then $(\mathbf{i} + 3\mathbf{j}) \cdot \left(-\frac{1}{\sqrt{5}}\mathbf{i} - \frac{2}{\sqrt{5}}\mathbf{j}\right) = -\frac{7}{\sqrt{5}}$

33. $\mathbf{R}(t) = (\cos 3t)\mathbf{i} + (\sin 3t)\mathbf{j} + 3t\,\mathbf{k} \Rightarrow \mathbf{v}(t) = (-3\sin 3t)\mathbf{i} + (3\cos 3t)\mathbf{j} + 3\,\mathbf{k}$

$\mathbf{v}\left(\frac{\pi}{3}\right) = -3\mathbf{j} + 3\mathbf{k}$. $f(x,y,z) = xyz \Rightarrow \nabla f = yz\mathbf{i} + xz\mathbf{j} + xy\,\mathbf{k}\Big|_{(-1,0,\pi)} = -\pi\mathbf{j}$

$\nabla f \cdot \mathbf{u} = (-\pi\mathbf{j}) \cdot \left(-\frac{1}{\sqrt{2}}\mathbf{j} + \frac{1}{\sqrt{2}}\mathbf{k}\right) = \frac{\pi}{\sqrt{2}}$

35. $\frac{\partial w}{\partial r} = \frac{\partial w}{\partial x}\frac{\partial x}{\partial r} + \frac{\partial w}{\partial y}\frac{\partial y}{\partial r} = \frac{\partial w}{\partial x}(\cos\theta) + \frac{\partial w}{\partial y}(\sin\theta) = \nabla w \cdot \mathbf{u}_r$

$\frac{\partial w}{\partial \theta} = \frac{\partial w}{\partial x}\frac{\partial x}{\partial \theta} + \frac{\partial w}{\partial y}\frac{\partial y}{\partial \theta} = \frac{\partial w}{\partial x}(-r\sin\theta) + \frac{\partial w}{\partial y}(r\cos\theta) = r\nabla w \cdot \mathbf{u}_\theta$

$\frac{\partial w}{\partial r}\mathbf{u}_r = \left[\frac{\partial w}{\partial x}(\cos\theta) + \frac{\partial w}{\partial y}(\sin\theta)\right](\cos\theta)\mathbf{i} + (\sin\theta)\mathbf{j}$

$\frac{1}{r}\frac{\partial w}{\partial \theta}\mathbf{u}_\theta = \left[\frac{\partial w}{\partial x}(-\sin\theta) + \frac{\partial w}{\partial y}(\cos\theta)\right](-\sin\theta)\mathbf{i} + (\cos\theta)\mathbf{j}$

$\therefore \frac{\partial w}{\partial r}\mathbf{u}_r + \frac{1}{r}\frac{\partial w}{\partial \theta}\mathbf{u}_\theta + \frac{\partial w}{\partial z}\mathbf{k} = \frac{\partial w}{\partial x}(\cos^2\theta + \sin^2\theta)\mathbf{i} + \frac{\partial w}{\partial y}(\cos^2\theta + \sin^2\theta)\mathbf{j} + \frac{\partial w}{\partial z}\mathbf{k}$

$= \frac{\partial w}{\partial x}\mathbf{i} + \frac{\partial w}{\partial y}\mathbf{j} + \frac{\partial w}{\partial z}\mathbf{k} = \nabla w$

37. $\mathbf{u}_\rho = \sin\phi\cos\theta\,\mathbf{i} + \sin\phi\sin\theta\,\mathbf{j} + \cos\phi\,\mathbf{k}$

$\mathbf{u}_\phi = \cos\phi\cos\theta\,\mathbf{i} + \cos\phi\sin\theta\,\mathbf{j} - \sin\phi\,\mathbf{k}$

$\mathbf{u}_\theta = -\sin\theta\,\mathbf{i} + \cos\theta\,\mathbf{j}$

$$\nabla w \cdot \mathbf{u}_\rho = \frac{\partial w}{\partial x}\sin\phi\cos\theta + \frac{\partial w}{\partial y}\sin\phi\sin\theta + \frac{\partial w}{\partial z}\cos\phi$$

$$= \frac{\partial w}{\partial x}\frac{\partial x}{\partial \rho} + \frac{\partial w}{\partial y}\frac{\partial y}{\partial \rho} + \frac{\partial w}{\partial z}\frac{\partial z}{\partial \rho} = \frac{\partial w}{\partial \rho}$$

$$\nabla w \cdot \mathbf{u}_\phi = \rho\left[\frac{\partial w}{\partial x}\cos\phi\cos\theta + \frac{\partial w}{\partial y}\cos\phi\sin\theta + \frac{\partial w}{\partial z}\cos\phi\right] = \rho\frac{\partial w}{\partial \phi}$$

$$\nabla w \cdot \mathbf{u}_\theta = \rho\left[\frac{\partial w}{\partial x}(-\sin\theta) + \frac{\partial w}{\partial y}\cos\theta\right] = \rho\sin\phi\frac{\partial w}{\partial \theta}$$

$$\therefore\ \nabla w = \frac{\partial w}{\partial \rho}\mathbf{u}_\rho + \frac{1}{\rho}\frac{\partial w}{\partial \phi}\mathbf{u}_\phi + \frac{1}{\rho\sin\phi}\frac{\partial w}{\partial \theta}\mathbf{u}_\theta$$

39. (a) $\nabla(kf) = (kf)_x\mathbf{i} + (kf)_y\mathbf{j} + (kf)_z = k(f_x)\mathbf{i} + k(f_y)\mathbf{j} + k(f_z)\mathbf{k}$

$= k(f_x\mathbf{i} + f_y\mathbf{j} + f_z\mathbf{k}) = k\nabla f$

(b) $\nabla(f+g) = (f+g)_x\mathbf{i} + (f+g)_y\mathbf{j} + (f+g)_z\mathbf{k}$

$= (f_x\mathbf{i} + f_y\mathbf{j} + f_z\mathbf{k}) + (g_x\mathbf{i} + g_y\mathbf{j} + g_z\mathbf{k}) = \nabla f + \nabla g$

(c) $\nabla(fg) = (fg)_x\mathbf{i} + (fg)_y\mathbf{j} + (fg)_z\mathbf{k}$

$= (fg_x + f_x g)\mathbf{i} + (fg_y + f_y g)\mathbf{j} + (fg_z + f_z g)\mathbf{k}$

$= f(g_x\mathbf{i} + g_y\mathbf{j} + g_z\mathbf{k}) + g(f_x\mathbf{i} + f_y\mathbf{j} + f_z\mathbf{k}) = f\nabla g + g\nabla f$

## 16.7 TANGENT PLANES AND NORMAL LINES

1. $x^2 + y^2 + z^2 = 3$ at $P_0(1,1,1)$

$\nabla f = 2x\mathbf{i} + 2y\mathbf{j} + 2z\mathbf{k}$ $\quad \nabla f\Big|_{(1,1,1)} = 2\mathbf{i} + 2\mathbf{j} + 2\mathbf{k}$

Tangent plange: $x + y + z = 3$

Normal at $P_0$: $x = 1 + 2t,\ y = 1 + 2t,\ z = 1 + 2t$

3. $z^2 - x^2 - y^2 = 0$ at $P_0(3,4,-5)$

$\nabla f = -2x\,\mathbf{i} - 2y\,\mathbf{j} + 2z\,\mathbf{k}\Big|_{(3,4,-5)} = -6\mathbf{i} - 8\mathbf{j} - 10\,\mathbf{k}$

Tangent plane: $3x + 4y + 5z = 0$

Normal at $P_0$: $x = 3 + 3t,\ y = 4 + 4t,\ z = -5 + 5t$

5. $z - \ln(x^2 + y^2) = 0$ at $P_0(1,0,0)$

$$\nabla f = -\frac{2x}{x^2+y^2}\mathbf{i} - \frac{2y}{x^2+y^2}\mathbf{j} + \mathbf{k}\Big|_{(1,0,0)} = -2\mathbf{i} + \mathbf{k}$$

Tangent plane: $2x - z = 2$

Normal at $P_0$: $x = 1 - 2t,\ y = 0,\ z = t$

7. $x^2 + 2xy - y^2 + z^2 = 7$ at $P_0(1,-1,3)$

$$\nabla f = (2x + 2y)\mathbf{i} + (2x - 2y)\mathbf{j} + 2z\,\mathbf{k}\Big|_{(1,-1,3)} = 4\mathbf{j} + 6\mathbf{k}$$

Tangent plane: $4y + 6z = 14$ or $2x + 3y = 7$

Normal at $P_0$: $x = 1,\ y = -1 + 4t,\ z = 3 + 6t$

9. $x^2 - xy - y^2 - z = 0$ at $P_0(1,1,-1)$

$$\nabla f = (2x - y)\mathbf{i} + (-x - 2y)\mathbf{j} - \mathbf{k}\Big|_{(1,1,-1)} = \mathbf{i} - 3\mathbf{j} - \mathbf{k}$$

Tangent plane: $x - 3y - z = -1$

Normal at $P_0$: $x = 1 + t,\ y = 1 - 3t,\ z = -1 - t$

11. $\cos\frac{\pi x}{2} - z = 0$ at $P_0(1,0,0)$

$$\nabla f = -\frac{\pi}{2}\sin\frac{\pi x}{2}\mathbf{i} - \mathbf{k}\Big|_{(1,0,0)} = -\frac{\pi}{2}\mathbf{i} - \mathbf{k}$$

Tangent plane: $\frac{\pi}{2}x + z = \frac{\pi}{2}$

Normal at $P_0$: $x = 1 - \frac{\pi}{2}\mathbf{i},\ y = 0,\ z = -t$

13. $x^2 + y^2 - 2xy - x + 3y - z = -4$ at $P_0(2,-3,18)$

$$\nabla f = (2x - 2y - 1)\mathbf{i} + (2y - 2x + 3)\mathbf{j} - \mathbf{k}\Big|_{(2,-3,18)} = 9\mathbf{i} - 7\mathbf{j} - \mathbf{k}$$

Tangent plane: $9x - 7y - z = 21$

Normal at $P_0$: $x = 2 + 9t,\ y = -3 - 7t,\ z = 18 - t$

15. $x + y^2 + z^2 = 1$ at $P_0(0,0,1)$

$$\nabla f = \mathbf{i} + 2y\,\mathbf{j} + 2z\,\mathbf{k}\Big|_{(0,0,1)} = \mathbf{i} + 2\mathbf{k}$$

Tangent plane: $x + 2z = 2$

Normal at $P_0$: $x = t,\ y = 0,\ z = 1 + 2t$

17. $\sin x - y = 0$ at $P_0(0,0,0)$

$\nabla f = (\cos x)\mathbf{i} - \mathbf{j}\Big|_{(0,0,0)} = \mathbf{i} - \mathbf{j}$

Tangent plane: $x - y = 0$

Normal at $P_0$: $x = t$, $y = -t$, $z = 0$

19. $x^2 + y^2 - z = 0$ $\quad \nabla f = 2x\mathbf{i} + 2y\mathbf{j} - \mathbf{k}$ $\quad \nabla f\Big|_{(1,1,2)} = 2\mathbf{i} + 2\mathbf{j} - \mathbf{k}$

21. $x^2 + y^2 + z = 4$ $\quad \nabla f = 2x\mathbf{i} + 2y\mathbf{j} + \mathbf{k}$ $\quad \nabla f\Big|_{(-1,-1,2)} = -2\mathbf{i} - 2\mathbf{j} + \mathbf{k}$

23. $x^2 + y^2 = 4$ $\quad \nabla f = 2x\mathbf{i} + 2y\mathbf{j}$ $\quad \nabla f\Big|_{(-1,\sqrt{3},1)} = -2\mathbf{i} + 2\sqrt{3}\mathbf{j}$

25. $4y^2 + 9z^2 = 36$ $\quad \nabla f = 8y\mathbf{j} + 18z\mathbf{k}$ $\quad \nabla f\Big|_{(0,3/2,\sqrt{3})} = 12\mathbf{j} + 18\sqrt{3}\mathbf{k}$

27. $x^2 + y^2 - z^2 = 1$ $\quad \nabla f = 2x\mathbf{i} + 2y\mathbf{j} - 2z\mathbf{k}$ $\quad \nabla f\Big|_{(1,1,-1)} = 2\mathbf{i} + 2\mathbf{j} + 2\mathbf{k}$

29. Let $f(x,y,z) = x + y^2 + 2z - 4$ and $g(x,y,z) = x - 1$ at $P_0(1,1,1)$

$\nabla f = \mathbf{i} + 2y\mathbf{j} + 2\mathbf{k}\Big|_{(1,1,1)} = \mathbf{i} + 2\mathbf{j} + 2\mathbf{k}$

$\nabla g = \mathbf{i}$

$$\nabla f \times \nabla g = \begin{vmatrix} \mathbf{i} & \mathbf{j} & \mathbf{k} \\ 1 & 2 & 2 \\ 1 & 0 & 0 \end{vmatrix} = 2\mathbf{j} - 2\mathbf{k}$$

The line is: $x = 1$, $y = 1 + 2t$, $z = 1 - 2t$

31. Let $f(x,y,z) = x^2 + 2y + 2z - 4$ and $g(x,y,z) = y - 1$ at $P_0\left(1,1,\frac{1}{2}\right)$

$\nabla f = 2x\mathbf{i} + 2\mathbf{j} + 2\mathbf{k}\Big|_{(1,1,1/2)} = 2\mathbf{i} + 2\mathbf{j} + 2\mathbf{k}$

$\nabla g = \mathbf{j}$

$$\nabla f \times \nabla g = \begin{vmatrix} \mathbf{i} & \mathbf{j} & \mathbf{k} \\ 2 & 2 & 2 \\ 0 & 1 & 0 \end{vmatrix} = -2\mathbf{i} + 2\mathbf{k}$$

The line is: $x = 1 - 2t$, $y = 1$, $z = \frac{1}{2} + 2t$

33. Let $f(x,y,z) = x^3 + 3x^2y^2 + y^3 + 4xy - z^2$ and $g(x,y,z) = x^2 + y^2 + z^2 - 11$

$$\nabla f = (3x^2 + 6xy^2 + 4y)\mathbf{i} + (6x^2y + 3y^2 + 4x)\mathbf{j} - 2z\,\mathbf{k}\Big|_{(1,1,3)} = 13\mathbf{i} + 13\mathbf{j} - 6\mathbf{k}$$

$$\nabla g = 2x\mathbf{i} + 2y\mathbf{j} + 2z\mathbf{k}\Big|_{(1,1,3)} = 2\mathbf{i} + 2\mathbf{j} + 6\mathbf{k}$$

$$\nabla f \times \nabla g = \begin{vmatrix} \mathbf{i} & \mathbf{j} & \mathbf{k} \\ 13 & 13 & -6 \\ 2 & 2 & 6 \end{vmatrix} = 90\mathbf{i} - 90\mathbf{j}$$

The line is: $x = 1 + 90t$, $y = 1 - 90t$, $z = 3$

35. $x^2 + y^2 = 4$ at $P_0(\sqrt{2}, \sqrt{2})$

$$\nabla f = 2x\mathbf{i} + 2y\mathbf{j}\Big|_{(\sqrt{2},\sqrt{2})} = 2\sqrt{2}\,\mathbf{i} + 2\sqrt{2}\,\mathbf{j}$$

The line is: $2\sqrt{2}\,x + 2\sqrt{2}\,y = 8$ or $x + y = 2\sqrt{2}$

37. $4x^2 + 9y^2 = 36$ at $P_0\left(2, \frac{2\sqrt{5}}{3}\right)$

$$\nabla f = 8x\mathbf{i} + 18y\mathbf{j}\Big|_{(2,2\sqrt{5}/3)} = 16\mathbf{i} + 12\sqrt{5}\,\mathbf{j}$$

The line is: $4x + 3\sqrt{5}y = 18$

39. $xy = -4$ at $P_0(2, -2)$

$$\nabla f = y\mathbf{i} + x\mathbf{j}\Big|_{(2,-2)} = -2\mathbf{i} + 2\mathbf{j}$$

The line is: $-2x + 2y = -8$ or $x = y = 4$

41. $(y + z)^2 + (z - x)^2 = 16$

$$\nabla f = -2(z - x)\mathbf{i} + 2(y + z)\mathbf{j} + 2(y + z + z - x)$$

We need x constant $\Rightarrow \frac{\partial f}{\partial x} = 0 \Rightarrow x = z$. Then $y + z = \pm 4$.

$\therefore\ x = t,\ y = \pm 4 - t,\ z = t$

43. $\mathbf{R}(t) = \sqrt{t}\,\mathbf{i} + \sqrt{t}\,\mathbf{j} - \frac{1}{4}(t + 3)\mathbf{k}$

$$\mathbf{v}(t) = \frac{1}{2\sqrt{t}}\mathbf{i} + \frac{1}{2\sqrt{t}}\mathbf{j} - \frac{1}{4}\mathbf{k}\Big|_{t=1} = \frac{1}{2}\mathbf{i} + \frac{1}{2}\mathbf{j} - \frac{1}{4}\mathbf{k}$$

$$f(x,y,z) = x^2 + y^2 - z \Rightarrow \nabla f = 2x\mathbf{i} + 2y\mathbf{j} - \mathbf{k}\Big|_{(1,1,-1)} = 2\mathbf{i} + 2\mathbf{j} - \mathbf{k}$$

Note that $\nabla f = 4\mathbf{v}$.

## 16.8 HIGHER ORDER DERIVATIVES

1. $f(x,y) = \ln(x^2+y^2)$

$$\frac{\partial f}{\partial x} = \frac{2x}{x^2+y^2} \qquad \frac{\partial f}{\partial y} = \frac{2y}{x^2+y^2}$$

$$\frac{\partial^2 f}{\partial x^2} = \frac{2(x^2+y^2) - 2x(2x)}{(x^2+y^2)^2} = \frac{2(y^2-x^2)}{(x^2+y^2)^2}$$

$$\frac{\partial^2 f}{\partial y^2} = \frac{2(x^2+y^2) - 2y(2y)}{(x^2+y^2)^2} = \frac{2(x^2-y^2)}{(x^2+y^2)^2}$$

$$\frac{\partial^2 f}{\partial y\,\partial x} = \frac{(0)(x^2+y^2) - 2x(2y)}{(x^2+y^2)^2} = \frac{-4xy}{(x^2+y^2)^2}$$

3. $f(x,y) = x^2 y + \cos y + y \sin x$

$$\frac{\partial f}{\partial x} = 2xy + y\cos x \qquad \frac{\partial f}{\partial y} = x^2 - \sin y + \sin x$$

$$\frac{\partial^2 f}{\partial x^2} = 2y - y\sin x \qquad \frac{\partial^2 f}{\partial y^2} = -\cos y \qquad \frac{\partial^2 f}{\partial y\,\partial x} = 2x + \cos x$$

5. $f(x,y,z) = xyz$

$$\frac{\partial f}{\partial x} = yz \qquad \frac{\partial f}{\partial y} = xz \qquad \frac{\partial^2 f}{\partial x^2} = 0 \qquad \frac{\partial^2 f}{\partial y^2} = 0 \qquad \frac{\partial^2 f}{\partial y\,\partial x} = z$$

7. $w = \ln(2x+3y)$

$$w_x = \frac{2}{2x+3y} \qquad w_{yx} = \frac{-6}{(2x+3y)^2} \qquad w_y = \frac{3}{2x+3y} \qquad w_{xy}:$$

9. $w = xy^2 + x^2y^3 + x^3y^4$

$$w_x = y^2 + 2xy^3 + 3x^2y^4 \qquad w_{yx} = 2y + 6xy^2 + 12x^2y^3$$

$$w_y = 2xy + 3x^2y^2 + 4x^3y^3 \qquad w_{xy} = 2y + 6xy^2 + 12x^2y^3$$

11. (a) x first (leaves one term)

(b) y first ($f_y = 0$)

(c) x first (leaves one term)

(d) x first (leaves one term)

(e) y first (leaves one term)

(f) y first (simpler)

13. $w = f(u, v)$, where $u = x + y$ and $v = xy$

$$\frac{\partial w}{\partial y} = \frac{\partial w}{\partial u}\frac{\partial u}{\partial y} + \frac{\partial w}{\partial v}\frac{\partial v}{\partial y} = \frac{\partial w}{\partial u}(1) + \frac{\partial w}{\partial v}(x) = f_u + xf_v$$

$$\frac{\partial w}{\partial x\,\partial y} = \frac{\partial}{\partial x}\left(\frac{\partial f}{\partial u} + x\frac{\partial f}{\partial v}\right).$$ Now, taking each summand:

$$\frac{\partial}{\partial x}\left(\frac{\partial f}{\partial u}\right) = \frac{\partial}{\partial u}\left(\frac{\partial f}{\partial u}\right)\cdot\frac{\partial u}{\partial x} + \frac{\partial}{\partial v}\left(\frac{\partial f}{\partial u}\right)\cdot\frac{\partial v}{\partial x} = \frac{\partial^2 f}{\partial u^2}(1) + \frac{\partial^2 f}{\partial v\partial u}(y) = f_{uu} + yf_{vu}.$$

$$\frac{\partial}{\partial x}\left(x\frac{\partial f}{\partial v}\right) = x\cdot\frac{\partial}{\partial x}\left(\frac{\partial f}{\partial v}\right) + \frac{\partial f}{\partial v}(1).$$ Finally,

$$\frac{\partial}{\partial x}\left(\frac{\partial f}{\partial v}\right) = \frac{\partial}{\partial u}\left(\frac{\partial f}{\partial v}\right)\cdot\frac{\partial u}{\partial x} + \frac{\partial}{\partial v}\left(\frac{\partial f}{\partial v}\right)\cdot\frac{\partial v}{\partial x} = f_{uv} + yf_{vv}.$$ Combining, we have

$$w_{xy} = f_{uu} + yf_{vu} + x(f_{uv} + yf_{vv}) + f_y$$
$$= f_{uu} + (y + x)f_{uv} + xy\,f_{vv} + f_v = f_{uu} + u\,f_{uv} + v\,f_{vv} + f_v$$

15. $u = f(x, y)$, where $x = r^2 + s^2$ and $y = 2rs$

$$\frac{\partial u}{\partial s} = \frac{\partial f}{\partial x}\frac{\partial x}{\partial s} + \frac{\partial f}{\partial y}\frac{\partial y}{\partial s} = 2s\frac{\partial f}{\partial x} + 2r\frac{\partial f}{\partial y}$$

$$\frac{\partial^2 u}{\partial s^2} = \left(2\cdot\frac{\partial f}{\partial x} + 2s\frac{\partial}{\partial s}\left(\frac{\partial f}{\partial x}\right)\right) + \left(0\cdot\frac{\partial f}{\partial y} + 2r\frac{\partial}{\partial s}\left(\frac{\partial f}{\partial y}\right)\right)$$

$$= 2\cdot\frac{\partial f}{\partial x} + 2s\left[\frac{\partial^2 f}{\partial x^2}\cdot\frac{\partial x}{\partial s} + \frac{\partial^2 f}{\partial y\,\partial x}\cdot\frac{\partial y}{\partial s}\right] + 2r\left[\frac{\partial^2 f}{\partial x\,\partial y}\cdot\frac{\partial x}{\partial s} + \frac{\partial^2 f}{\partial y^2}\cdot\frac{\partial y}{\partial s}\right]$$

$$= 2f_x + 2s(2sf_{xx} + 2rf_{xy}) + 2r(2sf_{xy} + 2rf_{yy})$$

$$= 2f_x + 4s^2 f_{xx} + 8rs\,f_{xy} + 4r^2 f_{yy}$$

17. $w = f(x, y)$, where $x = \sin t$ and $y = t^2$

$$\frac{\partial w}{\partial t} = \frac{\partial f}{\partial x}\frac{\partial x}{\partial t} + \frac{\partial f}{\partial y}\frac{\partial y}{\partial t} = \cos t\frac{\partial f}{\partial x} + 2t\frac{\partial f}{\partial y}$$

$$\frac{\partial^2 w}{\partial t^2} = \left(-\sin t\cdot\frac{\partial f}{\partial x} + \cos t\frac{\partial}{\partial t}\left(\frac{\partial f}{\partial x}\right)\right) + \left(2\cdot\frac{\partial f}{\partial y} + 2t\frac{\partial}{\partial t}\left(\frac{\partial f}{\partial y}\right)\right)$$

$$= -\sin t\frac{\partial f}{\partial x} + \cos t\left[\frac{\partial^2 f}{\partial x^2}\frac{\partial x}{\partial t} + \frac{\partial^2 f}{\partial y\,\partial x}\frac{\partial y}{\partial t}\right] + 2\frac{\partial f}{\partial y} + 2t\left[\frac{\partial^2 f}{\partial x\,\partial y}\frac{\partial x}{\partial t} + \frac{\partial^2 f}{\partial y^2}\frac{\partial y}{\partial t}\right]$$

$$= (-\sin t)f_x + \cos t(\cos t f_{xx} + 2tf_{xy}) + 2f_y + 2t(\cos t f_{xy} + 2tf_{yy})$$

$$= (-\sin t)f_x + 2f_y + (\cos^2 t)f_{xx} + (4t\cos t)f_{xy} + 4t^2 f_{yy}$$

19. $\frac{\partial w}{\partial \theta} = \frac{\partial w}{\partial x}\frac{\partial x}{\partial \theta} + \frac{\partial w}{\partial y}\frac{\partial y}{\partial \theta} = (-r\sin\theta)\frac{\partial w}{\partial x} + (r\cos\theta)\frac{\partial w}{\partial y}$

$$\frac{\partial^2 w}{\partial \theta^2} = (-r\cos\theta)\frac{\partial w}{\partial x} + (-r\sin\theta)\frac{\partial}{\partial \theta}\left(\frac{\partial w}{\partial x}\right) + (-r\sin\theta)\frac{\partial w}{\partial y} + (r\cos\theta)\frac{\partial}{\theta}\left(\frac{\partial w}{\partial y}\right)$$

$$= (-r\cos\theta)\frac{\partial w}{\partial x} + (-r\sin\theta)\left(\frac{\partial^2 w}{\partial x^2}\frac{\partial x}{\partial \theta} + \frac{\partial^2 w}{\partial y\partial x}\frac{\partial y}{\partial \theta}\right) + (-r\sin\theta)\frac{\partial w}{\partial y}$$

$$+ (r\cos\theta)\left(\frac{\partial^2 w}{\partial x\partial y}\frac{\partial x}{\partial \theta} + \frac{\partial^2 w}{\partial y^2}\frac{\partial y}{\theta}\right)$$

$$= 0 + (-2)\Big[(1)(-2) + (1)(0)\Big] + (-2)(1) + 0 = 4 - 2 = 2$$

21. $f(x,y,z) = 2z^3 - 3z(x^2 + y^2)$

$f_x = -6zx \qquad f_y = -6zy \qquad f_z = 6z^2 - 3(x^2 + y^2)$

$f_{xx} = -6z \qquad f_{yy} = -6z \qquad f_{zz} = 12z$

$f_{xx} + f_{yy} + f_{zz} = -6z - 6z + 12z = 0$

23. $f(x,y) = \ln\sqrt{x^2 + y^2} = \frac{1}{2}\ln(x^2 + y^2)$

$f_x = \frac{x}{x^2 + y^2} \qquad f_y = \frac{y}{x^2 + y^2}$

$f_{xx} = \frac{y^2 - x^2}{x^2 + y^2} \qquad f_{yy} = \frac{x^2 - y^2}{x^2 + y^2}$

$f_{xx} + f_{yy} = 0$

25. $f(x,y,z) = e^{3x+4y}\cos 5z$

$f_x = 3e^{3x+4y}\cos 5z \qquad f_y = 4e^{3x+4y}\cos 5z \qquad f_z = -5e^{3x+4y}\sin 5z$

$f_{xx} = 9e^{3x+4y}\cos 5z \qquad f_{yy} = 16e^{3x+4y}\cos 5z \qquad f_{zz} = -25e^{3x+4y}\cos 5z$

$f_{xx} + f_{yy} + f_{zz} = 9e^{3x+4y}\cos 5z + 16e^{3x+4y}\cos 5z - 25e^{3x+4y}\cos 5z = 0$

27. $f(x,y,z) = \cos 3x\cos 4y\sinh 5z$

$f_x = -3\sin 3x\cos 4y\sinh 5z \qquad f_y = -4\cos 3x\sin 4y\sinh 5z$

$f_z = 5\cos 3x\cos 4y\cosh 5z$

$f_{xx} = -9\cos 3x\cos 4y\sinh 5z \qquad f_{yy} = -16\cos 3x\cos 4y\sinh 5z$

$f_{zz} = 25\cos 3x\cos 4y\sinh 5z$

$f_{xx} + f_{yy} + f_{zz} = 0$

29. Let $u_1 = f(r)$, $r = x - iy$. Then $\frac{\partial u_1}{\partial x} = \frac{\partial f}{\partial r}\frac{\partial r}{\partial x} = \frac{\partial f}{\partial r}$ and $\frac{\partial u_1}{\partial y} = \frac{\partial f}{\partial r}\frac{\partial r}{\partial y} = -i\frac{\partial f}{\partial r}$.

$$\frac{\partial^2 u_1}{\partial x^2} = \frac{\partial^2 f}{\partial r^2}\frac{\partial r}{\partial x} = \frac{\partial^2 f}{\partial r^2} \text{ and } \frac{\partial^2 u_1}{\partial y^2} = -i\frac{\partial^2 f}{\partial r^2}\frac{\partial r}{\partial y} = i^2\frac{\partial^2 f}{\partial r^2} = -\frac{\partial^2 f}{\partial r^2}.$$

Hence $\frac{\partial^2 u_1}{\partial x^2} + \frac{\partial^2 u_1}{\partial y^2} = 0$. Now let $u_2 = g(s)$, $s = x + iy$. Similarly,

$\frac{\partial^2 u_2}{\partial x^2} + \frac{\partial^2 u_2}{\partial y^2} = 0$. Since $u = u_1 + u_2$, the result follows.

31. (a) $f(x,y) = ax^2 + bxy + cy^2$; $f_x = 2ax + by$

$f_y = bx + 2cy$; $f_{xx} = 2a$ $f_{yy} = 2c$

$2a + 2c = 0 \Rightarrow a = -c$, $b$ arbitrary.

(b) $f(x,y) = ax^3 + bx^2y + cxy^2 + dy^3$; $f_x = 3ax^2 + 2bxy + cy^2$

$f_y = bx^2 + 2cxy + 3dy^2$; $f_{xx} = 6ax + 2by$; $f_{yy} = 2cx + 6dy$

$6ax + 2by + 2cx + 6dy = 0$ if $6a + 2c = 0$ and $2b + 6d = 0$

$\Rightarrow a = \frac{1}{3}c$, $b = -3d$, $c$ and $d$ arbitrary.

33. $\omega = \cos(2x + 2ct)$

$$\frac{\partial \omega}{\partial t} = -2c\sin(2x + 2ct) \qquad \frac{\partial^2 \omega}{\partial t^2} = -4c^2\cos(2x + 2ct)$$

$$\frac{\partial \omega}{\partial x} = -2\sin(2x + 2ct) \qquad \frac{\partial^2 \omega}{\partial x^2} = -4\cos(2x + 2ct)$$

$$\therefore c^2\frac{\partial^2 \omega}{\partial x^2} = c^2(-4\cos(2x + 2ct)) = \frac{\partial^2 \omega}{\partial t^2}$$

35. $\omega = \ln(2x + 2ct)$

$$\frac{\partial \omega}{\partial t} = \frac{c}{x + ct} \qquad \frac{\partial^2 \omega}{\partial t^2} = -\frac{c^2}{(x + ct)^2}$$

$$\frac{\partial \omega}{\partial x} = \frac{1}{x + ct} \qquad \frac{\partial^2 \omega}{\partial x^2} = \frac{-1}{(x + ct)^2}$$

$$\therefore c^2\frac{\partial^2 \omega}{\partial x^2} = c^2\left(\frac{-1}{(x + ct)^2}\right) = \frac{\partial^2 \omega}{\partial t^2}$$

37. $\omega = 5\cos(3x+3ct) - 7\sinh(4x-4ct)$

$$\frac{\partial\omega}{\partial t} = -15c\sin(3x+3ct) + 28\cosh(4x-4ct)$$

$$\frac{\partial^2\omega}{\partial t^2} = -45c^2\cos(3x+3ct) - 112c^2\sinh(4x-4ct)$$

$$\frac{\partial\omega}{\partial x} = -15\sin(3x+3ct) \; -28\cosh(4x-4ct)$$

$$\frac{\partial^2\omega}{\partial x^2} = -45\cos(3x+3ct) - 112\sinh(4x-4ct)$$

$$\therefore\; c^2\frac{\partial^2\omega}{\partial x^2} = c^2(-45\cos(3x+3ct) - 112\sinh(4x-4ct)) = \frac{\partial^2\omega}{\partial t^2}$$

39. $w = e^{rt}\sin\pi x$ $\qquad w_t = re^{rt}\sin\pi x$

$w_x = \pi e^{rt}\cos\pi x$ $\qquad w_{xx} = -\pi^2 e^{rt}\sin\pi x$

$re^{rt}\sin\pi x = -c^2\pi^2 e^{rt}\sin\pi x \Rightarrow e^{rt}\sin\pi x\,(r + c^2\pi^2) = 0 \Rightarrow$

$r = -c^2\pi^2$. $\therefore\; w = e^{-c^2\pi^2 t}\sin\pi x$

41. $u = f(y)$ where $y = x - t\,g(u)$.

$$\frac{\partial u}{\partial x} = \frac{df}{dy}\frac{\partial y}{\partial x} \text{ and } \frac{\partial u}{\partial t} = \frac{df}{dy}\frac{\partial y}{\partial t}. \text{ But } \frac{\partial y}{\partial x} = 1 - t\frac{\partial g}{\partial x} = 1 - t\frac{dg}{du}\frac{\partial u}{\partial x}$$

$$\text{and } \frac{\partial y}{\partial t} = -g - t\frac{\partial g}{\partial t} = -g - t\frac{dg}{du}\frac{\partial u}{\partial t}. \text{ Thus}$$

$$\frac{\partial u}{\partial x} = \frac{df}{dy}\left(1 - t\frac{dg}{du}\frac{\partial u}{\partial x}\right) \Rightarrow \frac{\partial u}{\partial x}(1 + t\,g'(u)\,f'(y)) = f'(y) \Rightarrow \frac{\partial u}{\partial x} = \frac{f'(y)}{1 + t\,g'(u)\,f'(y)}$$

$$\text{and } \frac{\partial u}{\partial t} = \frac{df}{dy}\left(-g - t\frac{dg}{du}\frac{\partial u}{\partial t}\right) \Rightarrow (1 + t\,f'(y)\,g'(u))\frac{\partial u}{\partial t} = -g(u)f'(y) \Rightarrow$$

$$\frac{\partial u}{\partial t} = \frac{-g(u)f'(y)}{(1 + t\,f'(y)\,g'(u))}. \quad \therefore\; \frac{\partial u}{\partial t} = -g(u)\frac{\partial u}{\partial x}.$$

## 16.M MISCELLANEOUS

1. We need $\sin\pi xy \geq 0$ which will occur on the sets $0 \leq \pi xy \leq \pi$, $2\pi \leq \pi xy \leq 3\pi$, $4\pi \leq \pi xy \leq 5\pi \ldots, 2n\pi \leq xy \leq (2n+1)\pi$. These are the regions in the first and third quadrants between the hyperbolas $0 \leq xy \leq 1$, $2 \leq xy \leq 3$, $\ldots$, $2n \leq xy \leq 2n+1$. (See graph in Answer of the text.)

3. We will calculate the limit along the lines $y = mx$:

$$\lim_{(x,y)\to(0,0)} \frac{x^2 - m^2x^2}{x^2 + m^2x^2} = \frac{1-m^2}{1+m^2},$$ which depends on the value of m.

$$\therefore \quad \lim_{(x,y)\to(0,0)} \frac{x^2 - y^2}{x^2 + y^2}$$ = does not exist, and hence $f(0,0)$ cannot be defined in such a way as to make $f$ continuous at $(0,0)$.

5. If f is constant, the result is obvious. Otherwise, choose c so that $f(c)$ is not an absolute maximum or absolute minimum value of $f$. Let P and Q be points such that $f(P) < c$ and $f(Q) > c$. The Intermediate Value Theorem holds along any connected path from P to Q. Since there are arbitrarily many such paths, there are arbitrarily many points $P_i$ for which $f(P_i) = c$.

7. (a) $f(x, y) = (\sin xy)^2$

$$\frac{\partial f}{\partial x} = 2y(\sin xy)(\cos xy) \qquad \frac{\partial f}{\partial y} = 2x(\sin xy)(\cos xy)$$

(b) $f(x, y) = \sin (xy)^2$

$$\frac{\partial f}{\partial x} = 2xy^2 \cos (xy)^2 \qquad \frac{\partial f}{\partial y} = 2x^2y \cos (xy)^2$$

9. $r = \sqrt{x^2 + y^2} \Rightarrow \dfrac{\partial r}{\partial x} = \dfrac{x}{\sqrt{x^2+y^2}} = \cos\theta$. If $x = r\cos\theta$, then

$$\frac{\partial x}{\partial r} = \cos\theta, \text{ so } \left(\frac{\partial x}{\partial r}\right)^{-1} \neq \frac{\partial r}{\partial x}$$ (except where $\cos\theta = 0$)

11. (a) $\displaystyle\lim_{r\to 0} \frac{\sin 6r}{6r} = 1$

(b) $$f_r(0,0) = \lim_{h\to 0} \frac{f(h,0) - f(0,0)}{h} = \lim_{h\to 0} \frac{\frac{\sin 6h}{6h} - 1}{h} = \lim_{h\to 0} \frac{\sin 6h - 6h}{6h^2} =$$

$$\lim_{h\to 0} \frac{6\cos 6h - 6}{12h} = \lim_{h\to 0} \frac{-36\sin 6h}{12} = 0$$

(c) $f_\theta(r, \theta) = 0$ since $\dfrac{\partial}{\partial\theta}\left(\dfrac{\sin 6r}{6r}\right) = 0$

13. $w = f(r,\theta)$, where $r = \sqrt{x^2 + y^2}$ and $\theta = \tan^{-1}\frac{y}{x}$

$$\frac{\partial w}{\partial x} = \frac{\partial w}{\partial r}\frac{\partial r}{\partial x} + \frac{\partial w}{\partial \theta}\frac{\partial \theta}{\partial x} = \frac{\partial w}{\partial r}\left(\frac{x}{\sqrt{x^2+y^2}}\right) + \frac{\partial w}{\partial \theta}\left(\frac{-yx^{-2}}{1+(yx^{-1})^2}\right)$$

$$= \cos\theta\,\frac{\partial w}{\partial r} - \frac{\sin\theta}{r}\frac{\partial w}{\partial \theta}$$

$$\frac{\partial w}{\partial y} = \frac{\partial w}{\partial r}\frac{\partial r}{\partial y} + \frac{\partial w}{\partial \theta}\frac{\partial \theta}{\partial y} = \frac{\partial w}{\partial r}\left(\frac{y}{\sqrt{x^2+y^2}}\right) + \frac{\partial w}{\partial \theta}\left(\frac{x^{-1}}{1+(yx^{-1})^2}\right)$$

$$= \sin\theta\,\frac{\partial w}{\partial r} + \frac{\cos\theta}{r}\frac{\partial w}{\partial \theta}$$

15. $w = u^3 + \tanh u + \cos u$, where $u = ax + by$

$\frac{\partial u}{\partial y} = b$ and $\frac{\partial u}{\partial x} = a$. $\therefore$ $\frac{\partial w}{\partial y} = \frac{\partial u}{\partial y}\frac{\partial w}{\partial u} = b\frac{\partial w}{\partial u}$ and $\frac{\partial w}{\partial x} = \frac{\partial u}{\partial x}\frac{\partial w}{\partial u} = a\frac{\partial w}{\partial u}$.

Hence $a\frac{\partial w}{\partial y} = ab\frac{\partial w}{\partial u} = b\frac{\partial w}{\partial x}$.

17. $w = \ln(x^2 + y^2 + 2z)$, where $x = r + s$, $y = r - s$, and $z = 2rs$

$$\frac{\partial w}{\partial x} = \frac{2x}{x^2+y^2+2z} = \frac{2(r+s)}{(r+s)^2+(r-s)^2+4rs} = \frac{2(r+s)}{2(r+s)^2} = \frac{1}{r+s}$$

$$\frac{\partial w}{\partial y} = \frac{2y}{x^2+y^2+2z} = \frac{r-s}{(r+s)^2};\quad \frac{\partial w}{\partial z} = \frac{2}{x^2+y^2+2z} = \frac{1}{(r+s)^2}$$

$$\therefore\ \frac{\partial w}{\partial r} = \frac{\partial w}{\partial x}\frac{\partial x}{\partial r} + \frac{\partial w}{\partial y}\frac{\partial y}{\partial r} + \frac{\partial w}{\partial z}\frac{\partial z}{\partial r} = \frac{1}{r+s} + \frac{r-s}{(r+s)^2} + \frac{2s}{(r+s)^2} = \frac{2}{r+s}$$

$$\frac{\partial w}{\partial s} = \frac{\partial w}{\partial x}\frac{\partial x}{\partial s} + \frac{\partial w}{\partial y}\frac{\partial y}{\partial s} + \frac{\partial w}{\partial z}\frac{\partial z}{\partial s} = \frac{1}{r+s} - \frac{r-s}{(r+s)^2} + \frac{2r}{(r+s)^2} = \frac{2}{r+s}$$

19. $F(x,y) = f(u,v) = f\left(\frac{x-y}{2}, \frac{x+y}{2}\right)$ so

$$\frac{\partial F}{\partial x} = \frac{\partial f}{\partial u}\frac{\partial u}{\partial x} + \frac{\partial f}{\partial v}\frac{\partial v}{\partial x} = \frac{1}{2}\left(\frac{\partial f}{\partial u} + \frac{\partial f}{\partial v}\right)$$

$$\frac{\partial F}{\partial y} = \frac{\partial f}{\partial u}\frac{\partial u}{\partial y} + \frac{\partial f}{\partial v}\frac{\partial v}{\partial y} = \frac{1}{2}\left(-\frac{\partial f}{\partial u} + \frac{\partial f}{\partial v}\right)$$

21. $g(u,v) = \int_{u(x)}^{v(x)} f(t)\,dt$

$$\frac{dg}{du} = \frac{dg}{du}\frac{du}{dx} + \frac{dg}{dv}\frac{dv}{dx}$$

$$= \left(\frac{d}{du}\int_{u(x)}^{v(x)} f(t)\,dt\right)\frac{du}{dx} + \frac{d}{dv}\left(\int_{u(x)}^{v(x)} f(t)\,dt\right)\frac{dv}{dx}$$

$$= \left(-\frac{d}{du}\int_{v(x)}^{u(x)} f(t)\,dt\right)\frac{du}{dx} + \frac{d}{dv}\left(\int_{u(x)}^{v(x)} f(t)\,dt\right)\frac{dv}{dx}$$

$$= f(v(x))\frac{dv}{dx} - f(u(x))\frac{du}{dx}$$

23. $\frac{df}{dx} = (x+3)(5-x-3)(1) - x(5-x)(1)$ (by Leibniz's Rule)

$= 6 - 6x = 0$ when $x = 1$. $\frac{d^2f}{dx^2} = -6 \Rightarrow x = 1$ maximizes the integral.

25. $z = f(x,y) + g(x,y) \Rightarrow 0 = \frac{dg}{dx} = \frac{\partial g}{\partial x} + \frac{\partial g}{\partial y}\frac{dy}{dx} \Rightarrow \frac{dy}{dx} = -\frac{\partial g/\partial x}{\partial g/\partial y}$

$$\frac{dz}{dx} = \frac{\partial f}{\partial x}\frac{dx}{dx} + \frac{\partial f}{\partial y}\frac{dy}{dx} + \frac{\partial g}{\partial x}\frac{dx}{dx} + \frac{\partial g}{\partial y}\frac{dy}{dx}$$

$$= \frac{\partial f}{\partial x} + \frac{\partial g}{\partial x} + \frac{dy}{dx}\left(\frac{\partial f}{\partial y} + \frac{\partial g}{\partial y}\right) = f_x + g_x - \frac{g_x}{g_y}(f_y + g_y)$$

$\therefore \quad h'(x) = f_x - \left(\frac{g_x}{g_y}\right)f_y$

If $f(x,y) = x^2 + y^2$ and $g(x,y) = x^3 + y^2 - x = 0$, then

$h(x) = x^2 - x^3 - x$ and $h'(x) = 2x - 3x^2 - 1$.

Also, $f_x = 2x$, $f_y = 2y$, $g_x = 3x^2 - 1$ and $g_y = 2y$ so

$$h'(x) = 2x - \frac{3x^2 - 1}{2y}(2y) = 2x - 3x^2 + 1$$

27. $z = f(u)$ where $u = \frac{1}{y}(x - y) = xy^{-1} - 1$

$$x\frac{\partial z}{\partial x} + y\frac{\partial z}{\partial y} = x\frac{\partial z}{\partial u}\frac{\partial u}{\partial x} + y\frac{\partial z}{\partial u}\frac{\partial u}{\partial y} = \frac{\partial z}{\partial u}[x y^{-1} + y(-xy^{-2})] = 0$$

29. $f(x,y,z) = (x-1)^2 + 2(y+1)^2 + 3(z-2)^2 - 6$ at $(2,0,1)$ in direction of $\mathbf{A} = \mathbf{i} - \mathbf{j} + 2\mathbf{k}$. $\mathbf{u} = \frac{1}{\sqrt{6}}(\mathbf{i} - \mathbf{j} + 2\mathbf{k})$

$f_x = 2(x-1)\Big|_{(2,0,1)} = 2 \quad f_y = 4(y+1)\Big|_{(2,0,1)} = 4. \quad f_z = 6(z-2)\Big|_{(2,0,1)} = -6$

$\nabla f\Big|_{(1,-1,2)} = 2\mathbf{i} + 4\mathbf{j} - 6\mathbf{k}.$

$(D_{\mathbf{u}}f)\Big|_{(1,-1,2)} = \nabla f \cdot \mathbf{u} = (2\mathbf{i} + 4\mathbf{j} - 6\mathbf{k}) \cdot \frac{1}{\sqrt{6}}(\mathbf{i} - \mathbf{j} + 2\mathbf{k}) = -\frac{14}{\sqrt{6}}$

31. $f(x,y,z) = x^2 + y^2 - 3z$ at $(1,3,5)$

$\nabla f\Big|_{(1,3,5)} = 2x\mathbf{i} + 2y\mathbf{j} - 3\mathbf{k}\Big|_{(1,3,5)} = 2\mathbf{i} + 6\mathbf{j} - 3\mathbf{k}.$

The maximum value of $(D_{\mathbf{u}}f)|_{(1,3,5)} = |\nabla f| = \sqrt{4+36+9} = 7$

33. $f(x,y,z) = xyz$ at $(1,1,1)$

$\nabla f\Big|_{(1,1,1)} = yz\mathbf{i} + xz\mathbf{j} + xy\mathbf{k}\Big|_{(1,1,1)} = \mathbf{i} + \mathbf{j} + \mathbf{k}.$

The maximum value of $(D_{\mathbf{u}}f)|_{(1,1,1)} = |\nabla f| = \sqrt{3}$.

35. There are two contributing factors to the change in density. One, $\frac{\partial \rho}{\partial t}$, represents the dependence of the density on time independent of the motion of the fluid. The second arises from the motion of the fluid and is the product of its velocity and the directional derivative.

37. $D_{\mathbf{u}}\, r(x,y,z) = |\nabla r| = \left|\frac{x}{r}\mathbf{i} + \frac{y}{r}\mathbf{j} + \frac{z}{r}\mathbf{k}\right| = 1$ if $(x,y,z) \neq (0,0,0)$, but

$\frac{\partial r}{\partial x} = \lim_{h\to 0} \frac{r(h,0,0) - r(0,0,0)}{h} = \lim_{h\to 0} \frac{|h|}{h}$ does not exist, and so the gradient can not exist.

39. $\theta = \tan^{-1}\frac{y}{x} \Rightarrow \nabla\theta = \frac{-yx^{-2}}{1+(yx^{-1})^2}\mathbf{i} + \frac{x^{-1}}{1+(yx^{-1})^2}\mathbf{j} = \frac{-y}{x^2+y^2}\mathbf{i} + \frac{x}{x^2+y^2}\mathbf{j}.$

The direction of $\nabla\theta$ is $\frac{\pi}{2} + \theta$.

$$|\nabla\theta| = \sqrt{\frac{y^2+x^2}{(x^2+y^2)^2}} = \sqrt{\frac{1}{x^2+y^2}} = \frac{1}{r}$$

41. (a) If $f(x, y) = ay - bx + C$, then $f_x = -b$, $f_y = a$ and $af_x + bf_y = -ab + ab = 0$.

If $f(x, y) = e^{ay-bx} + C$, then $f_x = -be^{ay-bx}$, $f_y = ae^{ay-bx}$, and

$af_x + bf_y = (-ab + ab)\, e^{ay-bx} = 0$.

(b) If $\nabla f = -bk(x, y)\mathbf{i} + ak(x, y)\mathbf{j}$, then $f_x = -bk(x, y)$, $f_y = ak(x, y)$ and

$af_x + bf_y = (-ab + ab)k(x, y) = 0$.

43. Let $f(x, y, z) = x^2 + y^2 - 3z$. Then $\nabla f = 2x\mathbf{i} + 2y\mathbf{j} - 3\mathbf{k}\Big|_{(1,3,10/3)} =$
$2\mathbf{i} + 6\mathbf{j} - 3\mathbf{k}$. Then $\mathbf{u} = \frac{2}{7}\mathbf{i} + \frac{6}{7}\mathbf{j} - \frac{3}{7}\mathbf{k}$.

45. $f(x, y, z) = xy + z - 2$. Then $\nabla f = y\mathbf{i} + x\mathbf{j} + \mathbf{k}\Big|_{(1,1,1)} = \mathbf{i} + \mathbf{j} + \mathbf{k}$.

The normal line has equation $x = 1 + t$, $y = 1 + t$, $z = 1 + t$ which passes through the origin when $t = -1$.

47. (a) Let $f(x, y, z) = \sqrt{x^2 + y^2} + (x^2 + y^2)^{3/2} - z$. Then

$$\nabla f = \frac{x}{\sqrt{x^2 + y^2}}(1 + 3x^2 + 3y^2)\mathbf{i} + \frac{y}{\sqrt{x^2 + y^2}}(1 + 3x^2 + 3y^2)\mathbf{j} - \mathbf{k}$$

(b) $$\cos\gamma = \frac{-1}{|\nabla f|} = \frac{-1}{\sqrt{1 + (1 + 3x^2 + 3y^2)^2}}$$

$$\lim_{(x,y,z)\to(0,0,0)} \cos\gamma = -\frac{1}{\sqrt{2}}$$

49. (a) See graph in answer section of book.

(b) $\nabla f = 2x\mathbf{i} - 2y\mathbf{j} + 2z\mathbf{k}\Big|_{(2,-3,3)} = 4\mathbf{i} + 6\mathbf{j} + 6\mathbf{k}$

(c) Tangent plane: $4x + 6y + 6z = 8$ or $2x + 3y + 3z = 4$

Normal line: $x = 2 + 4t$, $y = -3 + 6t$, $z = 3 + 6t$

51. Let $f(x, y, z) = (x - a)^2 + (y - b)^2 + (z - a)^2 - 1$ and $g(x, y, z) = x^2 + y^2 + z^2 - 1$

$\nabla f = 2(x - a)\mathbf{i} + 2(y - b)\mathbf{j} + 2(z - c)\mathbf{k}$ and $\nabla g = 2x\mathbf{i} + 2y\mathbf{j} + 2z\mathbf{k}$.

$\nabla f \perp \nabla g \Rightarrow \nabla f \bullet \nabla g = 0 \Rightarrow 4x(x - a) + 4y(y - b) + 4z(z - c) = 0 \Rightarrow ax + by + cz = 1$.

If $(x_0, y_0, z_0)$ is a point of intersection of the spheres, then

$x_0^2 + y_0^2 + z_0^2 = (x_0 - a)^2 + (y_0 - b)^2 + (z_0 - c)^2 \Rightarrow$

$0 = -2(ax_0 + by_0 + cz_0) + a^2 + b^2 + c^2$. $\therefore$ all points $(a, b, c)$ for which

$a^2 + b^2 + c^2 = 2$.

53. Let $f(x,y,z) = (x-a)^2 + y^2 + z^2 - 3$ and $g(x,y,z) = x^2 + (y-1)^2 + z^2 - 1$

$\nabla f = 2(x-a)\mathbf{i} + 2y\,\mathbf{j} + 2z\,\mathbf{k}$ and $\nabla g = 2x\mathbf{i} + 2(y-1)\mathbf{j} + 2z\mathbf{k}$.

$\nabla f \perp \nabla g \Rightarrow \nabla f \cdot \nabla g = 0 \Rightarrow 4x(x-a) + 4y(y-1) + 4z^2 = 0 \Rightarrow$

(1) $x^2 + y^2 + z^2 - ax - y = 0$.

We also know (2) $x^2 + y^2 + z^2 - 2y = 0$ and (3) $x^2 + y^2 + z^2 - 2xa + a^2 = 0$

Substituting (2) into (1) yields $y = ax$. Substituting this into (3) gives $a = \pm\sqrt{3}$.

55. If we express the surface $f(x,y,z)$ as $z - f(x,y) = 0$, then we see that a normal to the surface at $P_0(x_0, y_0, z_0)$ is

$$\mathbf{n} = -f_x(x_0, y_0)\mathbf{i} - f_y(x_0, y_0)\mathbf{j} + \mathbf{k}.$$

If we parametize $C_x$ by $x = t$, $y = y_0$, $z = f(t, y_0)$, then

$\frac{dC_x}{dt} = \mathbf{i} + \frac{d}{dt}f(t, y_0)\,\mathbf{k} = \mathbf{i} + f_x(x_0, y_0)\mathbf{k}$. Similarly,

$\frac{dC_y}{dt} = \mathbf{j} + f_y(x_0, y_0)\mathbf{k}$. A normal to the plane spanned by these is

$\frac{dC_x}{dt} \times \frac{dC_y}{dt} = -f_x(x_0, y_0)\mathbf{i} - f_y(x_0, y_0)\mathbf{j} + \mathbf{k}$. Hence the tangent plane is coincident with this plane.

57. $f(x(t)), y(t)) = 0 \Rightarrow 0 = \frac{df}{dt} = \frac{\partial f}{\partial x}\frac{dx}{dt} + \frac{\partial f}{\partial y}\frac{dy}{dt} = \left(\frac{\partial f}{\partial x}\mathbf{i} + \frac{\partial f}{\partial y}\mathbf{j}\right) \cdot \left(\frac{dx}{dt}\mathbf{i} + \frac{dy}{dt}\mathbf{j}\right)$

so $\nabla f$ is normal to the tangent vector.

59. $F(x,y) = f(u,v) = f(x+y, xy^2)$. $F_x = f_u u_x + f_v v_x = f_u + y^2 f_v$.

$F_{yx} = \frac{\partial}{\partial y}(f_u + y^2 f_v) = f_{uu}\,u_y + f_{vu}\,v_y + y^2(f_{uv}u_y + f_{vv}\,v_y) + 2y\,f_v$

$= f_{uu} + (y^2 + 2xy)f_{uv} + 2yf_v + 2xy^3 f_{vv}$.

61. $\frac{\partial g}{\partial \theta} = \frac{\partial f}{\partial x}\frac{\partial x}{\partial \theta} + \frac{\partial f}{\partial y}\frac{\partial y}{\partial \theta} = (-r \sin \theta)\frac{\partial f}{\partial x} + (r \cos \theta)\frac{\partial f}{\partial y}$

$$\frac{\partial^2 g}{\partial \theta^2} = (-r \sin \theta)\left(\frac{\partial^2 f}{\partial x^2}\frac{\partial x}{\partial \theta} + \frac{\partial^2 f}{\partial y\, \partial x}\frac{\partial y}{\partial \theta}\right) - (r \cos \theta)\frac{\partial f}{\partial x} +$$

$$(r \cos \theta)\left(\frac{\partial^2 f}{\partial x\, \partial y}\frac{\partial x}{\partial \theta} + \frac{\partial f}{\partial y^2}\frac{\partial y}{\partial \theta}\right) - (r \sin \theta)\frac{\partial f}{\partial y}$$

$$= r^2 - r(\sin \theta + \cos \theta) - 2r^2 \sin \theta \cos \theta \frac{\partial^2 f}{\partial x\, \partial y} = 2 \text{ at } \left(2, \frac{\pi}{2}\right).$$

63. $r = \sqrt{x^2 + y^2 + z^2} \Rightarrow \frac{\partial r}{\partial x} = \frac{x}{r}, \frac{\partial r}{\partial y} = \frac{y}{r}$ and $\frac{\partial r}{\partial z} = \frac{z}{r}$.

If $f = f(r)$, then $\frac{\partial f}{\partial x} = \frac{df}{dr}\frac{\partial r}{\partial x} = \frac{x}{r}\frac{df}{dr}$ and

$$\frac{\partial^2 f}{\partial x^2} = \frac{1}{r}\frac{df}{dr} + x\frac{\partial}{\partial x}\left(\frac{1}{r}\frac{df}{dr}\right) = \frac{1}{r}\frac{df}{dr} + x\left[\frac{d}{dr}\left(\frac{1}{r}\frac{df}{dr}\right)\frac{\partial r}{\partial x}\right]$$

$$= \frac{1}{r}\frac{df}{dr} + \frac{x^2}{r}\left[-\frac{1}{r^2}\frac{df}{dr} + \frac{1}{r}\frac{d^2 f}{dr^2}\right] = \frac{1}{r}\frac{df}{dr} + \frac{x^2}{r^3}\left[r\frac{d^2 f}{dr^2} - \frac{df}{dr}\right].$$

Similarly, $\frac{\partial^2 f}{\partial y^2} = \frac{1}{r}\frac{df}{dr} + \frac{y^2}{r^3}\left[r\frac{d^2 f}{dr^2} - \frac{df}{dr}\right]$ and $\frac{\partial^2 f}{\partial z^2} = \frac{1}{r}\frac{df}{dr} + \frac{z^2}{r^3}\left[r\frac{d^2 f}{dr^2} - \frac{df}{dr}\right]$.

Adding and using the given relation, $\frac{3}{r}\frac{df}{dr} + \frac{x^2 + y^2 + z^2}{r^3}\left[r\frac{d^2 f}{dr^2} - \frac{df}{dr}\right] = 0$

or $\frac{d^2 f}{dr^2} + \frac{2}{r}\frac{df}{dr} = 0$. To solve, let $u = \frac{df}{dr}$ so that $\frac{du}{dr} = \frac{d^2 f}{dr^2}$. Then

$\frac{du}{u} = -2\frac{dr}{r} \Rightarrow \ln u = -2 \ln r + \ln C_1 \Rightarrow u = \frac{C_1}{r^2}$. $\frac{df}{dr} = \frac{C_1}{r^2} \Rightarrow$

$f(r) = -\frac{C_1}{r} + C_2$ or $f(r) = \frac{a}{r} + b$.

65. $\sin(x+y)+\sin(y+z)=1$. We have

$$\cos(x+y)+\cos(y+z)\frac{\partial z}{\partial x}=0 \Rightarrow \frac{\partial z}{\partial x}=\frac{-\cos(x+y)}{\cos(y+z)}, \text{ and}$$

$$\cos(x+y)+\cos(y+z)\left(1+\frac{\partial z}{\partial y}\right)=0 \Rightarrow 1+\frac{\partial z}{\partial y}=\frac{-\cos(x+y)}{\cos(y+z)}.$$

$$\frac{\partial^2 z}{\partial x\,\partial y}=-\frac{\cos(y+z)(-\sin(x+y))+\cos(x+y)\left(-\sin(y+z)\frac{\partial z}{\partial x}\right)}{\cos^2(y+z)}$$

$$=\frac{\cos^2(y+z)\sin(x+y)+\cos^2(x+y)\sin(y+z)}{\cos^3(y+z)}$$

67. $w=z\tan^{-1}\frac{x}{y} \Rightarrow \frac{\partial w}{\partial x}=yz(y^2+x^2)^{-1}, \frac{\partial w}{\partial y}=-xz(y^2+x^2)^{-1}$ and $\frac{\partial w}{\partial z}=\tan^{-1}\frac{x}{y}$.

Then $\frac{\partial^2 w}{\partial x^2}=-2xyz(x^2+y^2)^{-2}, \frac{\partial^2 w}{\partial y^2}=2xyz(x^2+y^2)^{-2}$ and $\frac{\partial^2 w}{\partial z^2}=0$.

$$\therefore \frac{\partial^2 w}{\partial x^2}+\frac{\partial^2 w}{\partial y^2}+\frac{\partial^2 w}{\partial z^2}=0$$

69. $f_x=\frac{y(x^4+4x^2y^2-y^4)}{(x^2+y^2)^2}$, $(x,y)\neq(0,0)$ and 0 if $(x,y)=(0,0)$

$f_y=\frac{-x(y^4+4x^2y^2-x^4)}{(x^2+y^2)^2}$, $(x,y)\neq(0,0)$ and 0 if $(x,y)=(0,0)$

$$f_{xy}(0,0)=\lim_{k\to 0}\frac{f_x(o,k)-f_x(0,0)}{k}=-1$$

$$f_{yx}(0,0)=\lim_{h\to 0}\frac{f_y(h,0)-f_y(0,0)}{h}=1$$

# CHAPTER 17

# APPLICATIONS OF PARTIAL DERIVATIVES

## 17.1 MAXIMA, MINIMA AND SADDLE POINTS

1. $f(x,y) = x^2 + xy + y^2 + 3x - 3y + 4$

$f_x = 2x + y + 3 \quad f_y = x + 2y - 3$

$\begin{cases} 2x + y = -3 \\ x + 2y = 3 \end{cases} \Rightarrow x = -3,\ y = 3$

$f_{xx} = 2 \qquad f_{xy} = 1 \qquad f_{yy} = 2$

$f_{xx}f_{yy} - f_{xy}^2 = 4 - 1 = 3 > 0$ and $f_{xx} = 2 > 0 \Rightarrow f(-3,3) = -5$ is local minimum.

3. $f(x,y) = 5xy - 7x^2 + 3x - 6y + 2$

$f_x = 5y - 14x + 3 \qquad f_y = 5x - 6$

$\begin{cases} 5y - 14x = -3 \\ 5x - 6 = 0 \end{cases} \Rightarrow x = \frac{6}{5},\ y = \frac{69}{25}$

$f_{xx} = -14 \qquad f_{xy} = 5 \qquad f_{yy} = 0$

$f_{xx}f_{yy} - f_{xy}^2 = -25 < 0 \Rightarrow$ saddle point. $f\left(\frac{6}{5}, \frac{69}{25}\right) = -\frac{112}{25}$

5. $f(x,y) = x^2 + xy + 3x + 2y + 5$

$f_x = 2x + y + 3 \quad f_y = x + 2$

$\begin{cases} 2x + y + 3 = 0 \\ x + 2 = 0 \end{cases} \Rightarrow x = -2,\ y = 1$

$f_{xx} = 2 \qquad f_{xy} = 1 \qquad f_{yy} = 0$

$f_{xx}f_{yy} - f_{xy}^2 = -1 < 0 \Rightarrow$ saddle point. $f(-2,1) = 3$

7. $f(x,y) = 2xy - 5x^2 - 2y^2 + 4x - 4$

$f_x = 2y - 10x + 4$ $\qquad f_y = 2x - 4y$

$\begin{cases} 2y - 10x + 4 = 0 \\ 2x - 4y = 0 \end{cases} \Rightarrow x = \frac{4}{9},\ y = \frac{2}{9}$

$f_{xx} = -10 \qquad f_{xy} = 2 \qquad f_{yy} = -4$

$f_{xx}f_{yy} - f_{xy}^2 = 36 > 0,\ f_{xx} = -10 \Rightarrow f\left(\frac{4}{9}, \frac{2}{9}\right) = -\frac{28}{9}$ is local maximum.

9. $f(x,y) = x^2 + xy + y^2 + 3y + 3$

$f_x = 2x + y \qquad f_y = x + 2y + 3$

$\begin{cases} 2x + y = 0 \\ x + 2y + 3 \end{cases} \Rightarrow x = 1,\ y = -2$

$f_{xx} = 2 \qquad f_{xy} = 1 \qquad f_{yy} = 2$

$f_{xx}f_{yy} - f_{xy}^2 = 3 > 0,\ f_{xx} = 2 > 0 \Rightarrow f(1,-2) = 0$ is local minimum.

11. $f(x,y) = 2x^2 + 3xy + 4y^2 - 5x + 2y$

$f_x = 4x + 3y - 5 \qquad f_y = 3x + 8y + 2$

$\begin{cases} 4x + 3y - 5 = 0 \\ 3x + 8y + 2 \end{cases} \Rightarrow x = 2,\ y = -1$

$f_{xx} = 4 \qquad f_{xy} = 3 \qquad f_{yy} = 8$

$f_{xx}f_{yy} - f_{xy}^2 = 23 > 0,\ f_{xx} = 4 > 0 \Rightarrow f(2,-1) = -6$ is local minimum.

13. $f(x,y) = x^2 - 4xy + y^2 + 5x - 2y$

$f_x = 2x - 4y + 5 \qquad f_y = -4x + 2y - 2$

$\begin{cases} 2x - 4y + 5 = 0 \\ -4x + 2y - 2 = 0 \end{cases} \Rightarrow x = \frac{1}{6},\ y = \frac{4}{3}$

$f_{xx} = 2 \qquad f_{xy} = -4 \qquad f_{yy} = 2$

$f_{xx}f_{yy} - f_{xy}^2 = -12 < 0 \Rightarrow$ saddlepoint. $f\left(\frac{1}{6}, \frac{4}{3}\right) = -\frac{11}{12}$

15. $f(x,y) = x^2 - y^2 - 2x + 4y + 6$

$f_x = 2x - 2 \qquad f_y = -2y + 4$

$\begin{cases} 2x - 2 = 0 \\ -2y + 4 = 0 \end{cases} \Rightarrow x = 1,\ y = 2$

$f_{xx} = 2 \qquad f_{xy} = 0 \qquad f_{yy} = -2$

$f_{xx}f_{yy} - f_{xy}^2 = -4 < 0 \Rightarrow$ saddle point. $f(1,2) = 9$

17. $f(x,y) = x^2 + 2xy$

$f_x = 2x + 2y$ $\qquad f_y = 2x$

$x = 0,\ y = 0$

$f_{xx} = 2 \qquad f_{xy} = 2 \qquad f_{yy} = 0$

$f_{xx}f_{yy} - f_{xy}^2 = -4 < 0 \Rightarrow$ saddle point. $f(0,0) = 0$

19. $f(x,y) = x^2 + xy + y^2 + x - 4y + 5$

$f_x = 2x + y + 1$ $\qquad f_y = x + 2y - 4$

$\begin{cases} 2x + y + 1 = 0 \\ x + 2y - 4 = 0 \end{cases} \Rightarrow x = -2,\ y = 3$

$f_{xx} = 2 \qquad f_{xy} = 1 \qquad f_{yy} = 2$

$f_{xx}f_{yy} - f_{xy}^2 = 3 > 0,\ f_{xx} = 2 \Rightarrow f(-2,3) = -2$ is local minimum.

21. $f(x,y) = 3x^2 - xy + 2y^2 - 8x + 9y + 10$

$f_x = 6x - y - 8$ $\qquad f_y = -x + 4y + 9$

$\begin{cases} 6x - y - 8 = 0 \\ -x + 4y + 9 = 0 \end{cases} \Rightarrow x = 1,\ y = -2$

$f_{xx} = 6 \qquad f_{xy} = -1 \qquad f_{yy} = 4$

$f_{xx}f_{yy} - f_{xy}^2 = 23 > 0,\ f_{xx} = 6 \Rightarrow f(1,-2) = -3$ is local minimum.

23. $f(x,y) = x^3 - y^3 - 2xy + 6$

$f_x = 3x^2 - 2$ $\qquad f_y = 3y^2 - 2$

$\begin{cases} 3x^2 - 2 = 0 \\ 3y^2 - 2 = 0 \end{cases} \Rightarrow 27x^4 - 2x = 0 \Rightarrow x = 0,\ y = 0$ or $x = -\frac{2}{3},\ y = \frac{2}{3}$

$f_{xx} = 6x \qquad f_{xy} = 0 \qquad f_{yy} = 6y$

At $(0,0)$: $f_{xx}f_{yy} - f_{xy}^2 = -4 < 0 \Rightarrow$ saddlepoint; $f(0,0) = 6$

At $\left(-\frac{2}{3}, \frac{2}{3}\right)$: $f_{xx}f_{yy} - f_{xy}^2\ 12 > 0, f_{xx} = -4 < 0 \Rightarrow$
$f\left(-\frac{2}{3}, \frac{2}{3}\right) = \frac{170}{27}$ is local maximum

25. $f(x,y) = 6x^2 - 2x^3 + 3y^2 + 6xy$

$f_x = 12x - 6x^2 + 6y$ $\quad\quad f_y = 6y + 6x$

$\begin{cases} 12x - 6x^2 + 6y = 0 \\ 6y + 6x = 0 \end{cases} \Rightarrow x^2 - x = 0 \Rightarrow x = 0,\ y = 0 \text{ or } x = 1, y = -1$

$f_{xx} = 12 - 12x \quad f_{xy} = 6 \quad f_{yy} = 6$

At (0,0): $f_{xx}f_{yy} - f_{xy}^2 = 36 > 0$ and $f_{xx} > 0 \Rightarrow f(0,0) = 0$ is local minimum

At (1,−1): $f_{xx}f_{yy} - f_{xy}^2 = -36 < 0 \Rightarrow$ saddlepoint; $f(1,-1) = 1$

27. $f(x,y) = x^3 + y^3 - 3xy + 15$

$f_x = 3x^2 - 3y$ $\quad\quad f_y = 3y^2 - 3x$

$\begin{cases} 3x^2 - 3y = 0 \\ 3y^2 - 3x \end{cases} \Rightarrow x^4 - x = 0 \Rightarrow x = 0,\ y = 0 \text{ or } x = 1, y = 1$

$f_{xx} = 6x \quad f_{xy} = -3 \quad f_{yy} = 6y$

At (0,0): $f_{xx}f_{yy} - f_{xy}^2 = -9 < 0 \Rightarrow$ saddlepoint; $f(0,0) = 15$

At (1,1): $f_{xx}f_{yy} - f_{xy}^2 = 25 > 0, f_{xx} = 6 > 0 \Rightarrow f(1,1) = 14$ is local minimum

29. $f(x,y) = 4xy - x^4 - y^4$

$f_x = 4y - 4x^3$ $\quad\quad f_y = 4x - 4y^3$

$\begin{cases} 4y - 4x^3 = 0 \\ 4x - 4y^3 \end{cases} \Rightarrow x - x^9 = 0 \Rightarrow x = 0,\ y = 0 \text{ or } x = 1, y = 1 \text{ or } x = -1, y = 1$

$f_{xx} = -12x^2 \quad f_{xy} = 4 \quad f_{yy} = -12y^2$

At (0,0): $f_{xx}f_{yy} - f_{xy}^2 = -16 < 0 \Rightarrow$ saddlepoint; $f(0,0) = 0$

At (1,1): $f_{xx}f_{yy} - f_{xy}^2 > 0, f_{xx} < 0 \Rightarrow f(1,1) = 2$ is local maximum

At (−1,−1): $f_{xx}f_{yy} - f_{xy}^2 > 0, f_{xx} < 0 \Rightarrow f(-1,1) = 2$ is a local maximum.

31. $f(x, y) = 2x^2 - 4x + y^2 - 4y + 1$ on region bounded by $x = 0, y = 2, y = 2x$

I: $x = 0,\ 0 \le y \le 2$

$h(y) = f(0, y) = y^2 - 4y + 1 \Rightarrow h'(y) = 2y - 4 = 0$ if $y = 2$

$h(2) = -3$ is minimum, $h(0) = 1$ is maximum

II: $y = 2,\ 0 \le x \le 1$

$h(x) = f(x, 2) = 2x^2 - 4x - 3 \Rightarrow h'(x) = 4x - 4 = 0$ if $x = 1$

$h(1) = -5$ is minimum and $h(0) = -3$ is maximum

III: $y = 2x$

$h(x) = f(x, 2x) = 6x^2 - 12x + 1 \Rightarrow h' = 12x - 12 = 0$ if $x = 1$

$h(1) = -5$

IV: On the interior

$f_x = 4x - 4 \Rightarrow x = 1$ $\qquad$ $f_y = 2y - 4 \Rightarrow y = 2$

$\therefore$ Absolute minimum of $-5$ at $(1, 2)$; absolute maximum of $1$ at $(0, 0)$.

33. $f(x, y) = x^2 + y^2$ on region bounded by $x = 0, y = 0, y + 2x = 2$

I: $x = 0,\ 0 \le y \le 2$

$h(y) = f(0, y) = y^2$

$h(2) = 4$ is maximum, $h(0) = 0$ is minimum

II: $y = 0,\ 0 \le x \le 1$

$h(x) = f(x, 0) = x^2$

$h(0) = 0$ is minimum, $h(1) = 1$ is maximum

III: $y = -2x + 2$

$h(x) = f(x, -2x + 2) = x^2 - (2 - 2x)^2 \Rightarrow h' = 2x - 4(2 - 2x) = 0$ if $x = 1$

$h(1) = 1$

IV: On the interior

$f_x = 2x \Rightarrow x = 0$ $\qquad$ $f_y = 2y \Rightarrow y = 0$

$\therefore$ Absolute minimum of $0$ at $(0, 0)$; absolute maximum of $4$ at $(0, 2)$.

35. $T(x,y) = x^2 + xy + y^2 - 6x + 2$ on region bounded by $0 \le x \le 5, -3 \le y \le 0$

I: $x = 5,\ -3 \le y \le 0$

$$T(5,y) = h(y) = y^2 + 5y - 3;\ T' = 2y + 5 = 0 \text{ if } y = -\frac{5}{2}$$

$$h'' = 2 \Rightarrow h\left(-\frac{5}{2}\right) = -\frac{37}{4} \text{ a minimum; } h(-3) = -9;\ h(0) = -3 \text{ is maximum}$$

II: $y = 0,\ 0 \le x \le 5$

$$h(x) = T(x,0) = x^2 - 6x + 2 = (x-3)^2 - 7$$

$h(0) = 2$ is maximum, $h(3) = -7$ is miniimum

III: $x = 0,\ -3 \le y \le 0$

$$h(y) = T(0,y) = y^2 + 2$$

$h(0) = 2$ is minimum; $h(-3) = 11$ is maximum.

IV: $y = -3,\ 0 \le x \le 5$

$$h(x) = x^2 - 9x + 11 = \left(x - \frac{9}{2}\right)^2 - \frac{37}{4}$$

$$h\left(-\frac{9}{2}\right) = -\frac{37}{4} \text{ is minimum}$$

V: On the interior

$f_x = 2x + y - 6$ and $f_y = x + 2y \Rightarrow x = 4$ and $y = -2$

$f_{xx} = 2,\ f_{yy} = 2,\ f_{xy} = 1.\ f_{xx}\, f_{yy} - f_{xy}^2 = 3 > 0 \Rightarrow$ local minimum $= -10$

$\therefore$ Absolute minimum of $-10$ at $(4,-2)$; absolute maximum of 11 at $(0,-3)$.

37. $f(x,y) = (x^2 - 4x)\cos y$ on region bounded by $1 \le x \le 3, -\frac{\pi}{4} \le y \le \frac{\pi}{4}$.

$f(x,y) = (x^2 - 4x)\cos y = \left[(x-2)^2 - 4\right]\cos y$. For $-\frac{\pi}{4} \le y \le \frac{\pi}{4},\ \frac{1}{\sqrt{2}} \le y \le 1$.

For $1 \le x \le 3,\ -4 \le [(x-2)^2 - 4] \le -3$. $\therefore$ The minimum value of $f(x,y) = -4$ which occurs at $(2,0)$ and the maximum value is $-\frac{3\sqrt{2}}{2}$ which occurs at the corners $\left(1, \pm\frac{\pi}{4}\right)$ and $\left(3, \pm\frac{\pi}{4}\right)$.

39. $T(x,y) = x^2 + 2y^2 - x$ on $x^2 + y^2 \le 1$. Rewrite T as

$T(x,y) = \left(x - \frac{1}{2}\right)^2 + 2y^2 - \frac{1}{4}$ to see that the absolute minimum of $-\frac{1}{4}$ occurs at $\left(\frac{1}{2}, 0\right)$. On the boundary, $T(x, 1 - x^2) = 2 - x - x^2$.

$T' = -1 - 2x = 0$ if $x = -\frac{1}{2} \Rightarrow y = \pm\frac{\sqrt{3}}{2}$. $T\left(-\frac{1}{2}, \pm\frac{\sqrt{3}}{2}\right) = \frac{9}{4}$ is absolute maximum.

41. $f(x,y) = -x^2 - y^2 + 2x + 2y + 2 = 4 - (x-1)^2 - (y-1)^2$ has as absolute maximum value of 4 at $(1,1)$. On the boundary $x = 0$, $y \ge 0$, $f(0,y) = -(y-1)^2 + 3$ which has no minimum. Hence $f$ has no minimum value on this unbounded region.

43. The low point occurs at the origin but $\frac{\partial z}{\partial x}$ and $\frac{\partial z}{\partial y}$ do not exist there.

The high points occur at the corners $(\pm 1, \pm 1, \sqrt{2})$ but $\frac{\partial z}{\partial x}$ and $\frac{\partial z}{\partial y}$ are nonzero at these points.

45. (a) $f(x,y) = xy$ on $x = 2\cos t$, $y = 2\sin t$. $f(t) = 2\sin 2t$ and

$f'(t) = 4\cos 2t = 0$ if $t = \frac{\pi}{4}, \frac{3\pi}{4}, \frac{5\pi}{4}$ or $\frac{7\pi}{4}$.

(i) On $0 \le t \le \frac{\pi}{2}$, we have $f(0) = f\left(\frac{\pi}{2}\right) = 0$ is minimum and $f\left(\frac{\pi}{4}\right) = 2$ is maximum.

(ii) On $0 \le t \le \pi$, the minimum becomes $f\left(\frac{3\pi}{4}\right) = -2$.

(iii) On $0 \le t \le 2\pi$, there are no changes.

(b) $f(x, y) = x + y$ on $x = 2\cos t$, $y = 2\sin t$. $f(t) = 2\sin t + 2\cos t$ and

$f'(t) = -2\sin t + 2\cos t = 0$ if $t = \frac{\pi}{4}$ or $\frac{5\pi}{4}$.

(i) On $0 \le t \le \frac{\pi}{2}$, we have $f(0) = f\left(\frac{\pi}{2}\right) = 2$ is minimum

and $f\left(\frac{\pi}{4}\right) = 2\sqrt{2}$ is maximum.

(ii) On $0 \le t \le \pi$, the minimum becomes $f(\pi) = -2$.

(iii) On $0 \le t \le 2\pi$, the minimum becomes $f\left(\frac{5\pi}{4}\right) = -2\sqrt{2}$.

(c) $f(x, y) = 2x^2 + y^2$ on $x = 2\cos t$, $y = 2\sin t$. $f(t) = 8\cos^2 t + 4\sin^2 t$ and

$f'(t) = -8\sin t\cos t = 0$ if $t = 0, \frac{\pi}{2}, \pi$ or $\frac{3\pi}{2}$.

(i) On $0 \le t \le \frac{\pi}{2}$, we have $f(0) = 8$ is maximum

and $f\left(\frac{\pi}{2}\right) = 4$ is minimum.

(ii) On $0 \le t \le \pi$, there is no change.

(iii) On $0 \le t \le 2\pi$, there is no change.

47. (a) $f(x, y) = x^2 + 3y^2$ on $x = 3\cos t$, $y = 2\sin t$. $f(t) = 9\cos^2 t + 12\sin^2 t$ and

$f'(t) = 6\sin t\cos t = 0$ if $t = 0, \frac{\pi}{2}, \pi$ or $\frac{3\pi}{2}$.

(i) On $0 \le t \le \frac{\pi}{2}$, we have $f(0) = 9$ is minimum

and $f\left(\frac{\pi}{2}\right) = 12$ is maximum.

(ii) On $0 \le t \le \pi$, there is no change.

(iii) On $0 \le t \le 2\pi$, there is no change.

(b) $f(x,y) = 2x + 3y$ on $x = 3\cos t$, $y = 2\sin t$. $f(t) = 6\cos t + 6\sin t$.

$f'(t) = -6\sin t + 6\cos t = 0$ if $t = \frac{\pi}{4}$ or $\frac{5\pi}{4}$.

(i) On $0 \le t \le \frac{\pi}{2}$, we have $f(0) = 0$ is minimum

and $f\left(\frac{\pi}{4}\right) = 6\sqrt{2}$ is maximum.

(ii) On $0 \le t \le \pi$, $f(\pi) = -6$ is minimum.

(iii) On $0 \le t \le 2\pi$, $f\left(\frac{5\pi}{4}\right) = -6\sqrt{2}$ is minimum.

## 17.2 LINEAR APPROXIMATIONS AND INCREMENT ESTIMATES

1. $f(x,y) = x^2 + y^2 + 1$ $\quad f_x = 2x \quad f_y = 2y$

(a) $L(x,y) = f(0,0) + f_x(0,0)x + f_y(0,0)y = 1$

(b) $L(x,y) = f(1,1) + f_x(1,1)(x-1) + f_y(1,1)(y-1) = 3 + 2(x-1) + 2(y-1)$

$= 2x + 2y - 1$

3. $f(x,y) = e^x \cos y$ $\quad f_x = e^x \cos y \quad f_y = -e^x \sin y$

(a) $L(x,y) = f(0,0) + f_x(0,0)x + f_y(0,0)y = 1 + x$

(b) $L(x,y) = f\left(0,\frac{\pi}{2}\right) + f_x\left(0,\frac{\pi}{2}\right)x + f_y\left(0,\frac{\pi}{2}\right)\left(y - \frac{\pi}{2}\right)$

$= -\left(y - \frac{\pi}{2}\right)$

5. $f(x,y) = 3x - 4y + 5$ $\quad f_x = 3 \quad f_y = -4$

(a) $L(x,y) = f(0,0) + f_x(0,0)x + f_y(0,0)y = 5 + 3x - 4y$

(b) $L(x,y) = f(1,1) + f_x(1,1)(x-1) + f_y(1,1)(y-1)$

$= 4 + 3(x-1) - 4(y-1) = 3x - 4y + 5$

7. $f(x,y) = x^2 - 3xy + 5$ $\quad f_x = 2x - 3y; \quad f_y = -3x$

$L(x,y) = f(2,1) + f_x(2,1)x + f_y(2,1)y = x - 6y + 7$

$f_{xx} = 2;\ f_{xy} = -3;\ f_{yy} = -3$. Take $M = 3$. Then

$|E| \le \frac{1}{2}(3)(0.1 + 0.1)^2 = 0.06$

9. $f(x,y) = 1 + y + x\cos y \qquad f_x = \cos y\,;\ f_y = 1 - x\sin y$

$L(x,y) = f(0,0) + f_x(0,0)\,x + f_y(0,0)\,y = 1 + x + y$

$f_{xx} = -\sin y;\ f_{yy} = -x\cos y;\ f_{xy} = -\sin y$. If $|x| \le 0.2$, $|y| \le 0.2$,

then $|-x\cos y| \le (0.2)(1) = 0.2$ so $M = 1$.

$|E| \le \frac{1}{2}(1)(0.2 + 0.2)^2 = 0.08$

11. $f(x,y) = e^x\cos y \qquad f_x = e^x\cos y;\ f_y = -e^x\sin y$

$L(x,y) = f(0,0) + f_x(0,0)\,x + f_y(0,0)\,y = 1 + x$

$f_{xx} = e^x\cos y;\ f_{yy} = -e^x\cos y;\ f_{xy} = -e^x\sin y$. If $|x| \le 0.1$, $|y| \le 0.1$,

$|E| \le \frac{1}{2}(1.11)\,(0.1 + 0.1)^2 = 0.0222$

13. $dV = V_r\,dr + V_h\,dh = 2\pi rh\,dr + \pi r^2\,dh$. At $(r_0, h_0)$ to be equally sensitive to small changes in r and h, we need $2r_0 h_0 = r_0^2 \Rightarrow r_0 = 2h_0$.

15. (a) $f(x,y) = x^2(y+1) \Rightarrow f_x = 2xy + 2x$ and $f_y = x^2$. At $(1,0)$,

$df = 2dx + dy$ is more sensitive to changes in x.

(b) $2dx = -\,dy$ if $\frac{dx}{dy} = -\frac{1}{2}$.

17. $dV = 2\pi rh\,dr + \pi r^2\,dh \Rightarrow \frac{dV}{V} = \frac{2dr}{r} + \frac{dh}{h}$.

$\therefore \left|\frac{dV}{V}\right| \le \left|\frac{2dr}{r}\right| + \left|\frac{dh}{h}\right| = 2(0.01) + 0.01 = 0.03$. V can be calculated to within 3%.

19. $dV = 2\pi rh\,dr + \pi r^2\,dh = 12\pi\,dr + 4\pi\,dh = 16\pi\,dr$.

$\therefore |16\pi\,dr| \le 0.01$ if $|dr| < \frac{0.1}{16\pi} \approx 0.002$ m

21. $\frac{1}{R} = \frac{1}{x} + \frac{1}{y} \Rightarrow R = \frac{xy}{x+y}$ and $dR = \left(\frac{y}{x+y}\right)^2 dx + \left(\frac{x}{x+y}\right)^2 dy$

If $x = 20$, $y = 25$ and $dx = dy = 0.1$, then $dR = \frac{1}{90}$, $R = \frac{100}{9}$, and

$\frac{dR}{R} = 0.1\,\%$.

23. $f(x,y,z) = xy + yz + xz \Rightarrow f_x = y + z,\ f_y = x + z$ and $f_z = y + x$

(a) At (1,1,1): $L(x,y,z) = 3 + 2(x-1) + 2(y-1) + 2(z-1) = 2x + 2y + 2z - 3$

(b) At (1,0,0): $L(x,y,z) = y + z$

(c) At (0,0,0: $L(x,y,z) = 0$

25. $f(x,y,z) = \sqrt{x^2 + y^2 + z^2}$

$f_x = \dfrac{x}{\sqrt{x^2+y^2+z^2}} \qquad f_y = \dfrac{y}{\sqrt{x^2+y^2+z^2}} \qquad f_z = \dfrac{z}{\sqrt{x^2+y^2+z^2}}$

(a) At (1,0,0): $L(x,y,z) = 1 + (x-1) = x$

(b) At (1,1,0): $L(,y,z) = \sqrt{2} + \frac{1}{\sqrt{2}}(x-1) + \frac{1}{\sqrt{2}}(y-1) = \frac{1}{\sqrt{2}}(x+y)$

(c) At (1,2,2): $L(x,y,z) = 3 + \frac{1}{3}(x-1) + \frac{2}{3}(y-2) + \frac{2}{3}(z-2) = \frac{1}{3}(x + 2y + 2z)$

27. $f(x,y,z) = e^x + \cos(y+z)$

$f_x = e^x \qquad f_y = -\sin(y+z) \qquad f_z = -\sin(y+z)$

(a) At (0,0,0): $L(x,y,z) = 2 + x$

(b) At $\left(0, \frac{\pi}{2}, 0\right)$: $L(x,y,z) = 1 + x - \left(y - \frac{\pi}{2}\right) - z$

(c) At $\left(0, \frac{\pi}{4}, \frac{\pi}{4}\right)$: $L(x,y,z) = 1 + x - \left(y - \frac{\pi}{4}\right) - \left(z - \frac{\pi}{4}\right)$

29. $f(x,y,z) = xz - 3yz + 2$ at $P_0(1,1,2)$

$f_x = z \qquad f_y = -3z \qquad f_z = x - 3y$

$L(x,y,z) = -2 + 2(x-1) - 6(y-1) - 2(z-2) = 2x - 6y - 2z + 6$

$f_{xx} = 0 \quad f_{yy} = 0 \quad f_{zz} = 0 \quad f_{xy} = 0 \quad f_{xz} = 0 \quad f_{yz} = -3$

$|E| \le \frac{1}{2}(3)(0.01 + 0.01 + 0.02)^2 = 0.0024$

31. $f(x,y,z) = xy + 2yz - 3xz$ at $P_0(1,1,0)$

$f_x = y - 3z \qquad f_y = x + 2z \qquad f_z = 2y - 3x$

$L(x,y,z) = 1 + (x-1) + (y-1) - z = x + y - z + 1$

$f_{xx} = 0 \quad f_{yy} = 0 \quad f_{zz} = 0 \quad f_{xy} = 1 \quad f_{xz} = -3 \quad f_{yz} = 2$

$|E| \le \frac{1}{2}(3)(0.01 + 0.01 + 0.01)^2 = 0.00135$

33. (a) $S = C\frac{Px^4}{wh^3} \Rightarrow dS = C\left(\frac{4Px^3}{wh^3}dx + \frac{x^4}{wh^3}dP - \frac{3Px^4}{wh^4}dh - \frac{Px^4}{w^2h^3}dw\right)$

$$= \frac{Px^4}{wh^3}\left(\frac{4}{x}dx + \frac{1}{P}dP - \frac{3}{h}dh - \frac{1}{w}dw\right) = S_0\left(\frac{4}{x}dx + \frac{1}{P}dP - \frac{3}{h}dh - \frac{1}{w}dw\right)$$

$$= S_0\left(dx + \frac{dP}{100} - 30dh - 5\,dw\right)$$

(b) More sensitive to a change in height

35. $P = abc \Rightarrow dP = (ab)\,dc + (ac)db + (bc)\,da$

$$\frac{dP}{P} = \frac{dc}{c} + \frac{db}{b} + \frac{da}{a} \Rightarrow \left|\frac{dP}{P}\right| = 0.02 + 0.02 + 0.02 = 0.06 = 6\%$$

37. $K = \frac{1}{2}ab\sin C \Rightarrow dK = \frac{1}{2}[(ab\cos C)\,dC + (a\sin C)\,db + (b\sin C)\,da]$

$$= \frac{1}{2}\left[(150)(200)\left(\frac{1}{2}\right)\left(\frac{\pi}{90}\right) + (150)\left(\frac{\sqrt{3}}{2}\right)\left(\frac{1}{2}\right) + (200)\left(\frac{\sqrt{3}}{2}\right)\left(\frac{1}{2}\right)\right] = 337.58$$

$K = \frac{1}{2}(150)(200)\left(\frac{\sqrt{3}}{2}\right) = 12{,}990.4$. The error is 2%.

39. (a) $Q = \sqrt{\frac{2KM}{h}} \Rightarrow dQ = \sqrt{2KM}\left(-\frac{1}{2}h^{-3/2}\,dh\right) + \sqrt{\frac{2M}{h}}\left(\frac{1}{2}K^{-1/2}\,dk\right) + \sqrt{\frac{2K}{h}}\left(\frac{1}{2}M^{-1/2}\,dM\right)$

If $k = 2$, $M = 20$ and $h = 0.05$, then $dQ = -400\,dh + 10\,dK + dM$

(b) More sensitive to a change in height.

## 17.3 LAGRANGE MULTIPLIERS

1. $f(x, y) = xy$ on $x^2 + 2y^2 = 1$. We have $y = 2\lambda x$ and $x = 4\lambda y$ so

$x = 8\lambda^2 x$ if $x = 0$ or $\lambda = \pm\frac{1}{2\sqrt{2}} \Rightarrow y = \pm\frac{1}{\sqrt{2}}x$. Then $x^2 + 2\left(\pm\frac{1}{\sqrt{2}}x\right)^2 = 1$

$\Rightarrow x = \pm\frac{1}{\sqrt{2}}$ and $y = \pm\frac{1}{2}$. Then $f\left(\pm\frac{1}{\sqrt{2}}, \pm\frac{1}{2}\right) = \frac{1}{2\sqrt{2}}$ is maximum and

$f\left(\pm\frac{1}{\sqrt{2}}, \mp\frac{1}{2}\right) = -\frac{1}{2\sqrt{2}}$ is the minimum.

3. $f(x,y) = 49 - x^2 - y^2$ on $x + 3y = 10$. We have $-2x = \lambda$ and $-2y = 3\lambda \Rightarrow$

$\lambda = 2$. Then $x = -1$ and $y = -3 \Rightarrow f(-1,-3) = 39$ is maximum.

5. $f(x,y) = x^2y$ on $x + y = 3$. We have $2xy = \lambda$ and $x^2 = \lambda$ so $2xy = x^2$ if $x(x - 2y) = 0$ or if $x = 0$ or $x = 2y$. If $x = 0$, $y = 3$ and and $f(0,3) = 0$ is minimum. If $x = 2y$, then $3y = 3$ or $y = 1 \Rightarrow$ $x = 2$ and $f(2,1) = 4$ is maximum.

7. (a) $f(x,y) = x + y$ on $g(x,y) = xy - 16$. We have $1 = \lambda y$ and $1 = \lambda x$ so $\frac{1}{\lambda^2} - 16 = 0$ if $\lambda = \pm\frac{1}{4}$. $f(4,4) = 8$ is local maximum and $f(-4,-4) = -8$ is is local minimum.

(b) $f(x,y) = xy$ on $g(x,y) = x + y - 16$. We have $x = \lambda$ and $y = \lambda \Rightarrow 2\lambda - 16 = 0$ or $\lambda = 8$. $f(8,8) = 64$ is maximum. Comment: the curves $xy = 64$ and $x + y = 16$ are tangent at $(8,8)$.

9. $V(r,h) = \pi r^2 h - 16\pi$ and $S(r,h) = 2\pi r^2 + 2\pi rh$. We have $4\pi r + 2\pi h = 2\lambda\, \pi rh$ and $2\pi r = \lambda\, \pi r^2$. Then $r = 0$ or $r = \frac{2}{\lambda}$. Ignoring $r = 0$, we find that $h = 2r$. Then $2r^3 = 16 \Rightarrow r = 2$ and $h = 4$.

11. $T(x,y) = 4x^2 - 4xy + y^2$ and $g(x,y) = x^2 + y^2 - 25$. We have $8x - 4y = 2\lambda x$ and $-4x + 2y = 2\lambda y \Rightarrow \lambda x + 2\lambda y = 0 \Rightarrow \lambda = 0$ or $x = -2y$. If $\lambda = 0$, then $y = 2x$ and $x = \pm\sqrt{5}$, $y = \pm 2\sqrt{5}$. $T(\pm\sqrt{5}, \pm 2\sqrt{5}) = 0$ which is the lowest temperature. If $x = -2y$, then $y = \pm\sqrt{5}$ and $x = \pm 2\sqrt{5}$. $T(\pm 2\sqrt{5}, \pm\sqrt{5}) = 125$ which is the highest.

13. $f(x,y) = x^2 + y^2$ and $g(x,y) = x^2 - 2x + y^2 - 4y$. We have $2x = 2\lambda y$ and $2x - 2 = \lambda(2y - 4) \Rightarrow \lambda x + 2\lambda y = 0 \Rightarrow x = \lambda y \Rightarrow y = 2x$. Substituting into g, $5x^2 - 10x = 0 \Rightarrow x = 0$ or $2$.
$f(0,0) = 0$ is the minimum and $f(0,4) = 20$ is the maximum.

15. $f(x,y,z) = (x-1)^2 + (y-1)^2 + (z-1)^2$ and $g(x,y,z) = x + 2y + 3z - 13$. We have $2(x-1) = \lambda,\ 2(y-1) = 2\lambda$ and $2(z-1) = 3\lambda \Rightarrow$

$x = \dfrac{\lambda}{2} + 1,\ y = \lambda + 1$ and $z = \dfrac{3\lambda}{2} + 1$. Substituting into g,

we find $7\lambda + 6 = 13$ or $\lambda = 1 \Rightarrow x = \dfrac{3}{2},\ y = 2$ and $z = \dfrac{5}{2}$.

17. $f(x,y,z) = x^2 + y^2 + z^2$ and $g(x,y,z) = x^2 + y^2 - z^2 - 1$. We have

$2x = 2\lambda x,\ 2y = 2\lambda y$ and $2z = -2\lambda z$. The possibilities are:

$\lambda = 0 \Rightarrow x = y = z = 0$ which is impossible since (0,0,0) is not on g.
$\lambda = -1 \Rightarrow 1 = -z^2$ which is impossible.
$\lambda = 1 \Rightarrow z = 0$ and the points lie on $x^2 + y^2 = 1$ with minimum distance = 1.

19. $f(x,y,z) = x^2 + y^2 + z^2$ and $g(x,y,z) = z^2 - xy - 4$. We have

$2x = -\lambda y,\ 2y = -\lambda x$, and $z = \lambda z \Rightarrow x = 0$ or $\lambda = \pm 2$.
If $x = 0$ then $y = 0$ and $z = \pm 2$ which are 2 units from origin.
If $\lambda = 2$, then $x = \pm 2$ and we have the points $(2,-2,0)$ and $(-2,2,0)$ which are $2\sqrt{2}$ units from the origin. $\lambda = -2$ is impossible since $x^2 \neq -4$. The closes points are $(0,0,\pm 2)$.

21. $T(x,y,z) = 400\,xyz^2$ on $g(x,y,z) = x^2 + y^2 + z^2 - 1$. We have $400yz^2 = 2\lambda x,\ 400xz^2 = 2\lambda y$ and $800xyz = 2\lambda z$. Then $200xyz^2 = \lambda x^2$ and $200xyz^2 = \lambda y^2 \Rightarrow x^2 = y^2$. Similarly, $z^2 = 2y^2$. Substituting into g, $y = \pm\dfrac{1}{2} \Rightarrow x = \pm\dfrac{1}{2}$ and $z = \pm\dfrac{1}{\sqrt{2}}$.

There are eight critical points, one in each octant, at which the temperature is $50^\circ$.

23. $p(x,y,z) = xyz$ subject to $g(x,y,z) = x + y + z^2 - 16$. We have $yz = \lambda,\ xz = \lambda$ and $xy = 2z\lambda \Rightarrow xyz = \lambda x = \lambda y = 2\lambda z^2 \Rightarrow x = y$ and $z^2 = \dfrac{x}{2}$. Substituting into g, $x = \dfrac{32}{5},\ y = \dfrac{32}{5}$ and $z = \dfrac{4}{\sqrt{5}}$ for a

product $p = \dfrac{4096\sqrt{5}}{125}$.

25. $f(x,y) = x^2 + 3y^2 + 2y$ on $x^2 + y^2 \le 1$. On the boundary, we have $2x = 2\lambda x$ and $6y = 2\lambda y \Rightarrow \lambda = 1$ or $x = 0$. If $\lambda = 1$, $y = -\frac{1}{2}$ and $x = \pm\frac{\sqrt{3}}{2}$.

$f\left(\pm\frac{\sqrt{3}}{2}, -\frac{1}{2}\right) = \frac{1}{2}$. If $x = 0$, $y = \pm 1$ and $f(0,1) = 5$, $f(0,-1) = 1$.

On the interior, $f_x = 2x$ and $f_y = 6y + 2 \Rightarrow x = 0$ and $y = -\frac{1}{3}$.

$f\left(0, -\frac{1}{3}\right) = -\frac{1}{3}$ is the minimum and 5 is the maximum value.

27. $T(x,y,z) = 8x^2 + 4yz - 16z + 600$ subject to $g(x,y,z) = 4x^2 + y^2 + 4z^2 - 16$. We have $16x = 8\lambda x$, $4z = 2\lambda y$ and $4y - 16 = 8\lambda z$. From the first, $x = 0$ or $\lambda = 2$.

If $x = 0$, then $y = \frac{4}{1-\lambda^2}$ and $z = \frac{\lambda}{2}y = \frac{2\lambda}{1-\lambda^2}$. Substituting into g, $\lambda = 0$ or $\lambda = \pm\sqrt{3}$. (0,0,0) is not on g. $T(0,-2,\sqrt{3}) = 600 - 24\sqrt{3}$ and $T(0,-2,-\sqrt{3}) = 600 + 24\sqrt{3}$. If $\lambda = 2$, $y = -\frac{4}{3}$, $z = -\frac{43}{3}$, $x = \pm\frac{4}{3}$ and

$T\left(\pm\frac{4}{3}, -\frac{4}{3}, -\frac{4}{3}\right) = \frac{1928}{3}$ is the hottest temperature.

29. $U(x,y) = xy + 2x$ and $G(x,y) = 2x + y - 30$. We have $y + 2 = 2\lambda$ and $x = \lambda \Rightarrow \lambda = 8$. Then $x = 8$, $y = 14$ and $U(8,14) = 128$.

31. $w = a_1x_1 + a_2x_2 + \ldots + a_nx_n$ subject to $x_1^2 + x_2^2 + \ldots + x_n^2 = 1$.

For $i = 1,2,..n$, we have $a_i = 2\lambda x_i \Rightarrow x_i = \frac{a_i}{2\lambda}$. Then

$$1 = \sum_{i=1}^{n} x_i^2 = \sum_{i=1}^{n}\left(\frac{a_i}{2\lambda}\right)^2 \Rightarrow 4\lambda^2 = \sum_{i=1}^{n} a_i^2 \Rightarrow \lambda = \pm\frac{1}{2}\left(\sum_{i=1}^{n} a_i^2\right)^{1/2}$$

Since the $a_i$ are positive, the maximum of $\left(\sum_{i=1}^{n} a_i^2\right)^{1/2}$ occurs when

$$x_i = \frac{a_i}{\sqrt{a_1^2 + a_2^2 + \ldots + a_n^2}}, \quad i = 1,2,\ldots n.$$

33. $f(x,y,z) = x^2 + y^2 + z^2$ subject to $x + z = 6$ and $y + 2z = 12$. The planes intersect in the line $x = 6 - t$, $y = 12 - 2t$, $z = t$. $F(t) = (6-t)^2 + (12-2t)^2 + t^2$. $F'(t) = 12t - 60 = 0$ if $t = 5$. $F''(t) = 12 > 0$ so there is a minimum of $\sqrt{30}$ at the point (1,2,5).

35. (a) $w = xyz$ subject to $x + y + z = 40$ and $z = x + y$. The planes intersect in the line $x = t$, $y = 20 - t$, $z = 20$. $F(t) = 20t(20 - t) = 400t - 20t^2$. $F'(t) = 400 - 40t = 0$ if $t = 10$. $F''(t) = -40 < 0 \Rightarrow$ a maximum of 2000 occurs at the point (10, 10, 20).

(b) The line of intersection is parallel to the xy-plane, intersects the xz-plane at (0, 20, 20) and the yz-plane at (20, 20, 20). During the period it is in the first octant, the product is positive and is negative at all other times. Therefore, we must have found a maximum value.

37. The planes $z = 1 + x + y$ and $y = x$ intersect the surface only in two points. $y = x$ is not one of the problem's original constraints.

## 17.4 TAYLOR'S FORMULA, THE SECOND DERIVATIVE TEST AND ERROR ESTIMATES

1. $f(x, y) = e^x \cos y$

$f_x = e^x \cos y\Big|_{(0,0)} = 1$ $\quad f_y = -e^x \sin y\Big|_{(0,0)} = 0$

$f_{xx} = e^x \cos y\Big|_{(0,0)} = 1$ $\quad f_{yy} = -e^x \cos y\Big|_{(0\,0)} = -1$

$f_{xy} = -e^x \sin y\Big|_{(0,0)} = 0$

$\therefore\ e^x \cos y \approx 1 + x + \frac{1}{2}(x^2 - y^2) = 1 + x + \frac{1}{2}x^2 - \frac{1}{2}y^2$

3. $f(x, y) = \sin(x^2 + y^2)$

$f_x = 2x\cos(x^2 + y^2)\Big|_{(0,0)} = 0$ $\quad f_y = 2y\cos(x^2 + y^2)\Big|_{(0,0)} = 0$

$f_{xx} = 2\cos(x^2 + y^2) - 4x^2\sin(x^2 + y^2)\Big|_{(0,0)} = 2$

$f_{yy} = 2\cos(x^2 + y^2) - 4y^2\sin(x^2 + y^2)\Big|_{(0\,0)} = 2$

$f_{xy} = -4xy\sin(x^2 + y^2)\Big|_{(0,0)} = 0$

$\therefore\ \sin(x^2 + y^2) \approx x^2 + y^2$

5. $f(x,y) = \dfrac{1}{1-x-y}$ at (0,0)

$$f_x = (1-x-y)^{-2}\Big|_{(0,0)} = 1 \qquad f_y = (1-x-y)^{-2}\Big|_{(0,0)} = 1$$

$$f_{xx} = 2(1-x-y)^{-3}\Big|_{(0,0)} = 2 \qquad f_{yy} = 2(1-x-y)^{-3}\Big|_{(00)} = 2$$

$$f_{xy} = 2(1-x-y)^{-3}\Big|_{(0,0)} = 2$$

$$\therefore \quad \frac{1}{1-x-y} \approx 1 + x + y + \frac{1}{2}(2x^2 + 4xy + 2y^2) = 1 + (x+y) + (x+y)^2$$

7. $f(x,y) = \cos x \cos y$ at (0,0)

$$f_x = -\sin x \cos y\Big|_{(0,0)} = 0 \qquad f_y = -\cos x \sin y\Big|_{(0,0)} = 0$$

$$f_{xx} = -\cos x \sin y\Big|_{(0,0)} = -1 \qquad f_{yy} = -\cos x \cos y\Big|_{(00)} = -1$$

$$f_{xy} = \sin x \sin y\Big|_{(0,0)} = 0$$

$$\therefore \quad \cos x \cos y \approx 1 - \frac{1}{2}(x^2 + y^2)$$

If $|x| \le 0.1$, $|y| \le 0.1$,

$$E(x,y) \le \frac{1}{6}\left[(0.1)^3 + 3(0.1)^3 + 3(0.1)^3 + (0.1)^3\right] \le 0.0013$$

9. (a) If $F(t) = f(a+ht,\ b+kt,\ d+mt)$, then

$$F'(t) = \frac{\partial f}{\partial x}\frac{dx}{dt} + \frac{\partial f}{\partial y}\frac{dy}{dt} + \frac{\partial f}{\partial z}\frac{dz}{dt} = h\frac{\partial f}{\partial x} + k\frac{\partial f}{\partial y} + m\frac{\partial f}{\partial z}.$$

$$F''(t) = h\frac{\partial F'(t)}{\partial x} + k\frac{\partial F'(t)}{\partial y} + m\frac{\partial f'(t)}{\partial z}$$

$$= h\left[h\frac{\partial^2 f}{\partial x^2} + k\frac{\partial^2 f}{\partial x\,\partial y} + m\frac{\partial^2 f}{\partial x\,\partial z}\right] + k\left[h\frac{\partial^2 f}{\partial y\,\partial x} + k\frac{\partial^2 f}{\partial y^2} + m\frac{\partial^2 f}{\partial y\,\partial z}\right]$$

$$+ m\left[h\frac{\partial^2 f}{\partial z\,\partial x} + k\frac{\partial^2 f}{\partial z\,\partial y} + m\frac{\partial^2 f}{\partial z^2}\right]$$

$$= h^2\frac{\partial^2 f}{\partial x^2} + m^2\frac{\partial^2 f}{\partial z^2} + k^2\frac{\partial^2 f}{\partial y^2} + 2hk\frac{\partial^2 f}{\partial x\,\partial y} + 2\,km\frac{\partial^2 f}{\partial z\,\partial y} + 2hm\frac{\partial^2 f}{\partial x\,\partial z}.$$

Now $F(t) = F(t_0) + F'(t_0)\,t + \frac{1}{2}F''(c)\,t^2$, $0 \le c \le t_0$, or

$$f(a+h,\ b+k,\ d+m) = fa,b,d) + hf_x(a,b,d) + kf_y(a,b,d) + mf_z(a,b,d) +$$
$$\frac{1}{2}(h^2 f_{xx} + k^2 f_{yy} + m^2 f_{zz} + 2hkf_{xy} + 2kmf_{yz} + 2hmf_{xz})\Big]_{(a+ch,\ b+ck,\ d+cm)}$$

(b) If all the second partials are bounded by B in absolute value,

then $|R| \le \frac{1}{2}B(|h^2| + |k^2| + |m^2| + 2|h||k| + 2|h||m| + 2|k|m|)$

$$= \frac{1}{2}B\left[(|h^2| + 2|h||k| + |k^2|) + 2(|h| + |k|)|m| + |m^2|\right]$$

$$= \frac{1}{2}B\left[(|h| + |k|)^2 + 2(|h| + |k|)|m| + |m^2|\right]$$

$$= \frac{1}{2}B(|h| + |k| + |m|)^2$$

## 17.M MISCELLANEOUS

1. $f(x,y) = x^2 + xy + y^2 - 3x + 3y$, $x \ge 0$, $y \ge 0$, $x + y = 4$

I. $0 \le x \le 4$, $y = 0$: $f(x,0) = g(x) = x^2 - 3x$.

$g'(x) = 2x - 3 = 0$ if $x = \frac{3}{2}$. $g\left(\frac{3}{2}\right) = -\frac{9}{4}$. $g(0) = 0$, $g(4) = 4$

II. $0 \le y \le 4$, $x = 0$: $f(0,y) = g(y) = y^2 + 3y$

$g'(y) = 2y + 3 = 0$ if $y = -\frac{3}{2}$ which is not in domain.

$g(4) = 28$.

III. $x + y = 4$: $f(x, 4-x) = g(x) = x^2 - 10x + 28$. $g'(x) = 2x - 10 = 0$ if $x = 5$

which is not in domain.

IV. Interior: $f_x = 2x + y - 3$ and $f_y = 2y + x + 3$. Solving, we find

$x = 3$ and $y = -3$, which is not in the domain.

∴ Absolute maximum = 28 and absolute minimun = $-\frac{9}{4}$.

3. $f(x,y) = y^2 - xy - 3y + 2x$

I. $y = 2$, $-2 \le x \le 2$: $f(x,2) = -2$

II. $y = -2$, $-2 \le x \le 2$: $f(x,-2) = g(x) = 4x + 10$.

$g'(x) = 4 \ne 0$; $g(2) = 18$; $g(-2) = 2$

III. $x = 2$, $-2 \le y \le 2$: $f(2,y) = g(y) = y^2 - 5y + 4$. $g'(x) = 2y - 5 = 0$

$x = \frac{5}{2}$, which is not in domain.

IV. $x = -2$, $-2 \le y \le 2$: $f(-2,y) = g(y) = y^2 - y - 4$. $g'(y) = 2y - 1 = 0$

if $y = \frac{1}{2}$. $g\left(\frac{1}{2}\right) = -\frac{17}{4}$

Interior: $f_x = -y + 2$ and $f_y = 2y - x - 3$. Solving, we find

$x = -1$ and $y = -2$. $f(-1,-2) = 6$

∴ Absolute maximum = 18 and absolute minimun = $-\frac{17}{4}$.

5. $f(x,y) = x^2 - y^2 - 2x + 4y$

I. $x = 2,\ 0 \le y \le 4$: $f(2,y) = g(y) = -y^2 + 4y$

$g'(y) = -2y + 4 = 0$ if $y = 2$. $g(2) = 4$

II. $y = 0,\ -2 \le x \le 2$: $f(x,0) = g(x) = x^2 - 2x$.

$g'(x) = 2x - 2 = 0$ if $x = 1$; $g(2) = 0$; $g(-2) = 8$; $g(1) = -1$

III. $y = x + 2$: $f(x, x+2) = g(x) = -2x + 4$. $g'(x) = -2 \ne 0$

Interior: $f_x = 2x - 2$ and $f_y = -y^2 + 4y$. Solving, we find

$x = 1$ and $y = 0$ or $4$. $f(1,0) = -1$ and $(1,4)$ not in region.

$\therefore$ Absolute maximum $= 8$ and absolute minimun $= -1$.

7. $f(x,y) = x^3 + y^3 + 3x^2 - 3y^2$

I. $x = 1,\ -1 \le y \le 1$: $f(1,y) = g(y) = y^3 - 3y^2 + 4$

$g'(y) = 3y^2 - 6y = 0$ if $y = 2, 0$. $g(0) = 4$, $g(1) = 2$, $g(-1) = 0$

II. $x = -1,\ -1 \le y \le 1$: $f(-1,y) = g(y) = y^3 - 3y^2 + 2$.

$g'(y) = 3y^2 - 6y = 0$ if $y = 2, 0$; $g(0) = 2$

III. $y = 1,\ -1 \le x \le 1$: $f(x,1) = g(x) = x^3 + 3x^2 - 2$.

$g'(x) = 3x^2 + 3x = 0$ if $x = 0, -2$; $g(0) = -2$

IV. $y = -1,\ -1 \le x \le 1$: $f(x,-1) = g(x) = x^3 + 3x^2 - 4$

$g'(x) = 3x^2 + 3x = 0$ if $x = 0, -2$; $g(0) = -4$; $g(-1) = -2, g(1)=1$

Interior: $f_x = 3x^2 + 6x$ and $f_y = 3y^2 - 6y$. Solving, we find

$x = 0, -2$ and $y = 0, 2$. $f(0,0) = 0$ and the others are not in region.

$\therefore$ Absolute maximum $= 4$ and absolute minimum $= -4$.

9. $f(x,y) = x^2 - y^2$ and let $g(x,y) = x^2 + y^2 - 4$

$\nabla f = \lambda \nabla g \Rightarrow 2x\mathbf{i} - 2y\mathbf{j} = 2x\lambda\mathbf{i} + 2y\lambda\mathbf{j}$

$2x = 2x\lambda \Rightarrow x = 0$ or $\lambda = 1$

$-2y = 2y\lambda \Rightarrow y = 0$ or $\lambda = -1$

$x = 0 \Rightarrow y^2 = 4 \Rightarrow y = \pm 2$. $f(0, \pm 2) = -4$

$y = 0 \Rightarrow x^2 = 4 \Rightarrow x = \pm 2$. $f(\pm 2, 0) = 4$

$\lambda = 1 \Rightarrow -2y = 2y \Rightarrow y = 0$: $\lambda = -1 \Rightarrow 2x = -2x \Rightarrow x = 0$.

$f_x = 2x = 0$ if $x = 0$. $f_y = -2y = 0$ if $y = 0$. $f(0,0) = 0$

$\therefore$ Absolute maximum $= 4$; absolute minimum $= -4$

11. $z = f(x,y) = x^3 + y^3 - 9xy + 27$. $f_x = 3x^2 - 9y$ and $f_y = 3y^2 - 9x$.

$3x^2 = 9y \Rightarrow y = \frac{1}{3}x^2$ so $3\left(\frac{x^2}{3}\right)^2 - 9x = 0 \Rightarrow x = 0, 3$

$f_{xx} = 6x$, $f_{yy} = 6y$ and $f_{yx} = -9$. The discriminant $D = 36xy - 9$, so at $(0,0)$, $D < 0$ so $(0,0)$ is a saddlepoint. At $(3,3)$, $D > 0$ and $f_{xx} > 0$ so $f(3,3) = 0$ is a minimum value.

13. Let $f(x,y,z) = x^2 + y^2 + z^2$ and $g(x,y,z) = xyz - 1$. Then $\nabla f = \lambda \nabla g \Rightarrow$

$$\begin{cases} 2x = \lambda yz \\ 2y = \lambda xz \\ 2z = \lambda xy \end{cases} \Rightarrow \quad \begin{cases} 2x^2 = \lambda xyz \\ 2y^2 = \lambda xyz \end{cases} \Rightarrow y = \pm x$$

Similarly, $z = \pm x$. Then $x^3 = \pm 1$ so the points are $(1,1,1)$, $(1,-1,-1)$, $(-1,-1,1)$ and $(-1,1,-1)$.

15. The equation of a plane tangent to $\frac{x^2}{a^2} + \frac{y^2}{b^2} + \frac{z^2}{c^2} = 1$ at a point

$P(x_0, y_0, z_0)$ is $\left(\frac{x_0}{a^2}\right)x + \left(\frac{y_0}{b^2}\right)y + \left(\frac{z_0}{c^2}\right)z = 1$. This plane has intercepts

$\left(\frac{a^2}{x_0}, 0, 0\right)$, $\left(0, \frac{b^2}{y_0}, 0\right)$ and $\left(0, 0, \frac{c^2}{z_0}\right)$. The volume of the tetrahedron is

$V = \frac{1}{3}\left(\frac{1}{2}\right)\left(\frac{a^2}{x_0}\right)\left(\frac{b^2}{y_0}\right)\left(\frac{c^2}{z_0}\right)$. Therefore we need to minimize the function

$f(x,y,z) = \frac{(abc)^2}{6}(xyz)^{-1}$ subject to the constraint

$g(x,y,z) = \frac{x^2}{a^2} + \frac{y^2}{b^2} + \frac{z^2}{c^2} - 1$. We solve the system

$$-\frac{(abc)^2}{6}\cdot\frac{1}{yzx^2} = \frac{2x}{a^2}\lambda,\quad -\frac{(abc)^2}{6}\cdot\frac{1}{xzy^2} = \frac{2y}{b^2}\lambda,\quad -\frac{(abc)^2}{6}\cdot\frac{1}{xyz^2} = \frac{2z}{c^2}\lambda$$

to find $z = \frac{c}{\sqrt{3}}$, $y = \frac{b}{\sqrt{3}}$, $x = \frac{a}{\sqrt{3}}$ and $V = \frac{\sqrt{3}abc}{2}$.

17. If $f(t) = f(x(t), y(t))$ has a relative maximum or minimum at $t_0$, then $f'(t_0) = 0$. But $f'(t) = \frac{\partial f}{\partial x}\frac{dx}{dt} + \frac{\partial f}{\partial y}\frac{dy}{dt} = \nabla f \cdot \left(\frac{dx}{dt}\mathbf{i} + \frac{dy}{dt}\mathbf{j}\right)$. At $t_0$, $\nabla f \perp \left(\frac{dx}{dt}\mathbf{i} + \frac{dy}{dt}\mathbf{j}\right) \Rightarrow \nabla f$ is tangent to $g(x, y)$ at $P_0$. At this point $P_0$, $\nabla g$ is also $\perp \left(\frac{dx}{dt}\mathbf{i} + \frac{dy}{dt}\mathbf{j}\right)$, as so is $\parallel \nabla f$, that is $\nabla f = \lambda \nabla g$ for some $\lambda$.

# CHAPTER 18

# MULTIPLE INTEGRALS

## 18.1 DOUBLE INTEGRALS

1. $\displaystyle\int_0^3\int_0^2 (4 - y^2)\,dy\,dx = \int_0^3 \left(4y - \frac{1}{3}y^3\right)\Big]_0^2 dx = \int_0^3 \frac{16}{3}dx = 16$

3. $\displaystyle\int_0^3\int_{-2}^0 (x^2y - 2xy)dy\,dx = \int_0^3 \left(\frac{1}{2}x^2y^2 - xy^2\right)\Big]_{-2}^0 dx = \int_0^3 (4x - 2x^2)\,dx = 0$

5. $\displaystyle\int_0^{\pi}\int_0^x x\sin y\,dy\,dx = \int_0^{\pi} -x\cos y\Big]_0^x dx = \int_0^{\pi} (x - x\cos x)dx$

$$= \frac{1}{2}x^2 - x\sin x - \cos x\Big]_0^{\pi} = \frac{4 + \pi^2}{2}$$

7. $\displaystyle\int_0^{\pi}\int_0^{\sin x} y\,dy\,dx = \int_0^{\pi} \frac{1}{2}y^2\Big]_0^{\sin x} dx = \int_0^{\pi} \frac{1}{2}\sin^2 x\,dx = \frac{\pi}{4}$

9. $\displaystyle\int_{10}^1\int_0^{1/y} ye^{xy}\,dx\,dy = \int_{10}^1 y\left(\frac{e^{xy}}{y}\right)\Big]_0^{1/y} dy = \int_{10}^1 (e - 1)\,dy = 9 - 9e$

11. $\displaystyle\int_1^2\int_x^{2x} \frac{x}{y}\,dy\,dx = \int_1^2 x\ln y\Big]_x^{2x} dy = \int_1^2 x\ln 2\,dx = \frac{3}{2}\ln 2$

13. $\displaystyle\int_0^1\int_0^{1-x} (y - \sqrt{x})dy\,dx = \int_0^1 \left(\frac{1}{2}y^2 - y\sqrt{x}\right)\Big]_0^{1-x} dx$

$$= \int_0^1\left(\frac{(1 - x)^2}{2} - \sqrt{x} + x^{3/2}\right)dx = -\frac{1}{10}$$

15. $\displaystyle\int_1^2\int_1^2 \frac{1}{xy}\,dy\,dx = \int_1^2 \frac{1}{x}\ln y\Big]_1^2 dx = \int_1^2 \ln 2\,\frac{1}{x}dx = (\ln 2)^2$

17. $\displaystyle\int_0^2\int_0^{4-2x} dy\,dx = \int_0^2 (4 - 2x)\,dx = 4$

$$\int_0^4\int_0^{2-y/2} dx\,dy = \int_0^4 \left(2 - \frac{y}{2}\right)dy = 4$$

19. $\int_0^1\int_y^{\sqrt{y}} dx\,dy = \int_0^1 (\sqrt{y} - y)dy = \frac{1}{6}$

$\int_0^1\int_{x^2}^{x} dy\,dx = \int_0^1 (x - x^2)\,dx = \frac{1}{6}$

21. $\int_0^2\int_1^{e^x} dy\,dx = \int_0^2 (e^x - 1)\,dx = e^2 - 3$

$\int_1^{e^2}\int_{\ln y}^{2} dx\,dy = \int_1^{e^2} (2 - \ln y)\,dy = e^2 - 3$

23. $\int_0^{\sqrt{2}}\int_{-\sqrt{4-2y^2}}^{\sqrt{4-2y^2}} y\,dx\,dy = \int_0^{\sqrt{2}} 2y\sqrt{4-2y^2}\,dy = \frac{8}{3}$

$\int_{-2}^{2}\int_0^{\sqrt{(4-x^2)/2}} y\,dy\,dx = \frac{1}{2}\int_0^2 (4 - x^2)\,dx = \frac{8}{3}$

25. $\int_0^1\int_{x^2}^{x} f(x,y)\,dy\,dx = \int_0^1\int_y^{\sqrt{y}} f(x,y)\,dx\,dy$

27. $\int_0^1\int_1^{e^x} dy\,dx = \int_1^e\int_{\ln y}^{1} dx\,dy$

29. $\int_0^2\int_0^{x^3} f(x,y)\,dy\,dx = \int_0^8\int_{y^{1/3}}^{2} f(x,y)\,dx\,dy$

31. $\int_0^{\pi}\int_x^{\pi} \frac{\sin y}{y}\,dy\,dx = \int_0^{\pi}\int_0^{y} \frac{\sin y}{y}\,dy\,dx = \int_0^{\pi} \frac{x \sin y}{y}\Big]_0^y\,dy = \int_0^{\pi} \sin y\,dy = 2$

33. $\int_0^1\int_y^1 x^2 e^{xy}\,dx\,dy = \int_0^1\int_0^x x^2 e^{xy}\,dy\,dx = \int_0^1 xe^{xy}\Big]_0^x\,dx = \int_0^1 (xe^{x^2} - x)\,dx = \frac{e-2}{2}$

35. $\int_0^8\int_{x^{1/3}}^{2} \frac{1}{y^4+1}\,dy\,dx = \int_0^2\int_0^{y^3} \frac{1}{y^4+1}\,dy\,dx = \int_0^2 \frac{y^3\,dy}{y^4+1} = \frac{1}{4}\ln(y^4+1)\Big]_0^2 = \frac{1}{4}\ln 17$

37. $4 - x^2 = 3x$ if $x = 1$ or $-4$.

$V = \int_{-4}^{1}\int_{3x}^{4-x^2} (x+4)\,dy\,dx = \int_{-4}^{1} (16 - 8x - 7x^2 - x^3)\,dx = \frac{625}{12}$

39. $V = \int_0^3\int_0^2 (4 - y^2)\,dy\,dx = \int_0^3 \left(4y - \frac{1}{3}y^3\right)\Big]_0^2\,dx = 16$

41. $\int_0^2 \int_{y/2}^1 e^{x^2}\, dx\, dy = \int_0^1 \int_0^{2x} e^{x^2}\, dy\, dx = \int_0^1 2xe^{x^2}\, dx = e - 1$

43. $\int_{-a}^{a} \int_{-\sqrt{a^2-x^2}}^{\sqrt{a^2-x^2}} \frac{x^2+y^2}{a}\, dx\, dy = \int_{-a}^{a} \frac{2}{3a}(2x^2+a^2)\sqrt{a^2-x^2}\, dx$

$= \frac{4}{3a}\left[\frac{a^4}{8}\sin^{-1}\frac{x}{a} - \frac{1}{8}x\sqrt{a^2-x^2}\,(a^2-2x^2)\right] + \frac{2a}{3}\left[\frac{x}{2}\sqrt{a^2-x^2} + \frac{a^2}{2}\sin^{-1}\frac{x}{a}\right]_a^a = \frac{\pi a^3}{2}$

## 18.2 AREAS, MOMENTS AND CENTERS OF MASS

1. $\int_0^a \int_0^{a-x} dy\, dx = \int_0^a (a-x)\, dx = \frac{1}{2}a^2$

3. $\int_0^2 \int_{2x}^4 dy\, dx = \int_0^2 (4-2x)dx = 4$

5. $2y - y^2 = y^2 \Leftrightarrow y = 0$ or $1$.

$\int_0^1 \int_{y^2}^{2y-y^2} dx\, dy = \int_0^1 (2y - 2y^2)\, dy = \frac{1}{3}$

7. $\int_{-1}^1 \int_{-1}^{\sqrt{1-x^2}} dy\, dx = \int_{-1}^1 \left(\sqrt{1-x^2} + 1\right)dx = 2 + \frac{\pi}{2}$

9. $\int_0^1 \int_y^{\sqrt{y}} dx\, dy = \int_0^1 (\sqrt{y} - y)\, dy = \frac{1}{6}$ (See Answer section of text for graph.)

11. $\int_0^{\frac{\pi}{4}} \int_{\sin x}^{\cos x} dy\, dx = \int_0^{\frac{\pi}{4}} (\cos x - \sin x)\, dx = \sqrt{2} - 1$

(See Answer section of text for graph)

13. $\int_{-1}^0 \int_{-2x}^{1-x} dy\, dx + \int_0^2 \int_{-x/2}^{1-x} dy\, dx = \int_{-1}^0 (1+x)\, dx + \int_0^2 \left(1 - \frac{x}{2}\right) dx = \frac{3}{2}$

(See Answer section of text for graph)

15. $M = \int_0^1 \int_x^{2-x^2} 3dy\,dx = \int_0^1 (6 - 3x^2 - x)\,dx = \frac{7}{2}$

$M_y = \int_0^1 \int_x^{2-x^2} 3x\,dy\,dx = \int_0^1 (6x - 3x^3 - 3x^2)\,dx = \frac{5}{4}$

$M_x = \int_0^1 \int_x^{2-x^2} 3y\,dy\,dx = \frac{3}{2}\int_0^1 (4 - 5x^2 + x^4)\,dx = \frac{19}{5}$

$(\bar{x}, \bar{y}) = \left(\frac{5}{4}\cdot\frac{2}{7}, \frac{19}{5}\cdot\frac{2}{7}\right) = \left(\frac{5}{14}, \frac{38}{35}\right)$

17. $M = \int_0^2 \int_{y^2/2}^{4-y} dx\,dy = \int_0^2 \left(4 - y - \frac{1}{2}y^2\right) dy = \frac{14}{3}$

$M_y = \int_0^2 \int_{y^2/2}^{4-y} x\,dx\,dy = \frac{1}{2}\int_0^2 \left(16 - 8y + y^2 - \frac{1}{4}y^4\right) dy = \frac{128}{15}$

$M_x = \int_0^2 \int_{y^2/2}^{4-y} y\,dx\,dy = \int_0^2 \left(4y - y^2 - \frac{1}{2}y^3\right) dy = \frac{10}{3}$

$(\bar{x}, \bar{y}) = \left(\frac{128}{15}\cdot\frac{3}{14}, \frac{10}{3}\cdot\frac{3}{14}\right) = \left(\frac{64}{35}, \frac{5}{7}\right)$

19. $M = \int_{-2}^1 \int_{y-2}^{-y^2} \delta\,dx\,dy = \int_{-2}^1 \delta(2 - y - y^2)\,dy = \frac{9}{2}\delta$

$M_y = \int_{-2}^1 \int_{y-2}^{-y^2} \delta x\,dx\,dy = \frac{1}{2}\delta\int_{-2}^1 (y^4 - (y-2)^2)\,dy = -\frac{36}{5}\delta$

$M_x = \int_{-2}^1 \int_{y-2}^{-y^2} \delta\,y\,dx\,dy = \int_{-2}^1 \delta(2y - y^2 - y^3)\,dy = -\frac{9}{4}\delta$

$(\bar{x}, \bar{y}) = \left(-\frac{36}{5}\cdot\frac{2}{9}, -\frac{9}{4}\cdot\frac{2}{9}\right) = \left(-\frac{8}{5}, -\frac{1}{2}\right)$

$I_x = \int_{-2}^1 \int_{y-2}^{-y^2} \delta\,y^2\,dx\,dy = \int_{-2}^1 \delta(2y^2 - y^3 - y^4)\,dy = \frac{189}{60}\delta = 189$

$I_y = \int_{-2}^1 \int_{y-2}^{-y^2} \delta x^2\,dx\,dy = -\frac{1}{3}\delta\int_{-2}^1 (y^6 + (y-2)^3)\,dy = \frac{1269}{28}\delta = \frac{6345}{7}$

$I_0 = I_x + I_y = \frac{7668}{7}$; $R_x = \sqrt{\frac{I_x}{M}} = \sqrt{\frac{189\,\delta}{60}\cdot\frac{2}{9\delta}} = \sqrt{\frac{7}{10}}$

$R_y = \sqrt{\frac{I_y}{M}} = \sqrt{\frac{47}{14}}$; $R_0 = \sqrt{\frac{I_0}{M}} = \sqrt{\frac{142}{35}}$.

21. Let $\triangle$ABC be situated so that its vertices are A(0,0), B(b,0) and C(a,h). The equation of the line through AB is $y = \frac{h}{a}x$ and through CB is $y = \frac{h}{a-b}(x-b)$.

$$M = \int_0^a \int_0^{(h/a)x} \delta\, dy\, dx + \int_a^b \int_0^{\frac{h}{a-b}(x-b)} \delta\, dy\, dx$$

$$= \int_0^a \frac{\delta h}{a} x\, dx + \int_a^b \frac{\delta h}{a-b}(x-b)dx = \frac{\delta bh}{2}$$

$$I_x = \int_0^a \int_0^{(h/a)x} \delta y^2\, dy\, dx + \int_a^b \int_0^{\frac{h}{a-b}(x-b)} \delta\, y^2\, dy\, dx$$

$$= \int_0^a \frac{\delta h^3}{3a^3} x^3\, dx + \int_a^b \frac{\delta h^3}{3(a-b)^3}(x-b)^3\, dx = \frac{\delta bh^3}{12}.$$

$$R_x = \sqrt{\frac{I_x}{M}} = \frac{h}{\sqrt{6}}.$$

23. $M_x = \int_0^a \int_0^{\sqrt{a^2-x^2}} y\, dy\, dx = \frac{1}{2}\int_0^a (a^2 - x^2)\, dx = \frac{a^3}{3}$. $M = \frac{\pi a^2}{4}$. $\bar{x} = \bar{y} = \frac{4a}{3\pi}$.

25. $M = \int_0^{\pi} \int_0^{\sin x} dx\, dy = \int_0^{\pi} \sin x\, dx = 2$.

$$M_y = \int_0^{\pi} \int_0^{\sin x} x\, dy\, dx = \int_0^{\pi} x \sin x\, dx = \sin x - x\cos x \Big]_0^{\pi} = \pi.$$

$$M_x = \int_0^{\pi} \int_0^{\sin x} y\, dy\, dx = \frac{1}{2}\int_0^{\pi} \sin^2 x\, dx = \frac{\pi}{4}.\quad (\bar{x}, \bar{y}) = \left(\frac{\pi}{2}, \frac{\pi}{8}\right)$$

27. $I_x = \int_{-a}^{a} \int_{-b}^{b} y^2\, dy\, dx = \int_{-a}^{a} \frac{2b^3}{3}\, dx = \frac{4ab^3}{3} = I_y$. $I_0 = I_x + I_y = \frac{4ab}{3}(a^2 + b^2)$

29. $M = \int_0^1 \int_{-y}^{y} (y+1)\,dx\,dy = \int_0^1 2y(y+1)\,dy = \frac{5}{3}$

$M_x = \int_0^1 \int_{-y}^{y} y\,(y+1)\,dx\,dy = \int_0^1 2y^2\,(y+1)\,dy = \frac{7}{6}$

$M_y = \int_0^1 \int_{-y}^{y} x\,(y+1)\,dx\,dy = \int_0^1 (y+1)\,\frac{x^2}{2}\Big]_{-y}^{y} = 0.\ \therefore (\bar{x}, \bar{y}) = \left(0, \frac{7}{10}\right).$

$I_x = \int_0^1 \int_{-y}^{y} y^2\,(y+1)\,dx\,dy = \int_0^1 2y^3\,(y+1)\,dy = \frac{9}{10}$

$I_y = \int_0^1 \int_{-y}^{y} x^2\,(y+1)\,dx\,dy = \frac{2}{3}\int_0^1 (y^4 + y^3)dy = \frac{3}{10}.\ I_0 = \frac{9}{10} + \frac{3}{10} = \frac{6}{5}.$

$R_x = \sqrt{\frac{9}{10}\cdot\frac{3}{5}} = \frac{3\sqrt{6}}{10};\ R_y = \sqrt{\frac{3}{10}\cdot\frac{3}{5}} = \frac{3\sqrt{2}}{10};\ R_0 = \sqrt{\frac{6}{5}\cdot\frac{3}{5}} = \frac{3\sqrt{2}}{5}$

31. $M = 3\int_0^1 \int_x^{2-x} (2x+y+1)\,dy\,dx = 3\int_0^1 \left(2xy + \frac{y^2}{2} + y\right)\Big]_x^{2-x} dx = 3\int_0^1 (4 - 4x^2)\,dx = 8$

$M_x = 3\int_0^1 \int_x^{2-x} y\,(2x+y+1)\,dy\,dx = \int_0^1 (14 - 6x - 6x^2 - 2x^3)\,dx = \frac{17}{2}$

$M_y = 3\int_0^1 \int_x^{2-x} x\,(2x+y+1)\,dy\,dx = 3\int_0^1 (4x - 4x^3)\,dx = 3.\ \therefore (\bar{x}, \bar{y}) = \left(\frac{3}{8}, \frac{17}{16}\right)$

33. $M = \int_0^1 \int_{y^2}^{2y-y^2} (y+1)\,dx\,dy = \int_0^1 (2y - 2y^3)\,dy = \frac{1}{2}$

$M_x = \int_0^1 \int_{y^2}^{2y-y^2} y\,(y+1)\,dx\,dy = 2\int_0^1 (y^2 - y^4)\,dy = \frac{4}{15}$

$M_y = \int_0^1 \int_{y^2}^{2y-y^2} x\,(y+1)\,dx\,dy = 2\int_0^1 (y^2 - y^4)\,dy = \frac{4}{15}.\ \therefore (\bar{x}, \bar{y}) = \left(\frac{8}{15}, \frac{8}{15}\right)$

$I_x = \int_0^1 \int_{y^2}^{2y-y^2} y^2\,(y+1)\,dx\,dy = 2\int_0^1 (y^3 - y^5)\,dy = \frac{1}{6}$

35. $M = \int_0^1 \int_0^6 (x + y + 1)\, dx\, dy = \int_0^1 (24 + 6y)\, dy = 27$

$M_x = \int_0^1 \int_0^6 x\,(x + y + 1)\, dx\, dy = \int_0^1 (24y + 6y^2)\, dy = 14$

$M_y = \int_0^1 \int_0^6 x(x + y + 1)\, dx\, dy = \int_0^1 (90 + 18y)\, dy = 99.\ \therefore (\bar{x}, \bar{y}) = \left(\frac{11}{3}, \frac{14}{27}\right)$

$I_y = \int_0^1 \int_0^6 x^2\,(x + y + 1)\, dx\, dy = \int_0^1 (396 + 72y)\, dy = 432;\ R_y = \sqrt{\frac{432}{27}} = 4$

37. $M = \int_{-1}^1 \int_0^{x^2} (7y + 1)\, dy\, dx = \int_{-1}^1 \left(\frac{7}{2}x^4 + x^2\right) dx = \frac{31}{15}.$

$M_y = \int_{-1}^1 \int_0^{x^2} x\,(7y + 1)\, dy\, dx = \int_{-1}^1 \left(\frac{7}{2}x^5 + x^3\right) dx = 0$

$M_x = \int_{-1}^1 \int_0^{x^2} y\,(7y + 1)\, dy\, dx = \int_{-1}^1 \left(\frac{7}{3}x^6 + \frac{1}{2}x^4\right) dx = \frac{13}{15}.\ \therefore (\bar{x}, \bar{y}) = \left(0, \frac{13}{31}\right)$

$I_y = \int_{-1}^1 \int_0^{x^2} x^2\,(7y + 1)\, dy\, dx = \int_{-1}^1 \left(\frac{7}{2}x^6 + x^4\right) dx = \frac{7}{5}.\ R_y = \sqrt{\frac{21}{31}}.$

39. $M = \int_0^{20} \int_{-1}^1 \left(1 + \frac{x}{20}\right) dy\, dx = \int_0^{20} 2\left(\left(1 + \frac{x}{20}\right) dx = 60\right.$

$M_x = \int_0^{20} \int_{-1}^1 y\left(1 + \frac{x}{20}\right) dy\, dx = \int_0^{20} \left(1 + \frac{x}{20}\right)\frac{1}{2}y^2\Big]_{-1}^1 = 0$

$M_y = \int_0^{20} \int_{-1}^1 x\left(1 + \frac{x}{20}\right) dy\, dx = \int_0^{20} 2x\left(1 + \frac{x}{20}\right) dx = \frac{2000}{3}.\ \therefore (\bar{x}, \bar{y}) = \left(\frac{100}{9}, 0\right)$

$I_x = \int_0^{20} \int_{-1}^1 y^2\left(1 + \frac{x}{20}\right) dy\, dx = \frac{2}{3}\int_0^{20} \left(1 + \frac{x}{20}\right) dx = 20.\ R_x = \sqrt{\frac{1}{3}}$

41. $I_a = \int_0^4 \int_0^2 (y - a)^2\, dy\, dx = \int_0^4 \left[\frac{(2 - a)^3}{3} + \frac{a^3}{3}\right] dx = \frac{4}{3}\,[(2 - a)^3 + a^3].$

Let $f(a) = \frac{4}{3}\,[(2 - a)^3 + a^3]$. Then $f'(a) = \frac{4}{3}[-3\,(2 - a)^2 + 3a^2] = 0$

if $a = 1$. $f''(a) = 8\,(2 - a) + 8a$ and $f''(1) > 0 \Rightarrow f(1) = \frac{8}{3}$ is minimum.

43. (a) $\nabla w = x\mathbf{i} + y\mathbf{j} \Rightarrow D_{\mathbf{u}}w = u_1 x + u_2 y$. Area of triangle $= \frac{1}{2}$

$$\text{Average value} = 2\int_0^1\int_0^x (u_1 x + u_2 y)\, dy\, dx$$

$$= 2\int_0^1 \left[ u_1 x(1-x) + \frac{1}{2}u_2 (1-x)^2 \right] dx = \frac{u_1 + u_2}{3}.$$

(b) $\text{Average value} = \dfrac{1}{\text{area } R}\displaystyle\iint_R (u_1 x + u_2 y)\, dA =$

$$= \frac{u_1}{\text{area } R}\iint_R x\, dA + \frac{u_2}{\text{area } R}\iint_R y\, dA = u_1\bar{x} + u_2\bar{y}.$$

## 18.3 DOUBLE INTEGRALS IN POLAR FORM

1. $\displaystyle\int_{-1}^{1}\int_0^{\sqrt{1-x^2}} dy\, dx = \int_0^{\pi}\int_0^1 r\, dr\, d\theta = \int_0^{\pi} \frac{1}{2}\theta\, d\theta = \frac{\pi}{2}$

3. $\displaystyle\int_0^1\int_0^{\sqrt{1-y^2}} (x^2+y^2)\, dx\, dy = \int_0^{\frac{\pi}{2}}\int_0^1 r^3\, dr\, d\theta = \int_0^{\frac{\pi}{2}} \frac{1}{4}\theta\, d\theta = \frac{\pi}{8}$

5. $\displaystyle\int_{-a}^{a}\int_{-\sqrt{a^2-x^2}}^{\sqrt{a^2-x^2}} dy\, dx = \int_0^{2\pi}\int_0^a r\, dr\, d\theta = \int_0^{2\pi} \frac{a^2\,\theta}{2}\, d\theta = \pi a^2$

7. $\displaystyle\int_0^{a/\sqrt{2}}\int_y^{\sqrt{a^2-y^2}} x\, dx\, dy = \int_0^{\pi/4}\int_0^a (r\cos\theta)\, r\, dr\, d\theta = \int_0^{\pi/4} \frac{a^3}{3}\cos\theta\, d\theta = \frac{a^3\sqrt{2}}{6}$

9. $\displaystyle\int_0^3\int_0^{\sqrt{3}\,x} \frac{dy\, dx}{\sqrt{x^2+y^2}} = \int_0^{\pi/3}\int_0^{3\sec\theta} \frac{1}{r}\, r\, dr\, d\theta = 3\int_0^{\pi/3} \sec\theta\, d\theta$

$$= 3\ln|\sec\theta + \tan\theta|\Big]_0^{\pi/3} = 3\ln(2+\sqrt{3})$$

11. $\displaystyle\int_0^1\int_0^{\sqrt{1-x^2}} 5\sqrt{x^2+y^2}\, dy\, dx = \int_0^{\frac{\pi}{2}}\int_0^1 5r^2\, dr\, d\theta = \int_0^{\frac{\pi}{2}} \frac{5}{3} d\theta = \frac{5\pi}{6}$

13. $\displaystyle\int_0^2\int_0^{\sqrt{1-(x-1)^2}} \frac{x+y}{x^2+y^2}\, dy\, dx = \int_0^{\frac{\pi}{2}}\int_0^{2\cos\theta} (\cos\theta + \sin\theta)\, dr\, d\theta$

$$= \int_0^{\frac{\pi}{2}} (2\sin\theta\cos\theta + 2\cos^2\theta)\, d\theta = 1 + \frac{\pi}{2}$$

15. $\int_0^{\frac{\pi}{2}}\int_0^{\sqrt{2-\sin 2\theta}} r\,dr\,d\theta = \frac{1}{2}\int_0^{\frac{\pi}{2}} (2 - \sin 2\theta)\,d\theta = \frac{\pi - 1}{2}$

17. $\int_{-\frac{\pi}{6}}^{\frac{\pi}{6}}\int_0^{\cos 3\theta} r\,dr\,d\theta = \frac{1}{2}\int_{-\frac{\pi}{6}}^{\frac{\pi}{6}} \cos^2 3\theta\,d\theta = \frac{1}{2}\int_{-\frac{\pi}{6}}^{\frac{\pi}{6}} \left(\frac{1}{2} + \frac{1}{2}\cos 6\theta\right) d\theta = \frac{\pi}{12}$

19. $\int_0^{\frac{\pi}{2}}\int_0^{1+\sin\theta} r\,dr\,d\theta = \frac{1}{2}\int_0^{\frac{\pi}{2}} (1 + \sin\theta)^2\,d\theta = \frac{3\pi}{8} + 1$

21. $\int_0^{2\pi}\int_0^{\sqrt{3}/2} \frac{r}{1 - r^2}\,dr\,d\theta = \int_0^{2\pi} \left(-\frac{1}{2}\ln(1 - r^2)\right]_0^{\sqrt{3}/2} = \int_0^{2\pi} \ln 2\,d\theta = \pi \ln 4$

23. $M_x = \int_0^{\pi}\int_0^{1-\cos\theta} (3r\sin\theta)\,r\,dr\,d\theta = \int_0^{\pi} (1 - \cos\theta)^3 \sin\theta\,d\theta = 4$

25. $M = \int_0^{2\pi}\int_0^{1+\cos\theta} r\,dr\,d\theta = \int_0^{2\pi} \frac{1}{2}(1 + \cos\theta)^2\,d\theta = \frac{3\pi}{2}$

$M_y = \int_0^{2\pi}\int_0^{1+\cos\theta} r^2\,dr\,d\theta\ \frac{1}{3}\int_0^{2\pi} (1 + \cos\theta)^3\,d\theta = \frac{5\pi}{4}$. $M_x = 0$ by symmetry.

$\therefore\ (\bar{x}, \bar{y}) = \left(\frac{5}{6}, 0\right)$

27. $I_0 = \iint (x^2 + y^2)\,\delta\,dA = \int_0^{2\pi}\int_0^{1+\cos\theta} r^3\,dr\,d\theta = \frac{1}{4}\int_0^{2\pi} (1 + \cos\theta)^4\,d\theta = \frac{35\pi}{16}$

29. $\int_{-\pi/2}^{\pi/2}\int_1^{1+\cos\theta} r\cos\theta\,r\,dr\,d\theta = \frac{1}{3}\int_{-\pi/2}^{\pi/2} (3\cos^2\theta + 3\cos^3\theta + \cos^4\theta)\,d\theta = \frac{4}{3} + \frac{5\pi}{8}$

31. $\int_0^4\int_{y/2}^{y/2+1} \frac{2x - y}{2}\,dx\,dy = \frac{1}{2}\int_0^4 \left(\left(\frac{y}{2} + 1\right)^2 - y\left(\frac{y}{2} + 1\right) + \frac{y^2}{4}\right) dy = 2$

33. (a) $\begin{cases} u = x - y \\ v = 2x + y \end{cases} \Rightarrow \begin{cases} x = \frac{1}{3}(u + v) \\ y = \frac{1}{3}(v - 2u) \end{cases}$

$$J(u, v) = \begin{vmatrix} \frac{1}{3} & \frac{1}{3} \\ -\frac{2}{3} & \frac{1}{3} \end{vmatrix} = \frac{1}{3}$$

(b) $y + 2x = \frac{1}{3}(v - 2u) + \frac{2}{3}(u + v) = v$

$x - y = \frac{1}{3}(v - 2u) - \frac{1}{3}(u + v) = u$

$$\iint_R (2x^2 - xy - y^2)\,dx\,dy = \iint_R (2x + y)(x - y)\,dx\,dy$$

$$= \frac{1}{3}\int_{-1}^{2}\int_{4}^{7} uv\,dv\,du = \frac{1}{3}\int_{-1}^{2} \frac{33}{2}u\,du = \frac{33}{4}$$

35. $J(u,v) = \begin{vmatrix} \frac{1}{v} & -\frac{u}{v^2} \\ v & u \end{vmatrix} = \frac{2u}{v}.\quad \iint_R \left(\sqrt{\frac{y}{x}} + \sqrt{xy}\right) dx\,dy$

$$= \int_1^3\int_1^2 (v + u)\frac{2u}{v}\,dv\,du = 2\int_1^3 (\ln 2\,u^2 + u)\,du = \frac{52\ln 2}{3} + 8.$$

37. $J(r,\theta) = \begin{vmatrix} a\cos\theta & -ar\sin\theta \\ b\sin\theta & br\cos\theta \end{vmatrix} = abr$

$$\iint (x^2 + y^2)\,dy\,dx = \int_0^{2\pi}\int_0^1 r^2(a^2\cos^2\theta + b^2\sin^2\theta)(abr)\,dr\,d\theta$$

$$= \frac{ab}{4}\int_0^{2\pi} (a^2\cos^2\theta + b^2\sin^2\theta)\,d\theta = \frac{\pi ab}{4}(a^2 + b^2)$$

## 18.4 TRIPLE INTEGRALS IN RECTANGULAR COORDINATES. VOLUMES AND AVERAGE VALUES

1. $\int_0^1\int_0^{1-z}\int_0^2 dx\,dy\,dz = \int_0^1\int_0^{1-z} 2\,dy\,dz = \int_0^1 2(1 - z)\,dz = 1$

3. (a) $\int_0^1\int_0^{2-2x}\int_0^{(6-3y-6x)/2} dz\,dy\,dx$ (b) $\int_0^1\int_0^{3-3x}\int_0^{(6-2z-6x)/3} dy\,dz\,dx$

(c) $\int_0^3\int_0^{(6-2z)/3}\int_0^{(6-3y-2z)/6} dx\,dy\,dz$ (d) $\int_0^3\int_0^{(3-z)/3}\int_0^{(6-2z-6x)/3} dy\,dx\,dz$

(e) $\int_0^2\int_0^{(2-y)/2}\int_0^{(6-3y-6x)/3} dz\,dx\,dy$

(f) $\int_0^2\int_0^{(6-3y)/2}\int_0^{(6-3y-2z)/6} dx\,dz\,dy = \int_0^2\int_0^{(6-3y)/2} \left[1 - \frac{1}{6}(2z + 3y)\right] dz\,dy$

$$= \int_0^2 \frac{3}{8}(y - 2)^2\,dy = 1$$

5. $\int_0^1\int_0^1\int_0^1 (x^2+y^2+z^2)\,dz\,dy\,dx = \int_0^1\int_0^1\left(x^2+y^2+\frac{1}{3}\right)dy\,dx = \int_0^1\left(x^2+\frac{2}{3}\right)dx = 1$

7. $\int_1^e\int_1^e\int_1^e \frac{1}{xyz}dx\,dy\,dz = \int_1^e\int_1^e \frac{1}{yz}\,dy\,dz = \int_1^e \frac{1}{z}\,dz = \ln z\Big]_1^e = 1$

9. $\int_0^1\int_0^\pi\int_0^\pi y\sin z\,dx\,dy\,dz = \int_0^1\int_0^\pi \pi y\sin z\,dy\,dz = \int_0^1 \frac{\pi^3}{2}\sin z\,dz = \frac{\pi^3}{2}(1-\cos 1)$

11. $\int_{-1}^1\int_{-\sqrt{1-z^2}}^{\sqrt{1-z^2}}\int_{-\sqrt{1-y^2-z^2}}^{\sqrt{1-y^2-z^2}} dx\,dy\,dz = \int_{-1}^1\int_{-\sqrt{1-z^2}}^{\sqrt{1-z^2}} 2\sqrt{1-y^2-z^2}\,dy\,dz$

$= \int_{-1}^1\left(y\sqrt{1-y^2-z^2} + (1-z^2)\sin^{-1}\frac{y}{\sqrt{1-z^2}}\Big]_{-\sqrt{1-z^2}}^{\sqrt{1-z^2}}\right)dz$

$= \pi\int_{-1}^1 (1-z^2)\,dz = \frac{4\pi}{3}$

13. $\int_0^2\int_{-\sqrt{4-y^2}}^{\sqrt{4-y^2}}\int_0^{2x+y} dz\,dx\,dy = \int_0^2\int_{-\sqrt{4-y^2}}^{\sqrt{4-y^2}} (2x+y)\,dx\,dy = \int_0^2 2y\sqrt{4-y^2}\,dy = \frac{16}{3}$

15. $\int_{-1}^1\int_0^{\sqrt{1-x^2}}\int_0^1 (2-2x^2-2y^2)\,dz\,dy\,dx = \int_{-1}^1\int_0^{\sqrt{1-x^2}} (2-2x^2-2y^2)\,dy\,dx$

$\int_{-1}^1 \frac{4}{3}(1-x^2)^{3/2}\,dx = \frac{1}{3}\left[\frac{3}{2}x\sqrt{1-x^2} + \frac{3}{2}\sin^{-1}x + x(1-x^2)^{3/2}\right]_{-1}^1 = \frac{\pi}{2}$

17. $\int_0^\pi\int_0^\pi\int_0^\pi \cos(x+y+z)\,dx\,dy\,dz = \int_0^\pi\int_0^\pi [\sin(z+y+\pi) - \sin(z+y)]\,dy\,dz$

$= \int_0^\pi\int_0^\pi -2\sin(z+y)\,dy\,dz = \int_0^\pi 2[\cos(z+\pi) - \cos z]\,dz = -4\int_0^\pi \cos z\,dz = 0$

19. Volume $= (2)(2)(2) = 8$

Average value $= \frac{1}{8}\int_0^2\int_0^2\int_0^2 (x^2+9)\,dx\,dy\,dz = \frac{1}{8}\int_0^2\int_0^2 \frac{62}{3}\,dy\,dz = \frac{31}{12}\int_0^2 2\,dz = \frac{31}{3}$

21. Average value $= \int_0^1\int_0^1\int_0^1 (x^2+y^2+z^2)\,dx\,dy\,dz = \int_0^1\int_0^1\left(x^2+y^2+\frac{1}{3}\right)dy\,dz$

$= \int_0^1\left(x^2+\frac{2}{3}\right)dx = 1.$ (The volume of the cube $= 1$).

23. $\int_{-1}^{1}\int_{-\sqrt{1-x^2}}^{\sqrt{1-x^2}}\int_{x^2+y^2}^{2-x^2-y^2} dz\,dy\,dx = 2\int_{-1}^{1}\int_{-\sqrt{1-x^2}}^{\sqrt{1-x^2}} (1 - x^2 - y^2)\,dy\,dx$

$= \frac{8}{3}\int_{-1}^{1} (1 - x^2)^{3/2}\,dx = \pi$ (See problem 15 for integration)

25. $\int_0^1\int_0^{1-x}\int_0^{2-2z} dy\,dz\,dx = \int_0^1\int_0^{1-x} (2 - 2z)\,dz\,dx = \int_0^1 (1 - x^2)\,dx = \frac{2}{3}$

27. $\int_{-1}^{1}\int_0^{\sqrt{1-x^2}}\int_0^{y} dz\,dy\,dx = \int_{-1}^{1}\int_0^{\sqrt{1-x^2}} y\,dy\,dx = \int_{-1}^{1} \frac{1}{2}(1 - x^2)\,dx = \frac{2}{3}$

29. $\int_0^1\int_0^{1-x^2}\int_0^{x^2+z^2} dy\,dz\,dx = \int_0^1\int_0^{1-x^2} (x^2 + z^2)\,dz\,dx$

$= \int_0^1 \left[x^2 - x^4 + \frac{1}{3}(1 - x^2)^3\right]dx = \frac{2}{7}$

31. $\int_{-2}^{2}\int_{-\sqrt{16-4z^2}}^{\sqrt{16-4z^2}}\int_0^{4-y} dx\,dy\,dz = \int_{-2}^{2}\int_{-\sqrt{16-4z^2}}^{\sqrt{16-4z^2}} (4 - y)dy\,dz = \int_{-2}^{2} 16\sqrt{4 - z^2}\,dz = 32\pi$

33. $\int_0^c\int_0^{b(1-z/c)}\int_0^{a(1-y/b-z/c)} dx\,dy\,dz = \int_0^c\int_0^{b(1-z/c)}\left(a - \frac{a}{b}y - \frac{a}{c}z\right)dy\,dz$

$= \int_0^c \frac{ab}{2}\left(1 - \frac{z}{c}\right)^2 dz = \frac{abc}{6}$

35. $8\int_0^a\int_0^{\sqrt{a^2-x^2}}\int_0^{\sqrt{a^2-x^2}} dz\,dy\,dx = 8\int_0^a\int_0^{\sqrt{a^2-x^2}} \sqrt{a^2 - x^2}\,dy\,dx$

$= 8\int_0^a (a^2 - x^2)\,dx = \frac{16}{3}a^3$

37. $V = \int_{-a}^{a}\int_{-(b/a)\sqrt{a^2-x^2}}^{(b/a)\sqrt{a^2-x^2}}\int_{-c\sqrt{1-(x^2/a^2)-(y^2/b^2)}}^{c\sqrt{1-(x^2/a^2)-(y^2/b^2)}} dz\,dy\,dx$

$$= \int_{-a}^{a}\int_{-(b/a)\sqrt{a^2-x^2}}^{(b/a)\sqrt{a^2-x^2}} 2c\sqrt{1-(x/a)^2-(y/b)^2}\,dy\,dx$$

$$= \int_{-a}^{a}\int_{-(b/a)\sqrt{a^2-x^2}}^{(b/a)\sqrt{a^2-x^2}} \frac{2c}{b}\sqrt{\frac{b^2}{a^2}(a^2-x^2)-y^2}\,dy\,dx$$

$$= \frac{\pi bc}{a^2}\int_{-a}^{a}(a^2-x^2)\,dx = \frac{4}{3}\pi abc$$

39. On the xy-plane, the projection is the region bounded by $y = x^2$ and $y = 1$; on the yz-plane, it is the triangular region bounded by the axes and the line $y + z = 1$; on the xz-plane, it is the region bounded by $z = 1 - x^2$ and the x-axis. (See figure in answer section of text.)

(a) $\int_{-1}^{1}\int_{0}^{1-x^2}\int_{x^2}^{1-z} dy\,dz\,dx$ (b) $\int_{0}^{1}\int_{-\sqrt{1-z}}^{\sqrt{1-z}}\int_{x^2}^{1-z} dy\,dx\,dz$

(c) $\int_{0}^{1}\int_{0}^{1-z}\int_{-\sqrt{y}}^{\sqrt{y}} dx\,dy\,dz$ (d) $\int_{0}^{1}\int_{0}^{1-y}\int_{-\sqrt{y}}^{\sqrt{y}} dx\,dz\,dy$

(e) $\int_{0}^{1}\int_{-\sqrt{y}}^{\sqrt{y}}\int_{0}^{1-y} dz\,dx\,dy$

## 18.5 MASSES AND MOMENTS IN THREE DIMENSIONS

1. $I_x = \int_{-c/2}^{c/2}\int_{-b/2}^{b/2}\int_{-a/2}^{a/2} \delta(y^2+z^2)\,dx\,dy\,dz = \int_{-c/2}^{c/2}\int_{-b/2}^{b/2} a\delta((y^2+z^2)\,dy\,dz$

$$= \int_{-c/2}^{c/2}\left(\frac{ab^3\delta}{12} + ab\delta z^2\right)dz = \frac{abc\delta}{12}(b^2+c^2) = \frac{M}{12}(b^2+c^2)$$

$$R_x = \sqrt{\frac{I_x}{M}} = \sqrt{\frac{b^2+c^2}{12}};\ R_y = \sqrt{\frac{a^2+c^2}{12}};\ R_z = \sqrt{\frac{a^2+b^2}{12}}$$

3. $I_x = \int_0^c \int_0^b \int_0^a \delta(y^2 + z^2)\,dx\,dy\,dz = \int_0^c \int_0^b a\delta(y^2 + z^2)\,dy\,dz$

$= \int_0^c a\delta\left(\frac{b^3}{3} + b\,z^2\right)dz = \frac{abc\delta}{3}(b^2 + c^2) = \frac{M}{3}(b^2 + c^2)$

$I_y = \int_0^c \int_0^a \int_0^b \delta(x^2 + z^2)\,dy\,dx\,dz = \int_0^c \int_0^a b\delta(x^2 + z^2)\,dx\,dz$

$= \int_0^c b\,\delta\left(\frac{a^3}{3} + a\,z^2\right)dz = \frac{abc\delta}{3}(a^2 + c^2) = \frac{M}{3}(a^2 + c^2)$

$I_z = \int_0^a \int_0^b \int_0^c \delta(x^2 + y^2)\,dz\,dy\,dx = \int_0^a \int_0^b c\delta(x^2 + y^2)\,dy\,dx$

$= \int_0^a c\,\delta\left(\frac{b^3}{3} + bx^2\right)dx = \frac{abc\delta}{3}(a^2 + b^2) = \frac{M}{3}(a^2 + b^2)$

5. $M = \int_{-1}^1 \int_{-1}^1 \int_{4y^2}^4 \delta\,dz\,dy\,dx = \int_{-1}^1 \int_{-1}^1 4\delta(1 - y^2)\,dy\,dx = \int_{-1}^1 \frac{16}{3}\delta\,dx = \frac{32\,\delta}{3}$

$M_{yz} = \int_{-1}^1 \int_{4y^2}^4 \int_{-1}^1 \delta\,x\,dx\,dz\,dy = 0;\ M_{xz} = \int_{-1}^1 \int_{4y^2}^4 \int_{-1}^1 \delta\,y\,dx\,dz\,dy$

$= \int_{-1}^1 \int_{4y^2}^4 \int_{-1}^1 2\delta y\,dz\,dy = \int_{-1}^1 8\delta(y - y^3)\,dy = 0,\ M_{xy} = \int_{-1}^1 \int_{-1}^1 \int_{4y^2}^4 \delta\,z\,dz\,dy\,dx$

$= \int_{-1}^1 \int_{-1}^1 \frac{\delta}{2}(16 - 16y^4)\,dy\,dx = \int_{-1}^1 \frac{64}{5}\delta\,dx = \frac{128\delta}{5}.\ \therefore\ (\bar{x}, \bar{y}, \bar{z}) = \left(0, 0, \frac{12}{5}\right)$

$I_x = \int_{-1}^1 \int_{-1}^1 \int_{4y^2}^4 \delta(y^2 + z^2)\,dz\,dy\,dx = \int_{-1}^1 \int_{-1}^1 \delta\left(4y^2 - 4y^4 + \frac{64}{3} - \frac{64}{3}y^6\right)dy\,dx$

$= \int_{-1}^1 \frac{3952}{105}\delta\,dx = \frac{7904\,\delta}{105}$

$I_y = \int_{-1}^1 \int_{-1}^1 \int_{4y^2}^4 \delta(x^2 + z^2)\,dz\,dy\,dx = \int_{-1}^1 \int_{-1}^1 \left(4x^2 - 4x^2y^2 + \frac{64}{3} - \frac{64}{3}y^6\right)dy\,dx$

$= \int_{-1}^1 \delta\left(\frac{16}{3}x^2 + \frac{768}{21}\right)dx = \frac{4832\,\delta}{63}$

$I_z = \int_{-1}^1 \int_{-1}^1 \int_{4y^2}^4 \delta(x^2 + y^2)\,dz\,dy\,dx = \int_{-1}^1 \int_{-1}^1 (4x^2 + 4y^2 - 4y^2x^2 - 4y^4)\,dy\,dx$

$= \int_{-1}^1 \left(\frac{16}{3}x^2 + \frac{16}{15}\right)dx = \frac{256\,\delta}{45}$

7. (a) $M = \delta\int_0^{2\pi}\int_0^2\int_{r^2}^4 r\,dz\,dr\,d\theta = \delta\int_0^{2\pi}\int_0^2 r(4-r^2)\,dr\,d\theta = 4\,\delta\int_0^{2\pi} d\theta = 8\pi\,\delta$

$$M_{xy} = \delta\int_0^{2\pi}\int_0^2\int_{r^2}^4 rz\,dz\,dr\,d\theta = \frac{\delta}{2}\int_0^{2\pi}\int_0^2 (16-r^4)r\,dr\,d\theta = \frac{\delta}{2}\int_0^{2\pi}\frac{64}{3}d\theta = \frac{64\pi\,\delta}{3}$$

$\bar{x} = \bar{y} = 0$ by symmetry. $\bar{z} = \frac{8}{3}$

(b) $4\pi = \int_0^{2\pi}\int_0^{\sqrt{c}}\int_{r^2}^{c} r\,dz\,dr\,d\theta = \int_0^{2\pi}\int_0^{\sqrt{c}} (rc - r^3)\,dr\,d\theta = \int_0^{2\pi}\frac{1}{4}c^2\,d\theta = \frac{1}{2}\pi c^2$

$\frac{1}{2}\pi c^2 = 4\pi \Rightarrow c^2 = 8$ or $c = 2\sqrt{2}$

9. $V = \frac{1}{2}(3)(6)(4) = 36$

$$I_L = \int_{-2}^{2}\int_{-2}^{4}\int_{-1}^{-\frac{1}{2}y+1} [(y-6)^2 + z^2]\,dz\,dy\,dx$$

$$= \int_{-2}^{2}\left[\frac{(y-6)^2(2-y)}{2} + (y-6)^2 + \frac{(2-y)^3}{24} + \frac{1}{3}\right]_{-2}^{4} dx = \int_{-2}^{2}\frac{693}{2}\,dx = 1386.$$

$$R_L = \sqrt{\frac{1386}{36}} = \frac{77\sqrt{2}}{2}$$

11. $I_L = \delta\int_0^4\int_0^2\int_0^1 [(y-2)^2 + z^2]\,dz\,dy\,dx = \delta\int_0^4\int_0^2\left[(y-2)^2 + \frac{1}{3}\right]dy\,dx$

$= \delta\int_0^4 \frac{10}{3}\,dx = \frac{40\,\delta}{3}$. $M = (1)(2)(8)\delta = 8\delta$. $R_L = \sqrt{\frac{5}{3}}$.

13. $M = \int_0^2\int_0^{2-x}\int_0^{2-y-x} 2x\,dz\,dy\,dx = \int_0^2\int_0^{2-x} (4x - 2x^2 - 2xy)dy\,dx$

$= \int_0^2 (4x - 4x^2 + x^3)dx = \frac{4}{3}$

$M_{xy} = \int_0^2\int_0^{2-x}\int_0^{2-y-x} 2x\,z\,dz\,dy\,dx = \int_0^2\int_0^{2-x} [x(2-y-x)^2]dx\,dy$

$= \int_0^2 \frac{1}{3}x(2-x)^3\,dx = \frac{8}{15}$. $M_{xz} = \frac{8}{15}$ by symmetry.

$M_{yz} = \int_0^2\int_0^{2-x}\int_0^{2-y-x} 2x^2\,dz\,dy\,dx = \int_0^2\int_0^{2-x} [2x^2(2-x-y]\,dy\,dx$

$= \int_0^2 x^2(2-x)^2\,dx = \frac{16}{15}$. $\therefore (\bar{x}, \bar{y}, \bar{z}) = \left(\frac{4}{5}, \frac{2}{5}, \frac{2}{5}\right)$

15. $M = \int_0^1\int_0^1\int_0^1 (x+y+z+1)\,dz\,dy\,dx = \frac{5}{2}$

$M_{xy} = \int_0^1\int_0^1\int_0^1 (x+y+z+1)\,z\,dz\,dy\,dx = \int_0^1\int_0^1 \left[\frac{1}{3} + \frac{1}{2}(x+y+1)\right]dy\,dx$

$= \int_0^1 \left(\frac{13}{12} + \frac{1}{2}x\right)dx = \frac{4}{3}$. $M_{xz} = M_{yz} = M_{xy}$ by symmetry.

$I_z = \int_0^1\int_0^1\int_0^1 (x+y+z+1)(x^2+y^2)\,dz\,dy\,dx = \int_0^1\int_0^1 (x^2+y^2)\left(x+y+\frac{3}{2}\right)dy\,dx$

$= \int_0^1 \left(x^3 + 2x^2 + \frac{x}{3} + \frac{3}{4}\right)dx = \frac{11}{6}$. $I_x = I_y = I_z$.

$\therefore\ (\bar{x}, \bar{y}, \bar{z}) = \left(\frac{8}{15}, \frac{8}{15}, \frac{8}{15}\right)$. $R_x = R_y = R_z = \sqrt{\frac{11}{15}}$.

## 18.6 TRIPLE INTEGRALS IN CYLINDRICAL AND SPHERICAL COORDINATES

1. $\int_0^{2\pi}\int_0^1\int_r^{\sqrt{2-r^2}} dz\,r\,dr\,d\theta = \int_0^{2\pi}\int_0^1 \left(\sqrt{2-r^2} - r\right) r\,dr\,d\theta =$

$= \int_0^{2\pi}\left(\frac{\sqrt{8}}{3} - \frac{2}{3}\right)d\theta = \frac{2\pi\,(2\sqrt{2} - 2)}{3}$

3. $\int_0^{2\pi}\int_0^{\theta/2\pi}\int_0^{3+24r^2} dz\,r\,dr\,d\theta = \int_0^{2\pi}\int_0^{\theta/2\pi} (3 + 24r^2)\,r\,dr\,d\theta =$

$= \int_0^{2\pi}\left(\frac{3}{8\pi^2}\theta^2 + \frac{3}{8\pi^4}\theta^4\right)d\theta = \frac{17\pi}{5}$

5. $\int_0^{2\pi}\int_0^1\int_r^{1/\sqrt{2-r^2}} 3\,dz\,r\,dr\,d\theta = 3\int_0^{2\pi}\int_0^1 \left(\frac{r}{\sqrt{2-r^2}} - r^2\right)dr\,d\theta$

$= 3\int_0^{2\pi}\left(\sqrt{2} - \frac{4}{3}\right)d\theta = (6\sqrt{2} - 8)\pi$

7. $\int_0^{\pi}\int_0^{\pi}\int_0^{2\sin\phi} \rho^2 \sin\phi\,d\rho\,d\phi\,d\theta = \int_0^{\pi}\int_0^{\pi} \frac{8}{3}\sin^4\phi\,d\phi\,d\theta = \int_0^{\pi} \pi\,d\theta = \pi^2$

9. $$\int_0^{2\pi}\int_0^{\pi}\int_0^{(1-\cos\phi)/2} \rho^2 \sin\phi \, d\rho \, d\phi \, d\theta = \int_0^{2\pi}\int_0^{\pi} \frac{1}{24}(1-\cos\phi)^3 \sin\phi \, d\phi \, d\theta$$

$$= \int_0^{2\pi} \frac{1}{6} \, d\theta = \frac{\pi}{3}$$

11. $$\int_0^{2\pi}\int_0^{\pi/3}\int_{\sec\phi}^{2} 3\rho^2 \sin\phi \, d\rho \, d\phi \, d\theta = \int_0^{2\pi}\int_0^{\pi/3} (8-\sec^3\phi)\sin\phi \, d\phi \, d\theta$$

$$= \int_0^{2\pi}\left(-8\cos\phi - \frac{1}{2}\tan^2\phi\right)\Big]_0^{\pi/3} d\theta = \int_0^{2\pi} \frac{5}{2} \, d\theta = 5\pi$$

13. (a) $$V = \int_0^{2\pi}\int_0^{\pi}\int_0^{2} \rho^2 \sin\phi \, d\rho \, d\phi \, d\theta$$

(b) $$V = \int_0^{2\pi}\int_0^{2}\int_{-\sqrt{4-r^2}}^{\sqrt{4-r^2}} dz \, r \, dr \, d\theta$$

(c) $$V = \int_{-2}^{2}\int_{-\sqrt{4-x^2}}^{\sqrt{4-x^2}}\int_{-\sqrt{4-y^2-x^2}}^{\sqrt{4-y^2-x^2}} dz \, dy \, dx$$

15. (a) $$V = \int_{-1}^{1}\int_{-\sqrt{1-x^2}}^{\sqrt{1-x^2}}\int_0^{\sqrt{4-y^2-x^2}} \sqrt{x^2+y^2} \, dz \, dy \, dx$$

(b) $$V = \int_0^{2\pi}\int_0^{\pi/6}\int_0^{2} \rho^3 \sin^2\phi \, d\rho \, d\phi \, d\theta + \int_0^{2\pi}\int_{\pi/6}^{\pi/2}\int_0^{\csc\phi} \rho^3 \sin^2\phi \, d\rho \, d\phi \, d\theta$$

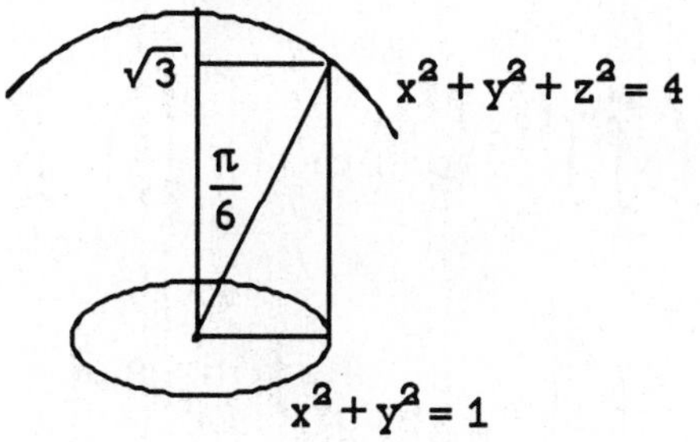


17. $$\int_{-\pi/2}^{\pi/2}\int_0^{\cos\theta}\int_0^{3r^2} f(r,\theta,z) \, dz \, r \, dr \, d\theta$$

19. (a) $$I_z = \int_0^{2\pi}\int_0^{1}\int_0^{\sqrt{1-r^2}} \delta r^2 \, dz \, r \, dr \, d\theta$$

(b) $$I_z = \int_0^{2\pi}\int_0^{\pi/2}\int_0^{1} (\rho^2 \sin^2\phi)\rho^2 \sin\phi \, d\rho \, d\phi \, d\theta$$

21. $V = \int_0^{2\pi}\int_0^1\int_0^{r^2} dz\, r\, dr\, d\theta = \int_0^{2\pi}\int_0^1 r^3\, dr\, d\theta = \int_0^{2\pi} \frac{1}{4} d\theta = \frac{\pi}{2}$

23. $V = \int_0^{2\pi}\int_0^2\int_0^{4-r^2} dz\, r\, dr\, d\theta = \int_0^{2\pi}\int_0^2 (4r - r^3)\, dr\, d\theta = \int_0^{2\pi} 4\, d\theta = 8\pi$

25. The paraboloids intersect when $4r^2 = 5 - r^2 \Rightarrow r = 1$.

$$V = \int_0^{2\pi}\int_0^1\int_{4r^2}^{5-r^2} dz\, r\, dr\, d\theta = \int_0^{2\pi}\int_0^1 (5r - 5r^3)\, dr\, d\theta = \int_0^{2\pi} \frac{5}{4}\, d\theta = \frac{5\pi}{2}$$

27. $V(\text{caps}) = 2\int_0^{2\pi}\int_0^{\pi/6}\int_0^{2a} \rho^2 \sin\phi\, d\rho\, d\phi\, d\theta = \frac{16\pi a^3}{3}(2 - \sqrt{3})$.

$V(\text{cylinder}) = 2\pi r^2 h = 2\sqrt{3}\pi a^3$. Total $= \frac{4\pi a^3}{3}(8 - 3\sqrt{3})$.

(See figure in problem 15 as an aid)

29. We orient the sphere with its center at the origin, and consider the bowl to be beneath the xy-plane. Then

$$V = \int_0^{2\pi}\int_0^4\int_{-\sqrt{25-r^2}}^{-3} dz\, r\, dr\, d\theta = \int_0^{2\pi}\int_0^4 \left[r\sqrt{25-r^2} - 3r\right] dr\, d\theta$$

$$= \int_0^{2\pi}\left[-\frac{1}{3}(25-r^2)^{3/2} - \frac{3}{2}r^2\right]_0^4 d\theta = \frac{52\pi}{3}.$$

31. Volume $= \pi r^2 h = \pi(1)^2(2) = 2\pi$

$$\text{Average value} = \frac{1}{2\pi}\int_0^{2\pi}\int_0^1\int_{-1}^1 (r)\, dz\, r\, dr\, d\theta = \frac{1}{2\pi}\int_0^{2\pi}\int_0^1 2r^2\, dr d\theta = \frac{1}{2\pi}\int_0^{2\pi}\frac{2}{3}\, d\theta = \frac{2}{3}$$

33. $M = \int_0^{2\pi}\int_0^1\int_0^r dz\, r\, dr\, d\theta = \int_0^{2\pi}\int_0^1 r^2\, dr\, d\theta = \int_0^{2\pi}\frac{1}{3} d\theta = \frac{2\pi}{3}$

$$M_{xy} = \int_0^{2\pi}\int_0^1\int_0^r z\, dz\, r\, dr\, d\theta = \int_0^{2\pi}\int_0^1 \frac{1}{2}r^3\, dr\, d\theta = \int_0^{2\pi}\frac{1}{8}\, d\theta = \frac{\pi}{4}.$$

$\bar{z} = \left(\frac{2\pi}{3}\right) \div \left(\frac{\pi}{4}\right) = \frac{3}{8}$. By symmetry, $\bar{x} = \bar{y} = 0$. $\therefore (\bar{x}, \bar{y}, \bar{z}) = \left(0, 0, \frac{3}{8}\right)$.

35. $M = \int_0^{2\pi}\int_1^2\int_0^4 dz\, r\, dr\, d\theta = \int_0^{2\pi}\int_1^2 4r\, dr\, d\theta = \int_0^{2\pi} 6\, d\theta = 12\pi$

$I_z = \int_0^{2\pi}\int_1^2\int_0^4 (x^2 + y^2)\, dz\, r\, dr\, d\theta = \int_0^{2\pi}\int_1^2 4r^3\, dr\, d\theta = \int_0^{2\pi} 15\, d\theta = 30\pi$

$R_z = \sqrt{\dfrac{30\pi}{12\pi}} = \dfrac{\sqrt{10}}{2}.$

37. $r^2 + z^2 = 2a^2$ and $r^2 = az \Rightarrow r^2 + z^2 = 2\left(\dfrac{r^4}{z^2}\right) \Rightarrow 2r^4 - r^2z^2 - z^4 = 0$ or

$(2r^2 + z^2)(r^2 - z^2) = 0 \Rightarrow r = z = a$. By symmetry, $\bar{x} = \bar{y} = 0$.

$M = \int_0^{2\pi}\int_0^a\int_{r^2/a}^{\sqrt{2a^2-r^2}} dz\, r\, dr\, d\theta = \int_0^{2\pi}\int_0^a \left(r\sqrt{2a^2 - r^2} - \dfrac{r^3}{a}\right) dr\, d\theta$

$= \int_0^{2\pi} \dfrac{8\sqrt{2} - 7}{12} a^3\, d\theta = \dfrac{\pi a^3 (8\sqrt{2} - 7)}{6}.$

$M_{xy} = \int_0^{2\pi}\int_0^a\int_{r^2/a}^{\sqrt{2a^2-r^2}} z\, dz\, r\, dr\, d\theta = \int_0^{2\pi}\int_0^a \left(\dfrac{2a^2 - r^2}{2} - \dfrac{r^4}{2a^2}\right) r\, dr\, d\theta$

$= \int_0^{2\pi} \left(\dfrac{7}{24}a^4\right) d\theta = \dfrac{7\pi a^4}{12}$. $\bar{z} = \left(\dfrac{7\pi a^4}{12}\right)\left(\dfrac{6}{\pi a^3 (8\sqrt{2} - 7)}\right) = \dfrac{7a}{2(8\sqrt{2} - 7)}.$

39. We orient the cone with its vertex at the origin and note that $\phi = \dfrac{\pi}{4}$.

$I_x = \int_0^{2\pi}\int_0^1\int_r^1 (y^2 + z^2)\, dz\, r\, dr\, d\theta = \int_0^{2\pi}\int_0^1\int_r^1 (r^2 \sin^2\theta + z^2)dz\, r\, dr\, d\theta$

$= \int_0^{2\pi}\int_0^1 \left[(r^3 - r^4)\sin^2\theta + \dfrac{1}{3}r - \dfrac{1}{3}r^4\right] dr\, d\theta$

$= \int_0^{2\pi} \left(\dfrac{1}{20}\sin^2\theta + \dfrac{1}{10}\right) d\theta = \dfrac{\pi}{20} + \dfrac{\pi}{5} = \dfrac{\pi}{4}.$

41. $\bar{z} = \bar{y} = 0$ by symmetry. $V = \frac{1}{3}\left(\frac{4}{3}\pi r^3\right) = \frac{4\pi}{9}$, or calculate:

$$M = \int_{-\pi/3}^{\pi/3}\int_0^1\int_{-\sqrt{1-r^2}}^{\sqrt{1-r^2}} dz\, r\, dr\, d\theta = \int_{-\pi/3}^{\pi/3}\int_0^1 2r\sqrt{1-r^2}\, dr\, d\theta = \int_{-\pi/3}^{\pi/3} \frac{2}{3} d\theta = \frac{4\pi}{9}.$$

$$M_{yz} = \int_{-\pi/3}^{\pi/3}\int_0^1\int_{-\sqrt{1-r^2}}^{\sqrt{1-r^2}} (r\cos\theta)\, dz\, r\, dr\, d\theta = \int_{-\pi/3}^{\pi/3}\int_0^1 2r^2\sqrt{1-r^2}\,(\cos\theta)\, dr\, d\theta$$

$$= \int_{-\pi/3}^{\pi/3} 2\cos\theta\left(-\frac{r}{4}(1-r^2)^{3/2} + \frac{1}{8}r(1-r^2)^{1/2} + \frac{1}{8}\sin^{-1} r\right)\Big]_0^1 d\theta$$

$$= \int_{-\pi/3}^{\pi/3} \frac{\pi}{8}\cos\theta\, d\theta = \frac{\sqrt{3}\pi}{8}. \quad \therefore\ \bar{x} = \frac{\sqrt{3}\pi}{8} \div \frac{4\pi}{9} = \frac{9\sqrt{3}}{32}.$$

43. (a) $M = \int_0^{2\pi}\int_0^1\int_r^1 z\, dz\, r\, dr\, d\theta = \int_0^{2\pi}\int_0^1\left(\frac{1}{2} - \frac{1}{2}r^2\right) r\, dr\, d\theta = \int_0^{2\pi} \frac{1}{8}\, d\theta = \frac{\pi}{4}$

$$M_{xy} = \int_0^{2\pi}\int_0^1\int_r^1 z^2\, dz\, r\, dr\, d\theta = \int_0^{2\pi}\int_0^1\left(\frac{1}{3} - \frac{1}{3}r^3\right) r\, dr\, d\theta = \int_0^{2\pi}\frac{1}{10} d\theta = \frac{\pi}{5}$$

$\bar{x} = \bar{y} = 0$ by symmetry. $\bar{z} = \frac{4}{5}$.

$$I_z = \int_0^{2\pi}\int_0^1\int_r^1 r^2 z\, dz\, r\, dr\, d\theta = \frac{1}{2}\int_0^{2\pi}\int_0^1 (r^3 - r^5)\, dr\, d\theta = \int_0^{2\pi}\frac{1}{24} d\theta = \frac{\pi}{12}$$

$$R_z = \sqrt{\frac{I_z}{M}} = \sqrt{\frac{1}{3}}.$$

(b) $M = \int_0^{2\pi}\int_0^1\int_r^1 z^2\, dz\, r\, dr\, d\theta = \frac{\pi}{5}$ (see part (a))

$$M_{xy} = \int_0^{2\pi}\int_0^1\int_r^1 z^3\, dz\, r\, dr\, d\theta = \frac{1}{4}\int_0^{2\pi}\int_0^1 (1 - r^4) r\, dr\, d\theta = \int_0^{2\pi}\frac{1}{12} d\theta = \frac{\pi}{6}$$

$\bar{x} = \bar{y} = 0$ by symmetry. $\bar{z} = \frac{5}{6}$.

$$I_z = \int_0^{2\pi}\int_0^1\int_r^1 r^2 z^2\, dz\, r\, dr\, d\theta = \frac{1}{3}\int_0^{2\pi}\int_0^1 (r^3 - r^6)\, dr\, d\theta = \int_0^{2\pi}\frac{1}{28}\, d\theta = \frac{\pi}{14}$$

$$R_z = \sqrt{\frac{I_z}{M}} = \sqrt{\frac{5}{14}}.$$

## Spherical Coordinates

45. $V = \int_0^{2\pi}\int_{\pi/3}^{2\pi/3}\int_0^a \rho^2 \sin\phi \, d\rho \, d\phi \, d\theta = \int_0^{2\pi}\int_{\pi/3}^{2\pi/3} \frac{a^3}{3} \sin\phi \, d\phi \, d\theta$

$= \int_0^{2\pi} \frac{a^3}{3} \, d\theta = \frac{2\pi a^3}{3}.$

47. $V = \int_0^{2\pi}\int_0^{\pi/3}\int_{\sec\phi}^{2} \rho^2 \sin\phi \, d\rho \, d\phi \, d\theta = \int_0^{2\pi}\int_0^{\pi/3} \left(\frac{8}{3} - \frac{\sec^3\phi}{3}\right) \sin\phi \, d\phi \, d\theta$

$= \int_0^{2\pi}\int_0^{\pi/3} \left(\frac{8}{3}\sin\phi - \frac{1}{3}\tan\phi \sec^2\phi\right) d\phi \, d\theta = \int_0^{2\pi} \frac{5}{6} \, d\theta = \frac{5\pi}{3}.$

49. $V = \int_0^{2\pi}\int_0^{\pi}\int_0^{1-\cos\phi} \rho^2 \sin\phi \, d\rho \, d\phi \, d\theta = \int_0^{2\pi}\int_0^{\pi} \frac{1}{3}(1-\cos\phi)^3 \sin\phi \, d\phi \, d\theta$

$= \int_0^{2\pi} \frac{4}{3} d\theta = \frac{8\pi}{3}.$

51. $V = \frac{4\pi}{3}$. Average value $= \frac{3}{4\pi}\int_0^{2\pi}\int_0^{\pi}\int_0^1 \rho^3 \sin\phi \, d\rho \, d\phi \, d\theta$

$= \frac{3}{4\pi}\int_0^{2\pi}\int_0^{\pi} \frac{1}{4} \sin\phi \, d\phi \, d\theta = \frac{3}{4\pi}\int_0^{2\pi} \frac{1}{2} \, d\theta = \frac{3}{4}.$

53. $M = \int_0^{2\pi}\int_0^{\pi/3}\int_0^a \rho^2 \sin\phi \, d\rho \, d\phi \, d\theta = \int_0^{2\pi}\int_0^{\pi/3} \frac{a^3}{3} \sin\phi \, d\phi \, d\theta = \int_0^{2\pi} \frac{a^3}{6} \, d\theta = \frac{\pi a^3}{3}$

$M_{xy} = \int_0^{2\pi}\int_0^{\pi/3}\int_0^a (\rho\cos\phi)\rho^2 \sin\phi \, d\rho \, d\phi \, d\theta = \int_0^{2\pi}\int_0^{\pi/3} \frac{a^4}{4} \cos\phi \sin\phi \, d\phi \, d\theta$

$= \int_0^{2\pi} \frac{3a^4}{32} \, d\theta = \frac{3\pi a^4}{16}$. Centroid at $\left(0, 0, \frac{9a}{16}\right)$.

55. $I_z = \int_0^{2\pi}\int_0^{\pi}\int_0^a \delta \rho^4 \sin^3\phi \, d\rho \, d\phi \, d\theta = \int_0^{2\pi}\int_0^{\pi} \delta \frac{a^5}{5} \sin^3\phi \, d\rho \, d\phi \, d\theta$

$= \frac{\delta a^5}{5}\int_0^{2\pi} \frac{4}{3} \, d\theta = \frac{8\pi\delta a^5}{15}$. $M = \frac{4}{3}\pi\delta a^3$. $R_z = a\sqrt{\frac{2}{5}}$.

57. $J(\rho,\phi,\theta) = \begin{vmatrix} \sin\phi\cos\theta & \rho\cos\phi\cos\theta & -\rho\sin\phi\sin\theta \\ \sin\phi\sin\theta & \rho\cos\phi\sin\theta & \rho\sin\phi\cos\theta \\ \cos\phi & -\rho\sin\phi & 0 \end{vmatrix}$

$$= \cos\phi(\rho^2\cos\phi\sin\phi\cos^2\theta + \rho^2\cos\phi\sin\phi\sin^2\theta)$$
$$+ \rho\sin\phi(\rho\sin^2\phi\cos^2\theta + \rho\sin^2\phi\sin^2\theta)$$
$$= \cos\phi(\rho^2\cos\phi\sin\phi) + \rho\sin\phi(\rho\sin^2\phi)$$
$$= \rho^2\sin\phi(\cos^2\phi + \sin^2\phi) = \rho^2\sin\phi$$

59. $J(u,v,w) = \begin{vmatrix} a & 0 & 0 \\ 0 & b & 0 \\ 0 & 0 & c \end{vmatrix} = abc$. The transformation takes

$R: \dfrac{x^2}{a^2} + \dfrac{y^2}{b^2} + \dfrac{z^2}{c^2} = 1$ into $R': u^2 + v^2 + w^2 = 1$ which is a unit sphere with $V = \dfrac{4}{3}\pi$. Therefore,

$$V = \iiint_R dx\,dy\,dz = \iiint_{R'} abc\,du\,dv\,dw = \frac{4}{3}\pi\,abc.$$

61. $x = u$, $y = \dfrac{v}{u}$ and $z = \dfrac{w}{3} \Rightarrow J(u,v,w) = \begin{vmatrix} 1 & 0 & 0 \\ -\dfrac{v}{u^2} & \dfrac{1}{u} & 0 \\ 0 & 0 & \dfrac{1}{3} \end{vmatrix} = \dfrac{1}{3u}$.

$$\iiint_R (x^2y + 3xyz)\,dx\,dy\,dz = \int_0^3\int_0^2\int_1^2 (uv + vw)\frac{1}{3u}\,du\,dv\,dw$$
$$= \int_0^3\int_0^2 \frac{1}{3}(v + \ln 2\,vw)\,dv\,dw = \frac{2}{3}\int_0^3 (1 + \ln 2\,w)\,dw = 2 + 3\ln 2.$$

## 18.M MISCELLANEOUS

1. $\displaystyle\int_0^4\int_{-\sqrt{4-y}}^{(y-4)/2} dx\,dy = \int_{-2}^0\int_{2x+4}^{4-x^2} dy\,dx = \int_{-2}^0 (-x^2 - 2x)\,dx = \frac{4}{3}$

3. $\displaystyle\int_0^\infty \frac{e^{-ax} - e^{-bx}}{x}\,dx = \int_0^\infty\int_a^b e^{-xy}\,dx\,dy = \int_a^b \left(\lim_{t\to\infty}\int_0^t e^{-xy}\,dx\right)dy$

$$= \int_a^b \left(\lim_{t\to\infty} -\frac{1}{y}e^{-xy}\Big]_0^t\right)dy = \int_a^b \frac{1}{y}\,dy = \ln\frac{b}{a}$$

5. $$\int_0^x\int_0^u e^{m(x-t)}f(t)\,dt\,du = \int_0^x\int_t^x e^{m(x-t)}f(t)\,du\,dt$$

$$= \int_0^x u\,e^{m(x-t)}f(t)\Big]_{u=t}^{u=x} dt = \int_0^x (x-t)e^{m(x-t)}f(t)\,dt$$

$$\int_0^x\int_0^v\int_0^u e^{m(x-t)}f(t)\,dt\,du\,dv = \int_0^x\int_t^x\int_t^v e^{m(x-t)}f(t)\,du\,dv\,dt$$

$$= \int_0^x\int_t^x (v-t)\,e^{m(x-t)}f(t)\,dv\,dt = \int_0^x\left[\frac{1}{2}(v-t)^2\,e^{m(x-t)}f(t)\right]_t^x dt$$

$$= \int_0^x \frac{1}{2}(x-t)^2\,e^{m(x-t)}f(t)\,dt$$

7. $$\int_{-1}^1\int_{x^2}^1 dy\,dx = \int_0^1\int_{-\sqrt{y}}^{\sqrt{y}} dx\,dy$$

9. $$\int_0^1\int_0^y (x^2+y^2)\,dx\,dy + \int_1^2\int_0^{2-y} (x^2+y^2)\,dx\,dy = \int_0^1\int_x^{2-x} (x^2+y^2)\,dy\,dx$$

11. $$\int_0^2\int_{2x}^4 (x^2+y^2)\,dy\,dx = \int_0^2\left(-\frac{14}{3}x^3 + 4x^2 + \frac{64}{3}\right)dx = \frac{104}{3}$$

13. $$\int_0^\infty\int_0^{e^{-(x^2/2)}} x\,dy\,dx = \int_0^\infty xe^{-(x^2/2)}\,dx = -\lim_{t\to\infty}\left[-e^{-(x^2/2)}\right]_0^t = 1$$

15. $$\text{Pressure} = \int_c^{c+a}\int_{-\sqrt{a^2-(y-c)^2}}^{\sqrt{a^2-(y-c)^2}} wy\,dx\,dy = \int_c^{c+a} 2wy\sqrt{a^2-(y-c)^2}\,dy$$

$$= \int_0^{\frac{\pi}{2}} 2wa^2\cos^2 t\,(a\sin t + c)\,dt = \frac{wa^2}{6}(3\pi c + 4a).$$

$$M_x = \int_c^{c+a}\int_{-\sqrt{a^2-(y-c)^2}}^{\sqrt{a^2-(y-c)^2}} wy^2\,dx\,dy = \int_c^{c+a} 2wy^2\sqrt{a^2-(y-c)^2}\,dy$$

$$= \frac{wa^2}{24}(3\pi a^2 + 12\pi c^2 + 32ac).\ \therefore\ \bar{y} = \frac{3\pi a^2 + 12\pi c^2 + 32ac}{4(3\pi c + 4a)}.$$

17. (a) $$\int_0^{\ln 2}\int_0^{\pi/2} e^x\cos y\,dx\,dy = \left(\int_0^{\ln 2}\cos y\,dy\right)\left(\int_0^{\pi/2} e^x\,dx\right) = \sin(\ln 2)(e^{\pi/2}-1)$$

(b) $$\int_1^2\int_{-1}^1 \frac{x}{y^2}\,dx\,dy = \left(\int_1^2\frac{1}{y^2}\,dy\right)\left(\int_{-1}^1 x\,dx\right) = 0$$

19. $M = \int_0^{\pi/4}\int_1^2 r\,dr\,d\theta = \int_0^{\pi/4} \frac{3}{2}\,d\theta = \frac{3\pi}{8}$

$M_x = \int_0^{\pi/4}\int_1^2 (r\sin\theta)r\,dr\,d\theta = \int_0^{\pi/4} \frac{7}{3}\sin\theta\,d\theta = \frac{7}{6}(2-\sqrt{2})$

$M_y = \int_0^{\pi/4}\int_1^2 (r\cos\theta)r\,dr\,d\theta = \int_0^{\pi/4} \frac{7}{3}\cos\theta\,d\theta = \frac{7\sqrt{2}}{6}$

$\therefore (\bar{x},\bar{y}) = \left(\frac{7\sqrt{2}}{6}\cdot\frac{8}{3\pi}, \frac{7}{6}(2-\sqrt{2})\cdot\frac{8}{3\pi}\right) = \left(\frac{28\sqrt{2}}{9\pi}, \frac{28(2-\sqrt{2})}{9\pi}\right)$

21. $\int_{-a}^{a}\int_0^{\sqrt{a^2-y^2}} x\,dx\,dy = \int_{-\pi/2}^{\pi/2}\int_0^a (r\cos\theta)r\,dr\,d\theta$

23. $J(u,v) = \begin{vmatrix} 1 & -1 \\ 0 & 1 \end{vmatrix} = 1$. We have $x = u+v$, $y = v$ and $y = x$ is transformed into $u = 0$, $y = 0$ into $v = 0$ so that the region is the first quadrant of the uv-plane. $\therefore \int_0^\infty e^{-sx}\,dx\int_0^x f(x-y)\,dy = \int_0^\infty\int_0^\infty e^{-s(u+v)} f(u,v)\,du\,dv$.

25. $M = \int_{-\pi/4}^{\pi/4}\int_0^{a\sqrt{\cos 2\theta}} r\,dr\,d\theta = \int_{-\pi/4}^{\pi/4} \frac{a^2}{2}\cos 2\theta\,d\theta = \frac{a^2}{4}\sin 2\theta\Big]_{\pi/4}^{\pi/4} = \frac{a^2}{2}$

$I_x = \int_{-\pi/4}^{\pi/4}\int_0^{a\sqrt{\cos 2\theta}} (r\sin\theta)^2\,r\,dr\,d\theta = \frac{a^4}{4}\int_{-\pi/4}^{\pi/4} \cos^2 2\theta\,\sin^2\theta\,d\theta$

$= \frac{a^4}{4}\int_{-\pi/4}^{\pi/4} \cos^2 2\theta\left(\frac{1}{2}-\frac{1}{2}\cos 2\theta\right)d\theta = \frac{a^4}{96}(3\pi - 8).$

$I_y = \int_{-\pi/4}^{\pi/4}\int_0^{a\sqrt{\cos 2\theta}} (r\cos\theta)^2\,r\,dr\,d\theta = \frac{a^4}{4}\int_{-\pi/4}^{\pi/4} \cos^2 2\theta\,\cos^2\theta\,d\theta$

$\frac{a^4}{4}\int_{-\pi/4}^{\pi/4} \cos^2 2\theta\left(\frac{1}{2}+\frac{1}{2}\cos 2\theta\right)d\theta = \frac{a^4}{96}(3\pi + 8).$

$\therefore \quad R_y = \frac{a}{4}\sqrt{\frac{3\pi+8}{3}}$ and $R_x = \frac{a}{4}\sqrt{\frac{3\pi-8}{3}}$

27. $K(a) = \int_0^{\beta}\int_0^{a} r \ln(r^2)\, dr\, d\theta = 2\int_0^{\beta} r \ln r\, dr\, d\theta$

$$= 2\int_0^{\beta}\left(\frac{a^2}{2}\ln a - \frac{a^2}{4}\right)d\theta = a^2\beta\left(\ln a - \frac{1}{2}\right)$$

Changing the order of integration, we have

$$K(a) = \int_0^{a\cos\beta}\int_0^{x\tan\beta} \ln(x^2+y^2)\, dy\, dx + \int_{a\cos\beta}^{a}\int_0^{\sqrt{a^2-x^2}} \ln(x^2+y^2)\, dy\, dx.$$

29. $(x^2+y^2)^2 - (x^2-y^2) = 0 \Rightarrow r^4 - r^2\cos 2\theta = 0$ or $r^2 = \cos 2\theta$.

$$\int_{-\pi/4}^{\pi/4}\int_0^{\sqrt{\cos 2\theta}} \frac{r}{(1+r^2)^2}\, dr\, d\theta = \frac{1}{2}\int_{-\pi/4}^{\pi/4}\left(1 - \frac{1}{1+\cos 2\theta}\right)d\theta$$

$$= \frac{1}{2}\int_{-\pi/4}^{\pi/4}\left(1 - \frac{1}{2\cos^2\theta}\right)d\theta = \frac{\pi-2}{4}$$

31. $M_{xy} = \int_0^1\int_{-(1-z)}^{1-z}\int_{-(1-z)}^{1-z} z\, dx\, dy\, dz = 4\int_0^1 z(1-z)^2\, dz = \frac{1}{3}$

$$V = \frac{1}{3}Bh = \frac{1}{3}(4)(1) = \frac{4}{3}.\quad \therefore (\bar{x}, \bar{y}, \bar{z}) = \left(0, 0, \frac{1}{4}\right).$$

33. $V = \int_0^{2\pi}\int_0^1\int_{r^2}^{(r^2+1)/2} dz\, r\, dr\, d\theta = \int_0^{2\pi}\int_0^1\left(\frac{r}{2} - \frac{r^3}{2}\right)dr\, d\theta = \frac{\pi}{4}$

35. Average value $= \frac{1}{8}\int_0^2\int_0^2\int_0^2 15xy\sqrt{x^2+y^2+1}\, dz\, dy\, dx$

$$= \frac{1}{8}\int_0^2\int_0^2 30xy\sqrt{x^2+y^2+1}\, dy\, dx = \frac{15}{4}\int_0^2 \frac{1}{3}x\left(\sqrt{x^2+y^2+1}\right)^3\Big]_0^2 dx$$

$$= \frac{5}{4}\int_0^2 x\left(\sqrt{x^2+5}\right)^3 - x\left(\sqrt{x^2+1}\right)^3 dx$$

$$= \frac{5}{4}\cdot\frac{1}{5}\left[(x^2+5)^{5/2} - (x^2+1)^{5/2}\right]_0^2 = \frac{122-25\sqrt{5}}{2}$$

37. $I_z = \int_0^{2\pi}\int_{b-a}^{b+a}\int_{-\sqrt{a^2-(b-r)^2}}^{\sqrt{a^2-(b-r)^2}} r^2\,dz\,r\,dr\,d\theta = 2\int_0^{2\pi}\int_{b-a}^{b+a} r^3\sqrt{a^2-(b-r)^2}\,dr\,d\theta$

$= 4\pi\int_{b-a}^{b+a} r^3\sqrt{a^2-(b-r)^2}\,dr$ (Let $r = b + a\sin u$)

$= 4\pi\int_{-\pi/2}^{\pi/2}(b+a\sin u)^3 a^2\cos^2 u\,du = \frac{\pi^2 a^2 b}{2}(3a^2+4b^2)$

39. $\int_0^{\pi/2}\int_0^{\sqrt{3}}\int_1^{\sqrt{4-r^2}} r^3\sin\theta\cos\theta\, z^2\,dz\,dr\,d\theta =$

$= \int_0^1\int_{\sqrt{1-x^2}}^{\sqrt{3-x^2}}\int_1^{\sqrt{4-x^2-y^2}} z^2 xy\,dz\,dy\,dx + \int_1^{\sqrt{3}}\int_0^{\sqrt{3-x^2}}\int_1^{\sqrt{4-x^2-y^2}} z^2 xy\,dz\,dy\,dx$

41. $V = 2\int_0^{\frac{\pi}{2}}\int_0^{a\sin\theta}\int_{-\sqrt{a^2-r^2}}^{\sqrt{a^2-r^2}} dz\,r\,dr\,d\theta = 2\int_0^{\frac{\pi}{2}}\int_0^{a\sin\theta} 2r\sqrt{a^2-r^2}\,dr\,d\theta$

$=2\int_0^{\frac{\pi}{2}} -\frac{2}{3}(a^2-r^2)^{3/2}\Big]_0^{a\sin\theta} d\theta = \frac{4a^3}{3}\int_0^{\frac{\pi}{2}}(1-\cos^3\theta)\,d\theta = \frac{2a^3}{9}(3\pi-4)$

43. $I_z = \int_0^{2\pi}\int_0^{\pi/3}\int_0^a \rho^2\sin^2\phi\,(\rho^2\sin\phi)\,d\rho\,d\phi\,d\theta = \frac{a^5}{5}\int_0^{2\pi}\int_0^{\pi/3}\sin^3\phi\,d\phi\,d\theta = \frac{\pi a^5}{12}$

45. $I_z = \int_0^{2\pi}\int_0^{\pi}\int_a^b (\rho^2\sin^2\phi)\rho^2\sin\phi\,d\rho\,d\phi\,d\theta = \frac{b^5-a^2}{5}\int_0^{2\pi}\int_0^{\pi}\sin^3\phi\,d\phi\,d\theta$

$= \frac{b^5-a^2}{5}\int_0^{2\pi}(1-\cos^2\phi)\sin\phi = \frac{8\pi}{15}(b^5-a^5)$

47. $I_x = \int_0^1\int_0^{2\pi}\int_{-\sqrt{4-r^2}}^{\sqrt{4-r^2}} (r^2\sin^2\theta + z^2)\,dz\,r\,d\theta\,dr$

$= \int_0^1\int_0^{2\pi}\left(2r^2\sqrt{4-r^2}\sin^2\theta + \frac{2}{3}(4-r^2)^{3/2}\right)r\,d\theta\,dr$

$= \int_0^1\left(2\pi r^2\sqrt{4-r^2} + \frac{4\pi}{3}(4-r^2)^{3/2}\right)r\,dr = \frac{2\pi}{15}(128-51\sqrt{3})$

49. We position the sphere so that its equation is $x^2 + y^2 + z^2 = a^2$, and take the axis tangent at P(a, 0, 0) parallel to z-axis.. Then

$$I = \int_0^a \int_0^{2\pi} \int_{-\sqrt{a^2-r^2}}^{\sqrt{a^2-r^2}} [(x-a)^2 + y^2]\, dz\, d\theta\, r\, dr$$

$$= \int_0^a \int_0^{2\pi} \int_{-\sqrt{a^2-r^2}}^{\sqrt{a^2-r^2}} [r^2 + a^2 - 2ar\cos\theta]\, dz\, d\theta\, r\, dr = \frac{28\pi a^5}{15}$$

51. Let $\mathbf{u} = \dfrac{x\mathbf{i} + y\mathbf{j} + (z-b)\mathbf{k}}{\sqrt{x^2+y^2+(z-b)^2}} = \dfrac{(r\cos\theta)^2\mathbf{i} + (r\sin\theta)^2\mathbf{j} + (z-b)\mathbf{k}}{\sqrt{r^2+(z-b)^2}}$.

$$\mathbf{F} = Gm \int_{-a}^{a} \int_0^{\sqrt{a^2-z^2}} \int_0^{2\pi} \frac{\delta\mathbf{u}}{r^2}\, d\theta\, r\, dr\, dz$$

$$= \left[ 2\pi\, Gm\, \delta \int_{-a}^{a} \int_0^{\sqrt{a^2-z^2}} (z-b)\,(r^2+(z-b)^2)^{-3/2}\, r\, dr\, dz \right]\mathbf{k}$$

$$= \left[ 2\pi\, Gm\, \delta \int_{-a}^{a} -(z-b)\,(r^2+(z-b)^2)^{-1/2} \Big]_0^{\sqrt{a^2-z^2}} dz \right]\mathbf{k}$$

$$= -2\pi\, Gm\, \delta \int_{-a}^{a} \left(1 + \frac{z-b}{\sqrt{a^2+b^2-2bz}}\right) dz\, \mathbf{k}$$

Now $\int_{-a}^{a} dz = 2a$ and $\int_{-a}^{a} \dfrac{-b\, dz}{\sqrt{a^2+b^2-2bz}} = \sqrt{a^2+b^2-2bz}\,\Big]_{-a}^{a} = -2a$

Remember that $|a-b| = b-a$. Let $w^2 = a^2 + b^2 - 2bz$. Then

$$\int_{-a}^{a} \frac{z\, dz}{\sqrt{a^2+b^2-2bz}} = \int_{b+a}^{b-a} \frac{w^2-a^2-b^2}{-2b\, w}\left(-\frac{w}{b}dw\right) = \frac{2a^3}{3b^2}$$

$$\therefore\ \mathbf{F} = -2\pi\, Gm\, \delta\mathbf{k} \left(\frac{2a^3}{3b^2}\right) = -\frac{GMm\delta}{b^2}\mathbf{k}.$$

# CHAPTER 19

# VECTOR FIELDS AND INTEGRATION

## 19.1 LINE INTEGRALS

1. (c) The initial point is (0,1) and the final point is (1,0). The path lies in the xy-plane.

3. (g) The path is the circle $x^2 + y^2 = a^2$ in the xy-plane.

5. (d) The initial point is (0,0,0) and the final point is (2,2,2).

7. (f) The initial point is (0,-1,0) and the final point is (0,0,2). The path lies in the yz-plane and is a part of the parabola $y = \frac{1}{4} z^2 - 1$.

9. $f(x,y,z) = x + y$ $\quad\quad$ $\mathbf{R}(t) = t\mathbf{i} + (1-t)\mathbf{j},\ 0 \le t \le 1$

$ds = \sqrt{1+1}\,dt = \sqrt{2}\,dt$

$$\int_C f(x,y,z)\,ds = \int_0^1 (t + 1 - t)\sqrt{2}\,dt = \sqrt{2}t\Big]_0^1 = \sqrt{2}$$

11. $f(x,y,z) = x - y + z - 2$ $\quad\quad$ $\mathbf{R}(t) = t\mathbf{i} + (1-t)\mathbf{j} + \mathbf{k},\ 0 \le t \le 1$

$ds = \sqrt{1+1}\,dt = \sqrt{2}\,dt$

$$\int_C f(x,y,z)\,ds = \int_0^1 (t - (1-t) + 1 - 2)\sqrt{2}\,dt = \int_0^1 (2t - 2)\sqrt{2}\,dt$$

$$= \sqrt{2}\,(t^2 - 2t)\Big]_0^1 = -\sqrt{2}$$

13. $f(x,y,z) = xy + y + z$ $\quad\quad$ $\mathbf{R}(t) = 2t\mathbf{i} + t\mathbf{j} + (2-2t)\mathbf{k},\ 0 \le t \le 1$

$ds = \sqrt{4+1+4}\,dt = 3\,dt$

$$\int_C f(x,y,z)\,ds = \int_0^1 (2t^2 + t + 2 - 2t)\,3dt = \int_0^1 (2t^2 - t + 2)\sqrt{2}\,dt$$

$$= 3\left(\frac{2}{3}t^3 - \frac{1}{2}t^2 + 2t\right)\Big]_0^1 = \frac{13}{2}$$

15. $f(x,y,z) = x + y$ $\quad\quad$ $\mathbf{R}(t) = (\cos t)\mathbf{i} + (\sin t)\mathbf{j} + t\mathbf{k},\ 0 \le t \le \frac{\pi}{2}$

$$ds = \sqrt{\sin^2 t + \cos^2 t + 1}\ dt = \sqrt{2}\ dt$$

$$\int_C f(x,y,z)\ ds = \int_0^1 (\cos t + \sin t)\sqrt{2}\ dt = \sqrt{2}(\sin t - \cos t)\Big]_0^{\frac{\pi}{2}} = 2\sqrt{2}$$

17. $f(x,y,z) = \sqrt{x^2 + y^2}$

$\mathbf{R}(t) = (t \sin t + \cos t)\mathbf{i} + (t \cos t - \sin t)\mathbf{j},\ 0 \le t \le \sqrt{3}$

$$f(t) = \sqrt{t^2 \sin^2 t + 2t \sin t \cos t + \cos^2 t + t^2 \cos^2 t - 2t \sin t \cos t + \sin^2 t}$$

$$= \sqrt{t^2 + 1}$$

$\mathbf{v}(t) = (t \cos t)\mathbf{i} + (t \sin t)\mathbf{j};\ ds = \sqrt{t^2 \cos^2 t + t^2 \sin^2 t}\ dt = |t|\ dt = t\ dt$

$$\int_C f(x,y,z)\ ds = \int_0^{\sqrt{3}} t\sqrt{t^2 + 1}\ dt = \frac{1}{3}(t^2 + 1)^{3/2}\Big]_0^{\sqrt{3}} = \frac{7}{3}$$

19. $f(x,y,z) = \dfrac{\sqrt{3}}{x^2 + y^2 + z^2}$ $\quad\quad$ $\mathbf{R}(t) = t\mathbf{i} + t\mathbf{j} + t\mathbf{k},\ 1 \le t \le 2$

$$ds = \sqrt{1 + 1 + 1}\ dt = \sqrt{3}\ dt$$

$$\int_C f(x,y,z)\ ds = \int_1^2 \left(\frac{\sqrt{3}}{3t^2}\right)\sqrt{3}\ dt = -\frac{1}{t}\Big]_1^2 = \frac{1}{2}$$

21. $f(x,y,z) = x + \sqrt{y} - z^2$

$\mathbf{R}_1(t) = t\mathbf{i} + t^2\mathbf{j},\ 0 \le t \le 1$ $\quad\quad$ $ds_1 = \sqrt{1 + 4t^2}\ dt$

$\mathbf{R}_2(t) = \mathbf{i} + \mathbf{j} + t\mathbf{k},\ 0 \le t \le 1$ $\quad\quad$ $ds_2 = dt$

$$\int_C f(x,y,z)\ ds = \int_0^1 2t\sqrt{1 + 4t^2}\ dt + \int_0^1 (2 - t^2)\ dt$$

$$= \frac{1}{6}(1 + 4t^2)^{3/2} + 2t - \frac{1}{3}t^3\Big]_0^1 = \frac{5\sqrt{5} + 9}{6}$$

23. $\mathbf{R}(t) = (\cos t)\mathbf{i} + (\sin t)\mathbf{j},\ 0 \le t \le 2\pi$. From Example 3, $M = 2\pi - 2$ and

$$ds = dt.\ I_z = \int_C (x^2 + y^2)(2 - y)\ ds = \int_0^{\pi} (2 - \sin t)\ dt = 2\pi - 2.$$

$$R_z = \sqrt{\frac{I_z}{M}} = \sqrt{\frac{2\pi - 2}{2\pi - 2}} = 1.$$

25. $\mathbf{R}(t) = (a\cos t)\mathbf{i} + (a\sin t)\mathbf{j}$ , $0 \le t \le 2\pi$. $ds = \sqrt{a^2\sin^2 t + a^2\cos^2 t}\,dt = a\,dt$

$$M = \int_0^{2\pi} \delta\, a\,dt = 2\pi\delta a. \quad I_z = \int_0^{2\pi} (x^2 + y^2)\,\delta\, a\,dt = 2\pi a^3\delta.$$

$$R_z = \sqrt{\frac{I_z}{M}} = a$$

27. $\mathbf{R}(t) = t\mathbf{i}$, $0 \le t \le L$. $M = \int_0^L \delta\,dt = \delta L$

$$I_z = \int_0^L (x^2 + y^2)\,\delta\,dt = \int_0^L \delta t^2\,dt = \frac{\delta L^3}{3} = \frac{L^2}{3}M.$$

29. $\mathbf{R}(t) = (a\cos t)\mathbf{i} + (a\sin t)\mathbf{j}$, $0 \le t \le \pi$. $ds = a\,dt$

$$M = \int_0^{\pi} \delta\,dt = \pi a\delta. \quad \bar{x} = 0 \text{ by symmetry}.$$

$$I_x = \int_0^{\pi} (z^2 + y^2)\,\delta\, a\,dt = \int_0^{\pi} \delta a^3 \sin^2 t\,dt = \frac{\pi a^3\delta}{2}. \quad R_x = \sqrt{\frac{I_x}{M}} = \frac{a}{\sqrt{2}}.$$

$$M_{xz} = \int_0^{\pi} y\,\delta\, a\,dt = \int_0^{\pi} \delta a^2 \sin t\,dt = 2a^2\delta. \quad \bar{y} = \frac{2a^2\delta}{\pi a\delta} = \frac{2a}{\pi}.$$

31. $\mathbf{R}(t) = (t^2 - 1)\mathbf{j} + (2t)\mathbf{k}$, $0 \le t \le 1$ . $ds = 2\sqrt{t^2 + 1}\,dt$. $\delta = \sqrt{t^2 + 1}$

$$M = \int \delta\,ds = \int_0^1 2(t^2 + 1)\,dt = \frac{8}{3}$$

$$I_x = \int (y^2 + z^2)\,\delta\,ds = 2\int_0^1 (t^2 + 1)^3\,dt = \frac{192}{35}. \quad R_x = \sqrt{\frac{I_x}{M}} = \sqrt{\frac{72}{35}}.$$

$$I_y = \int (x^2 + z^2)\delta\,ds = \int_0^1 8t^2(t^2 + 1)\,dt = \frac{64}{15}. \quad R_y = \sqrt{\frac{8}{5}}.$$

$$I_z = \int (x^2 + y^2)\delta\,ds = 2\int_0^1 (t^6 - t^4 - t^2 + 1)\,dt = \frac{128}{105}. \quad R_z = \sqrt{\frac{16}{35}}.$$

$$M_{xz} = \int y\,\delta\,ds = 2\int_0^1 (t^4 - 1)\,dt = -\frac{8}{5}. \quad M_{yz} = \int x\delta\,ds = 0.$$

$$M_{xy} = \int z\delta\,ds = 4\int_0^1 (t^3 + t)\,dt = 3. \quad (\bar{x}, \bar{y}, \bar{z}) = \left(0, -\frac{3}{5}, \frac{9}{8}\right)$$

## 19.2 LINE INTEGRALS IN VECTOR FIELDS. WORK, CIRCULATION, AND FLUX

1. $\mathbf{F}(x,y,z) = 2x\mathbf{i} + 3y\mathbf{j} + 4z\mathbf{k}$

(a) $\mathbf{R}_1(t) = t\mathbf{i} + t\mathbf{j} + t\mathbf{k},\ 0 \le t \le 1$

$$\text{Work} = \int_C \mathbf{F} \cdot d\mathbf{R}_1 = \int_0^1 (2t\mathbf{i} + 3t\mathbf{j} + 4t\mathbf{k}) \cdot (\mathbf{i} + \mathbf{j} + \mathbf{k})\, dt$$

$$= \int_0^1 9t\, dt = \frac{9}{2}$$

(b) $\mathbf{R}_2(t) = t\mathbf{i} + t^2\mathbf{j} + t^4\mathbf{k},\ 0 \le t \le 1$

$$\text{Work} = \int_C \mathbf{F} \cdot d\mathbf{R}_2 = \int_0^1 \left(2t\mathbf{i} + 3t^2\mathbf{j} + 4t^4\mathbf{k}\right) \cdot (\mathbf{i} + 2t\mathbf{j} + 4t^3\mathbf{k})\, dt$$

$$= \int_0^1 (2t + 6t^3 + 16t^7)\, dt = t^2 + \frac{3}{2}t^4 + 2t^8\Big]_0^1 = \frac{9}{2}$$

(c) $\mathbf{R}_1(t) = t\mathbf{i} + t\mathbf{j},\ 0 \le t \le 1$ $\quad\mathbf{R}_2(t) = \mathbf{i} + \mathbf{j} + t\mathbf{k},\ 0 \le t \le 1$

$$\text{Work} = \int_{C_1} \mathbf{F} \cdot d\mathbf{R}_1 + \int_{C_2} \mathbf{F} \cdot d\mathbf{R}_2$$

$$= \int_0^1 \left(2t\mathbf{i} + 3t\mathbf{j}\right) \cdot (\mathbf{i} + \mathbf{j})\, dt + \int_0^1 (2\mathbf{i} + 3\mathbf{j} + 4t\mathbf{k}) \cdot \mathbf{k}\, dt$$

$$= \int_0^1 9t\, dt = \frac{9}{2}t^2\Big]_0^1 = \frac{9}{2}$$

3. $\mathbf{F}(x,y,z) = \dfrac{1}{x^2+1}\mathbf{j}$

(a) $\mathbf{R}_1(t) = t\mathbf{i} + t\mathbf{j} + t\mathbf{k},\ 0 \le t \le 1$

$$\text{Work} = \int_C \mathbf{F} \cdot d\mathbf{R}_1 = \int_0^1 \left(\frac{1}{t^2+1}\mathbf{j}\right) \cdot (\mathbf{i} + \mathbf{j} + \mathbf{k})\, dt$$

$$= \int_0^1 \frac{1}{t^2+1}\, dt = \tan^{-1} t\Big]_0^1 = \frac{\pi}{4}$$

(b) $\mathbf{R}_2(t) = t\mathbf{i} + t^2\mathbf{j} + t^4\mathbf{k},\ 0 \le t \le 1$

$$\text{Work} = \int_C \mathbf{F} \cdot d\mathbf{R}_1 = \int_0^1 \left(\frac{1}{t^2+1}\mathbf{j}\right) \cdot (\mathbf{i} + 2t\mathbf{j} + 4t^3\mathbf{k})\, dt$$

$$= \int_0^1 \frac{2t}{t^2+1} dt = \ln(t^2+1)\Big]_0^1 = \ln 2$$

(c) $\mathbf{R}_1(t) = t\mathbf{i} + t\mathbf{j}, 0 \le t \le 1$ $\mathbf{R}_2(t) = \mathbf{i} + \mathbf{j} + t\mathbf{k}, 0 \le t \le 1$

$$\text{Work} = \int_0^1 \mathbf{F} \cdot d\mathbf{R}_1 + \int_0^1 \mathbf{F} \cdot d\mathbf{R}_2$$

$$= \int_0^1 \left(\frac{1}{t^2+1}\mathbf{j}\right) \cdot (\mathbf{i} + \mathbf{j})\, dt + \int_0^1 \left(\frac{1}{2}\mathbf{j}\right) \cdot \mathbf{k}\, dt$$

$$= \int_0^1 \frac{1}{t^2+1}\, dt = \tan^{-1} t\Big]_0^1 = \frac{\pi}{4}$$

5. $\mathbf{F}(x, y, z) = xy\mathbf{i} + yz\mathbf{j} + xz\mathbf{k}$

(a) $\mathbf{R}_1(t) = t\mathbf{i} + t\mathbf{j} + t\mathbf{k}, \ 0 \le t \le 1$

$$\text{Work} = \int_0^1 \mathbf{F} \cdot d\mathbf{R}_1 = \int_0^1 (t^2\mathbf{i} + t^2\mathbf{j} + t^2\mathbf{k}) \cdot (\mathbf{i} + \mathbf{j} + \mathbf{k})\, dt$$

$$= \int_0^1 3t^2\, dt = t^3\Big]_0^1 = 1$$

(b) $\mathbf{R}_2(t) = t\mathbf{i} + t^2\mathbf{j} + t^4\mathbf{k}, \ 0 \le t \le 1$

$$\text{Work} = \int_0^1 \mathbf{F} \cdot d\mathbf{R}_1 = \int_0^1 \left(t^3\mathbf{i} + t^6\mathbf{j} + t^5\mathbf{k}\right) \cdot (\mathbf{i} + 2t\mathbf{j} + 4t^3\mathbf{k})\, dt$$

$$= \int_0^1 (t^3 + 2t^7 + 4t^8)\, dt = \left(\frac{1}{4}t^4 + \frac{1}{4}t^8 + \frac{4}{9}t^9\right)\Big]_0^1 = \frac{17}{18}$$

(c) $\mathbf{R}_1(t) = t\mathbf{i} + t\mathbf{j}, 0 \le t \le 1$ $\mathbf{R}_2(t) = \mathbf{i} + \mathbf{j} + t\mathbf{k}, 0 \le t \le 1$

$$\text{Work} = \int_0^1 \mathbf{F} \cdot d\mathbf{R}_1 + \int_0^1 \mathbf{F} \cdot d\mathbf{R}_2$$

$$= \int_0^1 \left(t^2\mathbf{i}\right) \cdot (\mathbf{i} + \mathbf{j})\, dt + \int_0^1 \left(\mathbf{i} + t\mathbf{j} + t\mathbf{k}\right) \cdot \mathbf{k}\, dt$$

$$= \int_0^1 (t^2 + t)dt = \frac{1}{3}t^3 + \frac{1}{2}t^2\Big]_0^1 = \frac{5}{6}$$

7. $\mathbf{F}(x, y, z) = (y + z)\mathbf{i} + (z + x)\mathbf{j} + (x + y)\mathbf{k}$

(a) $\mathbf{R}_1(t) = t\mathbf{i} + t\mathbf{j} + t\mathbf{k}, \ 0 \le t \le 1$

$$\text{Work} = \int_0^1 \mathbf{F} \cdot d\mathbf{R}_1 = \int_0^1 (2t\mathbf{i} + 2t\mathbf{j} + 2t\mathbf{k}) \cdot (\mathbf{i} + \mathbf{j} + \mathbf{k})\, dt$$

$$= \int_0^1 6t\, dt = 3t^2\Big]_0^1 = 3$$

(b) $\mathbf{R}_2(t) = t\mathbf{i} + t^2\mathbf{j} + t^4\mathbf{k}$, $0 \le t \le 1$

$$\text{Work} = \int_0^1 \mathbf{F} \cdot d\mathbf{R}_1 = \int_0^1 \Big( (t^2 + t^4)\mathbf{i} + (t + t^4)\mathbf{j} + (t + t^2)\mathbf{k} \Big) \cdot (\mathbf{i} + 2t\mathbf{j} + 4t^3\mathbf{k})\, dt$$

$$= \int_0^1 (3t^2 + 5t^4 + 6t^5)\, dt = (t^3 + t^5 + t^6)\Big]_0^1 = 3$$

(c) $\mathbf{R}_1(t) = t\mathbf{i} + t\mathbf{j}$, $0 \le t \le 1$ $\mathbf{R}_2(t) = \mathbf{i} + \mathbf{j} + t\mathbf{k}$, $0 \le t \le 1$

$$\text{Work} = \int_0^1 \mathbf{F} \cdot d\mathbf{R}_1 + \int_0^1 \mathbf{F} \cdot d\mathbf{R}_2$$

$$= \int_0^1 \Big( t\mathbf{i} + t\mathbf{j} + 2t\mathbf{k} \Big) \cdot (\mathbf{i} + \mathbf{j})\, dt + \int_0^1 \Big( (1 + t)\mathbf{i} + (1 + t)\mathbf{j} + 2\mathbf{k} \Big) \cdot \mathbf{k}\, dt$$

$$= \int_0^1 (2t + 2)dt = t^2 + 2t\Big]_0^1 = 3$$

9. $\mathbf{F}(x, y, z) = xy\mathbf{i} + y\mathbf{j} - yz\mathbf{k}$

$\mathbf{R}(t) = t\mathbf{i} + t^2\mathbf{j} + t\mathbf{k}$, $0 \le t \le 1$

$$\text{Work} = \int_0^1 \mathbf{F} \cdot d\mathbf{R}_1 = \int_0^1 (t^3\mathbf{i} + t^2\mathbf{j} - t^3\mathbf{k}) \cdot (\mathbf{i} + 2t\mathbf{j} + \mathbf{k})\, dt$$

$$= \int_0^1 2t^3\, dt = \frac{1}{2}t^4\Big]_0^1 = \frac{1}{2}$$

11. $\mathbf{F}(x, y, z) = z\mathbf{i} + x\mathbf{j} + y\mathbf{k}$

$\mathbf{R}(t) = (\sin t)\mathbf{i} + (\cos t)\mathbf{j} + t\mathbf{k}$, $0 \le t \le 2\pi$

$$\text{Work} = \int_0^{2\pi} \mathbf{F} \cdot d\mathbf{R}_1 = \int_0^{2\pi} \Big( t\mathbf{i} + (\sin t)\mathbf{j} + (\cos t)\mathbf{k} \Big) \cdot \Big( (\cos t)\mathbf{i} - (\sin t)t\mathbf{j} + \mathbf{k} \Big)\, dt$$

$$= \int_0^{2\pi} (t \cos t - \sin^2 t + \cos t)\, dt$$

$$= \cos t + t \sin t - \frac{1}{2}t + \frac{1}{4}\sin 2t + \sin t\Big]_0^{2\pi} = -\pi$$

13. $\mathbf{F}(x, y, z) = -4xy\,\mathbf{i} + 8y\,\mathbf{j} + 2\,\mathbf{k}$

$\mathbf{R}(t) = t\mathbf{i} + t^2\mathbf{j} + \mathbf{k}$, $0 \le t \le 2$

$$\text{F.I.} = \int_0^2 \mathbf{F} \cdot d\mathbf{R} = \int_0^2 \Big( (-4t^3\mathbf{i} + 8t^2\mathbf{j} + 2\mathbf{k}) \cdot \Big( \mathbf{i} + 2t\mathbf{j} \Big) dt$$

$$= \int_0^2 12t^3\, dt = 3t^4\Big]_0^2 = 48$$

15. $\mathbf{F}(x, y, z) = (x - z)\mathbf{i} + x\mathbf{k}$; $\mathbf{R}(t) = (\cos t)t\mathbf{i} + (\sin t)\mathbf{k}$, $0 \le t \le \pi$

$$\text{F.I.} = \int_C \mathbf{F} \cdot d\mathbf{R} = \int_0^{\pi} \Big((\cos t - \sin t)t\mathbf{i} + (\cos t)\mathbf{k}\Big) \cdot ((-\sin t)\mathbf{i} + (\cos t)\mathbf{k})\, dt$$

$$= \int_0^{\pi} (1 - \cos t \sin t)\, dt = t + \frac{1}{2}\cos^2 t \Big]_0^{\pi} = \pi$$

17. $\mathbf{F}(x, y, z) = (x + y)\mathbf{i} - (x^2 + y^2)\mathbf{j}$

(a) $\mathbf{R}(t) = (\cos t)\mathbf{i} + (\sin t)\mathbf{j}$, $0 \le t \le \pi$

$$\text{F.I.} = \int_C \mathbf{F} \cdot d\mathbf{R} = \int_0^{\pi} \Big((\cos t + \sin t)\mathbf{i} - \mathbf{j}\Big) \cdot ((-\sin t)\mathbf{i} + (\cos t)\mathbf{j})\, dt$$

$$= \int_0^{\pi} (-\cos t \sin t - \sin^2 t - \cos t)\, dt$$

$$= \frac{1}{2}\cos^2 t - \sin t - \frac{1}{2}t + \frac{1}{4}\sin 2t \Big]_0^{\pi} = -\frac{\pi}{2}$$

(b) $\mathbf{R}(t) = -t\mathbf{i}$, $-1 \le t \le 1$

$$\text{F.I.} = \int_C \mathbf{F} \cdot d\mathbf{R} = \int_{-1}^{1} (-t\mathbf{i} - t^2\mathbf{j}) \cdot (-\mathbf{i})\, dt = \int_{-1}^{1} -t\, dt = 0$$

(c) $\mathbf{R}_1(t) = (1 - t)\mathbf{i} - t\mathbf{j}$, $0 \le t \le 1$; $\mathbf{R}_2(t) = -t\mathbf{i} + (t - 1)\mathbf{j}$ $0 \le t \le 1$

$$\text{F.I.} = \int_C \mathbf{F} \cdot d\mathbf{R} = \int_0^{1} \Big((1 - 2t)\mathbf{i} - (1 - 2t + 2t^2)\mathbf{j}\Big) \cdot \Big(-\mathbf{i} - \mathbf{j}\Big)\, dt$$

$$+ \int_0^{1} \Big((1 - 2t)\mathbf{i} + (2t^2 - 2t + 1)\mathbf{j}\Big) \cdot \Big(-\mathbf{i} + \mathbf{j}\Big)\, dt$$

$$\int_0^{1} (2t^2 - 2t^2 + 2t)\, dt = 1$$

19. $\mathbf{F}(x, y) = x\mathbf{i} + y\mathbf{j}$

$\mathbf{R}_1(t) = (a\cos t)t\mathbf{i} + (a\sin t)\mathbf{j}$, $0 \le t \le \pi$

$\mathbf{R}_2(t) = t\mathbf{i}$, $-a \le t \le a$

$$\text{Circ} = \int_0^{\pi} \Big((a\cos t + a\sin t)t\mathbf{i}\Big) \cdot \Big((-a\sin t)\mathbf{i} + (a\cos t)\mathbf{j}\Big)\, dt + \int_{-a}^{a} t\mathbf{i} \cdot \mathbf{i}\, dt$$

$$= \int_0^{\pi} (-a^2\cos t \sin t + a^2 \sin t \cos t)\, dt + \int_{-a}^{a} t\, dt = 0$$

$$\text{Flux} = \int M\, dy - N\, dx = \int_0^{\pi} (a\cos t)(a\cos t) - (a\sin t)(-a\sin t)\, dt + \int_{-a}^{a} 0\, dt = \pi a^2$$

21. $\mathbf{F}(x, y) = -y\mathbf{i} + x\mathbf{j}$

$\mathbf{R}_1(t) = (a\cos t)t\mathbf{i} + (a\sin t)\mathbf{j},\ 0 \le t \le \pi$

$\mathbf{R}_2(t) = t\mathbf{i},\ -a \le t \le a$

$$\text{Circ} = \int_0^{\pi} \big((-a \sin t\, t + a\cos t)t\mathbf{i}\big) \cdot \big((-a\sin t)\mathbf{i} + (a\cos t)\mathbf{j}\big)\, dt + \int_{-a}^{a} t\mathbf{j} \cdot \mathbf{i}\ dt$$

$$= \int_0^{\pi} a^2\, dt = \pi a^2$$

$$\text{Flux} = \int M\,dy - N\,dx = \int_0^{\pi} (-a\sin t)(a\cos t) - (a\cos t)(-a \sin t)\, dt + \int_{-a}^{a} -t\ dt = 0$$

23. $\mathbf{F}_1(x, y) = x\mathbf{i} + y\mathbf{j}$ $\qquad$ $\mathbf{F}_2(x, y) = -y\mathbf{i} + x\mathbf{j}$

(a) $\mathbf{R} = (\cos t)\mathbf{i} + (4 \sin t)\mathbf{j},\ 0 \le t \le 2\pi$

$$\mathbf{F}_1:\ \text{Circ} = \int_0^{2\pi} (\cos t)(-\sin t) + (4\sin t)(4 \cos t)\, dt = 0$$

$$\text{Flux} = \int_0^{2\pi} (4 \cos^2 t + 4\sin^2 t)\, dt = 8\pi$$

$$\mathbf{F}_2:\ \text{Circ} = \int_0^{2\pi} (4 \cos^2 t + 4\sin^2 t)\, dt = 8\pi$$

$$\text{Flux} = \int_0^{2\pi} (4\cos t)(-4\sin t) + (\sin t)(\cos t)\, dt = 0$$

(b) $\mathbf{R} = (4\cos t)\mathbf{i} + (\sin t)\mathbf{j},\ 0 \le t \le 2\pi$

$$\mathbf{F}_1:\ \text{Circ} = \int_0^{2\pi} (-15 \sin t \cos t)\, dt = 0$$

$$\text{Flux} = \int_0^{2\pi} (4 \cos^2 t + 4\sin^2 t)\, dt = 8\pi$$

$$\mathbf{F}_2:\ \text{Circ} = \int_0^{2\pi} (4 \cos^2 t + 4\sin^2 t)\, dt = 8\pi$$

$$\text{Flux} = \int_0^{2\pi} (15 \sin t \cos t)\, dt = 0$$

25. $\mathbf{F}(x, y) = y\mathbf{i} = f(t)\,\mathbf{i}.\ \therefore \int \mathbf{F} \cdot d\mathbf{R} = \int_a^b (f(t)\mathbf{i}) \cdot (\mathbf{i} + f'(t)\mathbf{j})\, dt$

$= \int_a^b f(t)\, dt =$ area under the graph of $f$ from $t = a$ to $t = b$.

## 19.3 GREEN'S THEOREM IN THE PLANE

1. $\mathbf{F}(x,y) = -y\mathbf{i} + x\mathbf{j}$

R: $x^2 + y^2 \le a^2$ C: $\mathbf{R}(t) = (a\cos t)\mathbf{i} + (a\sin t)\mathbf{j}$, $0 \le t \le 2\pi$

$M = -y$ $N = x$

$$\frac{\partial M}{\partial x} = 0 \quad \frac{\partial N}{\partial y} = 0 \quad \frac{\partial M}{\partial y} = -1 \quad \frac{\partial N}{\partial x} = 1$$

$$\oint_C M\,dy - N\,dx = \iint_R \left(\frac{\partial M}{\partial x} + \frac{\partial N}{\partial y}\right) dx\,dy$$

$$\int_0^{2\pi} \left[(-a\sin t)(a\cos t) - (a\cos t)(-a\sin t)\right] dt \overset{?}{=} \iint_C 0\,dx\,dy = 0$$

$$\int_0^{2\pi} -2a^2 \sin t\cos t\,dt = \int_0^{2\pi} -a^2 \sin 2t = -\frac{1}{2}a^2 \cos 2t\Big]_0^{2\pi} = 0$$

$$\oint_C M\,dx + N\,dy = \iint_R \left(\frac{\partial N}{\partial x} - \frac{\partial M}{\partial y}\right) dx\,dy$$

$$\int_0^{2\pi} \left[(-a\sin t)(-a\sin t) + (a\cos t)(a\cos t)\right] dt = \int_0^{2\pi} a^2\,dt \overset{?}{=} \iint_R 2\,dx\,dy = 2\pi a^2$$

3. $\mathbf{F}(x,y) = 2x\mathbf{i} - 3y\mathbf{j}$ $M = 2x$ $N = -3y$

R: $x^2 + y^2 \le a^2$ C: $\mathbf{R}(t) = (a\cos t)\mathbf{i} + (a\sin t)\mathbf{j}$, $0 \le t \le 2\pi$

$$\frac{\partial M}{\partial x} = 2 \quad \frac{\partial N}{\partial y} = -3 \quad \frac{\partial M}{\partial y} = 0 \quad \frac{\partial N}{\partial x} = 0$$

$$\oint_C M\,dy - N\,dx = \iint_R \left(\frac{\partial M}{\partial x} + \frac{\partial N}{\partial y}\right) dx\,dy$$

$$\int_0^{2\pi} \left[(2a\cos t)(a\cos t) - (-3a\sin t)(-a\sin t)\right] dt \overset{?}{=} \iint_R -\,dx\,dy = 0$$

$$\int_0^{2\pi} (2a^2\cos^2 t - 3a^2\sin^2 t)\,dt = -\pi a^2$$

$$\oint_C M\,dx + N\,dy = \iint_R \left(\frac{\partial N}{\partial x} - \frac{\partial M}{\partial y}\right) dx\,dy$$

$$\int_0^{2\pi} \left[(-a\sin t)(-a\sin t) + (a\cos t)(a\cos t)\right] dt \overset{?}{=} \iint_R 2\,dx\,dy = 2\pi a^2$$

$$\int_0^{2\pi} a^2\,dt = 2\pi a^2$$

5. $\mathbf{F}(x,y) = (x-y)\mathbf{i} + (x+y)\mathbf{j}$

C: The square bounded by $x=0$, $x=1$, $y=0$, $y=1$

$$\frac{\partial M}{\partial x} = 1 \quad \frac{\partial N}{\partial y} = 1 \quad \frac{\partial M}{\partial y} = -1 \quad \frac{\partial N}{\partial x} = 1$$

$$\text{Flux} = \iint_R \left(\frac{\partial M}{\partial x} + \frac{\partial N}{\partial y}\right) dx\,dy = \int_0^1\int_0^1 2\,dx\,dy = 2$$

$$\text{Circ} = \iint_R \left(\frac{\partial N}{\partial x} - \frac{\partial M}{\partial y}\right) dx\,dy = \int_0^1\int_0^1 2\,dx\,dy = 2$$

7. $\mathbf{F}(x,y) = (xy+x)\mathbf{i} + (xy-y)\mathbf{j}$

C: The square bounded by $x=0$, $x=1$, $y=0$, $y=1$

$$\frac{\partial M}{\partial x} = y+1 \quad \frac{\partial N}{\partial y} = x-1 \quad \frac{\partial M}{\partial y} = x \quad \frac{\partial N}{\partial x} = y$$

$$\text{Flux} = \iint_R \left(\frac{\partial M}{\partial x} + \frac{\partial N}{\partial y}\right) dx\,dy = \int_0^1\int_0^1 (y+x)\,dx\,dy = 1$$

$$\text{Circ} = \iint_R \left(\frac{\partial N}{\partial x} - \frac{\partial M}{\partial y}\right) dx\,dy = \int_0^1\int_0^1 (y-x)\,dx\,dy = 0$$

9. $\mathbf{F}(x,y) = (x^2-y^2)\mathbf{i} + (x^2+y^2)\mathbf{j}$

C: The triangle bounded by $x=1$, $y=0$, $y=x$

$$\frac{\partial M}{\partial x} = 2x \quad \frac{\partial N}{\partial y} = 2y \quad \frac{\partial M}{\partial y} = -2y \quad \frac{\partial N}{\partial x} = 2x$$

$$\text{Flux} = \iint_R \left(\frac{\partial M}{\partial x} + \frac{\partial N}{\partial y}\right) dx\,dy = \int_0^1\int_0^y (2y+2x)\,dx\,dy = 1$$

$$\text{Circ} = \iint_R \left(\frac{\partial N}{\partial x} - \frac{\partial M}{\partial y}\right) dx\,dy = \int_0^1\int_0^y (2x+2y)\,dx\,dy = 1$$

11. $\mathbf{F}(x,y) = xy\mathbf{i} + y^2\mathbf{j}$

C: The 1st. quadrant region bounded by $y=x^2$ and $y=x$

$$\frac{\partial M}{\partial x} = y \quad \frac{\partial N}{\partial y} = 2y \quad \frac{\partial M}{\partial y} = x \quad \frac{\partial N}{\partial x} = 0$$

$$\text{Flux} = \iint_R \left(\frac{\partial M}{\partial x} + \frac{\partial N}{\partial y}\right) dx\,dy = \int_0^1\int_{x^2}^x 3y\,dy\,dx = \frac{1}{5}$$

$$\text{Circ} = \iint_R \left(\frac{\partial N}{\partial x} - \frac{\partial M}{\partial y}\right) dx\,dy = \int_0^1\int_y^{\sqrt{y}} -x\,dx\,dy = -\frac{1}{12}$$

13. $$\oint_C (y^2\,dx + x^2\,dy) = \int_0^1\int_0^{1-y} (2x-2y)\,dx\,dy = 0$$

15. $\oint_C (6y + x)\,dx + (y + 2x)\,dy = \iint_R -4\,dx\,dy = -4\,(4\pi) = -16\pi$

17. $\oint_C 2xy^3\,dx + 4x^2y^2\,dy = \int_0^1\int_0^{x^3} 2xy^2\,dy\,dx = \dfrac{2}{33}$

19. (a) $\oint_C f(x)\,dx + g(y)\,dy = \iint_R \left(\dfrac{\partial}{\partial x}g(y) - \dfrac{\partial}{\partial y}f(x)\right)dx\,dy = 0$

(b) $\oint_C ky\,dx + hx\,dy = \iint_R (h-k)\,dx\,dy = (h-k)A$, where A is the area of the region bounded by C.

21. $\oint_C -y^3\,dx + x^3\,dy = \iint_R (3x^2 + 3y^2)\,dx\,dy \ge 0$ since $3x^2 + 3y^2 \ge 0$ for all x, y.

23. $\oint_C \dfrac{\partial f}{\partial y}dx + \dfrac{\partial f}{\partial x}dy = \iint_R -\left(\dfrac{\partial^2 f}{\partial x^2} + \dfrac{\partial^2 f}{\partial y^2}\right)dx\,dy = 0$

25. $\int_{x_1}^{x_2} \dfrac{\partial N}{\partial x}\,dx = N(x, y)\Big]_{x=g_1(y)}^{x=g_2(y)} = N(g_2(y), y) - N(g_1(y), y)$

$$\int_c^d \int_{g_1(y)}^{g_2(y)} \left(\frac{\partial N}{\partial x}\,dx\right)dy = \int_c^d \Big[N(g_2(y), y) - N(g_1(y), y)\Big]\,dy = \oint_C N\,dy$$

$$\therefore \oint_C N\,dy = \iint_R \left(\frac{\partial N}{\partial x}\,dx\right)dy$$

27. $A = \dfrac{1}{2}\oint_C x\,dy - y\,dx = \int_0^{2\pi} (a\cos t)(a\cos t) - (a\sin t)(-a\sin t)\,dt$

$$= \frac{1}{2}\int_0^{2\pi} a^2\,dt = \pi a^2$$

29. $A = \dfrac{1}{2}\oint_C x\,dy - y\,dx = \int_0^{2\pi} (a\cos^3 t)(-3a\cos^2 t\sin t) - (a\sin^3 t)(3a\sin^2 t\cos t)\,dt$

$$= \frac{3a^2}{2}\int_0^{2\pi} \cos^2 t\,\sin^2 t\,dt = \frac{3a^2\pi}{8}$$

## 19.4 SURFACE AREA AND SURFACE INTEGRALS

1. $F(x,y,z) = x^2 + y^2 - z$ $\quad \nabla F = 2x\mathbf{i} + 2y\mathbf{j} - \mathbf{k}$ $\quad |\nabla F| = \sqrt{4x^2 + 4y^2 + 1}$

$|\nabla F \bullet \mathbf{k}| = 1.$ $\quad R = \{(x,y): x^2 + y^2 = 2\}$

$$A = \iint \sqrt{4x^2 + 4y^2 + 1}\, dx\, dy = \int_0^{2\pi}\int_0^{\sqrt{2}} \sqrt{4r^2 + 1}\, r\, dr\, d\theta$$

$$= \int_0^{2\pi} \frac{1}{12}(4r^2 + 1)^{3/2}\Big]_0^{\sqrt{2}} d\theta = \int_0^{2\pi} \frac{13}{6} d\theta = \frac{13\pi}{3}$$

3. $F(x,y,z) = x + 2y + 2z - 5$ $\quad \nabla F = \mathbf{i} + 2\mathbf{j} + 2\mathbf{k}$ $\quad |\nabla F| = \sqrt{1 + 4 + 4} = 3$

$|\nabla F \bullet \mathbf{k}| = 2.$

$$A = \int_{-1}^{1}\int_{y^2}^{2-y^2} \frac{3}{2}\, dx\, dy = \frac{3}{2}\int_{-1}^{1} (2 - 2y^2)\, dy = 4$$

5. $F(x,y,z) = x^2 - 2y - 2z$ $\quad \nabla F = 2x\mathbf{i} - 2\mathbf{j} - 2\mathbf{k}$

$|\nabla F| = \sqrt{4x^2 + 8} = 2\sqrt{x^2 + 2}.$ $\quad |\nabla F \bullet \mathbf{k}| = 2.$

$$A = \int_0^2\int_0^{3x} \sqrt{x^2 + 2}\, dy\, dx = \int_0^2 3x\sqrt{x^2 + 2}\, dx = 6\sqrt{6} - 2\sqrt{2}$$

7. $F(x,y,z) = x^2 + y^2 + z^2 - 1$ $\quad \nabla F = 2x\mathbf{i} + 2y\mathbf{j} + 2z\mathbf{k}$

$|\nabla F| = 2\sqrt{x^2 + y^2 + z^2} = 2.$ $\quad |\nabla F \bullet \mathbf{k}| = 2z.$ $\quad R = \left\{(x,y): x^2 + y^2 = \frac{1}{2}\right\}$

$$A = \iint_R \frac{1}{z}\, dA = \int_0^{2\pi}\int_0^{1/\sqrt{2}} \frac{1}{\sqrt{1 - r^2}}\, r\, dr\, d\theta = \int_0^{2\pi}\left(1 - \frac{1}{\sqrt{2}}\right) d\theta = (2 - \sqrt{2})\pi$$

9. $F(x,y,z) = z - cx$ $\quad \nabla F = -c\mathbf{i} + \mathbf{k}$

$|\nabla F| = \sqrt{1 + c^2}.$ $\quad |\nabla F \bullet \mathbf{k}| = 1.$ $\quad R = \{(x,y): x^2 + y^2 = 1\}$

$$A = \iint_R \sqrt{1 + c^2}\, dA = \int_0^{2\pi}\int_0^1 \sqrt{1 + c^2}\, r\, dr\, d\theta = \frac{1}{2}\int_0^{2\pi} \sqrt{1 + c^2}\, d\theta = \pi\sqrt{1 + c^2}$$

11. $F(x,y,z) = x^2 + y + z^2 - 1 \quad \nabla F = 2x\mathbf{i} + \mathbf{j} + 2z\,\mathbf{k}$

$|\nabla F| = \sqrt{1 + 4x^2 + 4z^2}$. $|\nabla F \cdot \mathbf{j}| = 1$. $R = \{(x,z): x^2 + z^2 = 1\}$

$$A = \iint_R \sqrt{1 + 4x^2 + 4z^2}\, dA = \int_0^{2\pi}\int_0^1 \sqrt{1 + 4r^2}\, r\, dr\, d\theta$$

$$= \frac{1}{12}\int_0^{2\pi} (1 + 4r^2)^{3/2}\, d\theta = \frac{\pi}{6}(5\sqrt{5} - 1)$$

13. $F_1 = \int_0^1\int_0^1 (x + y)\, dx\, dy = \int_0^1 \left(\frac{1}{2} + y\right)dy = 1$

$F_2 = \int_0^1\int_0^1 (1 + x + y)\, dx\, dy = 2 \quad F_3 = \int_0^1\int_0^1 (x + z)\,dx\, dz = 1$

$F_4 = \int_0^1\int_0^1 (1 + x + z)\, dx\, dz = 2 \quad F_5 = \int_0^1\int_0^1 (y + z)\, dy\, dz = 1$

$F_6 = \int_0^1\int_0^1 (1 + y + z)\, dy\, dz = 2$. $\therefore \iint_S (x + y + z)\, d\sigma = 9$.

15. $\iint_S xyz\, d\sigma = \int_0^b\int_0^a cxy\, dx\, dy + \int_0^c\int_0^b ayz\, dy\, dz = \int_0^c\int_0^a b\, xz\, dx\, dz = \frac{abc}{4}(ab + bc + a$

17. $g(x,y,z) = x + y + z$. $F(x,y,z) = 2x + 2y + z = 2$

$\nabla F = 2\mathbf{i} + 2\mathbf{j} + \mathbf{k}$. $|\nabla F| = 3$. $\nabla F \cdot \mathbf{k} = 1$

$$\iint_R 3(x + y + z)\, d\sigma = \int_0^1\int_0^{1-y} 3(x + y + 2 - 2x - 2y)\, dx\, dy$$

$$= \frac{3}{2}\int_0^1 (y^2 - 4y + 3)\, dy = 2$$

19. $g(x,y,z) = x^2 + y^2 + z^2$. $F(x,y,z) = y^2 + z^2 - a^2$

$\nabla F = 2y\mathbf{j} + 2z\,\mathbf{k}$. $|\nabla F| = 2\sqrt{y^2 + z^2}$. $|\nabla F \cdot \mathbf{k}| = 2z$

$$2\iint_R (x^2 + y^2 + z^2)\frac{2\sqrt{y^2 + z^2}}{2z}\,dx\, dy = 2a\int_{-a}^a\int_0^h (x^2 + a^2)\frac{dx\, dy}{\sqrt{a^2 - y^2}} = \frac{2\pi ah}{3}(h^2 + 3a^2$$

21. $\mathbf{F}(x,y,z) = z\mathbf{k}$. $G(x,y,z) = x^2 + y^2 + z^2 - a^2$

$\nabla G = 2x\mathbf{i} + 2y\mathbf{j} + 2z\,\mathbf{k}$. $|\nabla G| = 2\sqrt{x^2 + y^2 + z^2} = 2a$. $|\nabla G \cdot \mathbf{k}| = 2z$

$\mathbf{n} = \frac{1}{a}(x\mathbf{i} + y\mathbf{j} + z\,\mathbf{k})$. $\mathbf{F} \cdot \mathbf{n} = \frac{z^2}{a}$

$$\iint_S \mathbf{F} \cdot \mathbf{n}\, d\sigma = \iint \frac{z^2}{a}\frac{a}{z}\, dA = \int_0^{\pi/2}\int_0^a \sqrt{a^2 - r^2}\, r\, dr\, d\theta = \frac{\pi a^3}{6}.$$

23. $\mathbf{F}(x,y,z) = y\mathbf{i} - x\mathbf{j} + \mathbf{k}$. $G(x,y,z) = x^2 + y^2 + z^2 - a^2$

$\nabla G = 2x\mathbf{i} + 2y\mathbf{j} + 2z\,\mathbf{k}$. $|\nabla G| = 2\sqrt{x^2 + y^2 + z^2} = 2a$. $|\nabla G \cdot \mathbf{k}| = 2z$

$\mathbf{n} = \frac{1}{a}(x\mathbf{i} + y\mathbf{j} + z\,\mathbf{k})$.

$$\iint_R \mathbf{F} \cdot \mathbf{n}\, d\sigma = \iint_R (y\mathbf{i} - x\mathbf{j} + \mathbf{k}) \cdot \frac{1}{a}(x\mathbf{i} + y\mathbf{j} + z\,\mathbf{k})\frac{a}{z}\, dA = \iint_R dA = \frac{\pi a^2}{4}$$

25. $\mathbf{F}(x,y,z) = x\mathbf{i} + y\mathbf{j} + z\,\mathbf{k}$. $G(x,y,z) = x^2 + y^2 + z^2 - a^2$

$\nabla G = 2x\mathbf{i} + 2y\mathbf{j} + 2z\,\mathbf{k}$. $|\nabla G| = 2\sqrt{x^2 + y^2 + z^2} = 2a$. $|\nabla G \cdot \mathbf{k}| = 2z$

$\mathbf{n} = \frac{1}{a}(x\mathbf{i} + y\mathbf{j} + z\,\mathbf{k})$.

$$\iint_R \mathbf{F} \cdot \mathbf{n}\, d\sigma = \iint_R (x\mathbf{i} + y\mathbf{j} + z\,\mathbf{k}) \cdot \frac{1}{a}(x\mathbf{i} + y\mathbf{j} + z\,\mathbf{k})\frac{a}{z}\, dA =$$

$$\int_0^{\pi/2}\int_0^a \frac{a^2}{\sqrt{a^2 - r^2}}\, r\, dr\, d\theta = \frac{\pi a^3}{2}.$$

27. $\mathbf{F}(x,y,z) = z^2\mathbf{i} + x\mathbf{j} - 3z\,\mathbf{k}$. $G(x,y,z) = y^2 + z - 4$

$\nabla G = 2y\mathbf{j} + \mathbf{k}$. $|\nabla G| = \sqrt{1 + 4y^2}$ $|\nabla G \cdot \mathbf{k}| = 1$

$$\iint_R \mathbf{F} \cdot \mathbf{n}\, d\sigma = \int_0^1\int_{-2}^2 \frac{2xy - 3(4 - y^2)}{\sqrt{1 + 4y^2}}\frac{\sqrt{1 + 4y^2}}{1}\, dy\, dx = -32$$

29. $\mathbf{F}(x,y,z) = -2\mathbf{i} + 2y\mathbf{j} + z\,\mathbf{k}$. $G(x,y,z) = e^x - y$

$\nabla G = e^x\mathbf{i} - \mathbf{j}$. $|\nabla G| = \sqrt{1 + e^{2x}}$. $|\nabla G \cdot \mathbf{i}| = e^x$

$$\iint_R \mathbf{F} \cdot \mathbf{n}\, d\sigma = \int_0^1\int_1^2 -\frac{2e^x + 2y}{\sqrt{1 + e^{2x}}}\frac{\sqrt{1 + e^{2x}}}{e^x}\, dy\, dx = \int_0^1\int_1^2 -4\, dy\, dx = -4$$

31. $\mathbf{F}(x,y,z) = xz\mathbf{i} + yz\mathbf{j} + \mathbf{k}$.

$G(x,y,z) = x^2 + y^2 + z^2 - 25$. $\nabla G = 2x\mathbf{i} + 2y\mathbf{j} + 2z\mathbf{k}$. $|\nabla G| = 10$. $|\nabla G \cdot \mathbf{k}| = 2z$

$$\iint_{S_1} \mathbf{F} \cdot \mathbf{n}\, d\sigma = \iint \frac{z}{5}(1 + x^2 + y^2)\frac{10}{2z}\, dx\, dy = \int_0^{2\pi}\int_0^4 (1 + r^2) r\, dr\, d\theta = 144\pi$$

$$\iint_{S_2} \mathbf{F} \cdot \mathbf{n}\, d\sigma = \iint (xz\mathbf{i} + yz\mathbf{j} + \mathbf{k}) \cdot (-\mathbf{k})\, dA = -16\pi. \quad \therefore \text{ Total} = 128\pi$$

33. $M = \frac{1}{8}(4\pi r^2) = \frac{\pi}{2}$. $M_{xy} = \iint z\, d\sigma = \iint z\left(\frac{1}{z}\right) dA = \int_0^{\pi/2}\int_0^1 r\, dr\, d\theta = \frac{\pi}{4}$.

$\bar{z} = \frac{\pi/4}{\pi/2} = \frac{1}{2}$. $\therefore (\bar{x}, \bar{y}, \bar{z}) = \left(\frac{1}{2}, \frac{1}{2}, \frac{1}{2}\right)$.

35. $M = \int_0^{2\pi}\int_1^2 \frac{\sqrt{r^2 + z^2}}{z}\, r\, dr\, d\theta = \int_0^{2\pi}\int_1^2 \frac{\sqrt{2r^2}}{r}\, r\, dr\, d\theta = \int_0^{2\pi}\int_1^2 \sqrt{2}\, r\, dr\, d\theta = 3\pi\sqrt{2}$

$M_{xy} = \int_0^{2\pi}\int_1^2 \sqrt{2}\, z\, r\, dr\, d\theta = \sqrt{2}\int_0^{2\pi}\int_1^2 r^2\, dr\, d\theta = \frac{14\pi\sqrt{2}}{3}$. $\bar{z} = \frac{14}{9}$. $\bar{x} = \bar{y} = 0$.

$I_z = \int_0^{2\pi}\int_1^2 (x^2 + y^2)\sqrt{2}\, r\, dr\, d\theta = \frac{15\sqrt{2}\,\pi}{2}$. $R_z = \sqrt{\frac{5}{2}}$.

37. (a) $M = 2\iint \delta \frac{a}{z}\, dx\, dy = 2\int_0^{2\pi}\int_0^a \frac{ar}{\sqrt{a^2 - r^2}}\, r\, dr\, d\theta = \pi^2 a^3$

(b) $M = 2\int_0^{2\pi}\int_0^a \frac{ar^2}{\sqrt{a^2 - r^2}}\, r\, dr\, d\theta = \frac{8\pi a^4}{3}$

## 19.5 THE DIVERGENCE THEOREM

1. $\mathbf{F}(x,y,z) = (x - y)\mathbf{i} + (y - z)\mathbf{j} + (x - y)\mathbf{k}$
D: the cube bounded by planes $x = \pm 1$, $y = \pm 1$, $z = \pm 1$

$$\text{div}\,\mathbf{F} = \frac{\partial}{\partial x}(x - y) + \frac{\partial}{\partial y}(y - z) + \frac{\partial}{\partial z}(x - y) = 1 + 1 + 0 = 2$$

$$\iiint_D \text{div}\,\mathbf{F}\, dV = \int_{-1}^1\int_{-1}^1\int_{-1}^1 2\, dV = 2\,(\text{volume of cube}) = 16$$

3. $\mathbf{F}(x,y,z) = x^2\mathbf{i} + y^2\mathbf{j} + z^2\mathbf{k}$

D: The cube bounded by planes $x = \pm 1$, $y = \pm 1$, $z = \pm 1$

$$\text{div}\,\mathbf{F} = \frac{\partial}{\partial x}x^2 + \frac{\partial}{\partial y}y^2 + \frac{\partial}{\partial z}z^2 = 2x + 2y + 2z$$

$$\iiint_D \text{div}\,\mathbf{F}\; dV = \int_{-1}^{1}\int_{-1}^{1}\int_{-1}^{1} (2x + 2y + 2z)\; dz\; dy\; dx = 0$$

5. $\mathbf{F}(x,y,z) = y\;\mathbf{i} + xy\;\mathbf{j} + z\;\mathbf{k}$

$$\text{div}\,\mathbf{F} = \frac{\partial}{\partial x}y + \frac{\partial}{\partial y}xy + \frac{\partial}{\partial z}z = x + 1$$

$$\iiint_D \text{div}\,\mathbf{F}\; dV = \int_0^{2\pi}\int_0^{2}\int_0^{r^2} (r\cos\theta + 1)r\; dz\; dr\; d\theta =$$

$$\int_0^{2\pi}\int_0^{2} r^2\,(r\cos\theta + 1)r\; dr\; d\theta = \int_0^{2\pi} \left[\frac{1}{5}r^5\cos\theta + \frac{1}{4}r^4\right]_0^2 =$$

$$\frac{32}{5}\sin\theta + 4\theta\Big]_0^{2\pi} = 8\pi$$

7. $\mathbf{F}(x,y,z) = x^2\mathbf{i} - 2xy\mathbf{j} + 3xz\mathbf{j}$

$$\text{div}\,\mathbf{F} = \frac{\partial}{\partial x}x^2 - \frac{\partial}{\partial y}2xy + \frac{\partial}{\partial z}3xz = 2x - 2x + 3x = 3x$$

$$\iiint_D \text{div}\,\mathbf{F}\; dV = \int_0^{\frac{\pi}{2}}\int_0^{\frac{\pi}{2}}\int_0^{2} 3\rho\,\sin\phi\,\cos\theta\;\rho^2\sin\phi\; d\rho\; d\phi\; d\theta$$

$$\int_0^{\frac{\pi}{2}}\int_0^{\frac{\pi}{2}} \frac{3}{4}\rho^4\Big]_0^2 \sin^2\phi\,\cos\theta\;\; d\phi\; d\theta = \int_0^{\frac{\pi}{2}} 12\,\sin\theta\Big]_0^{\frac{\pi}{2}} \sin^2\phi\; d\phi =$$

$$12\left[\frac{1}{2}\phi - \frac{1}{4}\sin 2\phi\right]_0^{\frac{\pi}{2}} = 3\pi$$

9. $\mathbf{F}(x,y,z) = 2xz\;\mathbf{i} + y\;\mathbf{j} - z^2\;\mathbf{k}$

$\text{div}\,\mathbf{F} = 2z + 1 - 2z = 1$

$$\iiint_D \text{div}\,\mathbf{F}\; dV = \int_0^{4}\int_0^{\frac{1}{2}\sqrt{16-x^2}}\int_0^{y} dz\; dy\; dx = \int_0^{4}\int_0^{\frac{1}{2}\sqrt{16-x^2}} y\; dy\; dx$$

$$= \frac{1}{8}\int_0^{4} (16 - x^2)\; dx = \frac{16}{3}$$

11. $\mathbf{F}(x,y,z) = \sqrt{x^2+y^2+z^2}\,(x\mathbf{i} + y\mathbf{j} + z\mathbf{k})$

$\operatorname{div}\mathbf{F} = 4\sqrt{x^2+y^2+z^2}$

$$\iiint_D \operatorname{div}\mathbf{F}\,dV = \int_0^{2\pi}\int_0^{\pi}\int_0^{a} (4\rho)\rho^2 \sin\phi\,d\rho\,d\phi\,d\theta$$

$$= \int_0^{2\pi}\int_0^{\pi} a^4 \sin\phi\,d\phi\,d\theta = \int_0^{2\pi} 2a^4\,d\theta = 4\pi a^4$$

13. $\mathbf{F}(x,y,z) = x\mathbf{i} - 2y\mathbf{j} + (z+3)\mathbf{k}$

$\operatorname{div}\mathbf{F} = 1 - 2 + 1 = 0$

Therefore the total flux $= \iiint_D \operatorname{div}\mathbf{F}\,dV = 0$. We calculate the across the faces in the coordinate planes:

xy − plane: $z = 0$, $\mathbf{n} = -\mathbf{k}$, $\iint \mathbf{F}\cdot\mathbf{n}\,d\sigma = -3\,(\text{area}) = -3$

yz − plane: $x = 0$, $\mathbf{n} = -\mathbf{i}$ and $\mathbf{F}\cdot\mathbf{n} = 0$

xz − plane: $y = 0$, $\mathbf{n} = -\mathbf{j}$ and $\mathbf{F}\cdot\mathbf{n} = 0$

$\therefore\ (-3) + (-3) + 1 + 0 + 0 +$ Flux across top $= 0$, so the flux across the top is 5.

15. (a) $\mathbf{F}(x,y,z) = x\mathbf{i} + y\mathbf{j} + z\mathbf{k} \Rightarrow \operatorname{div}\mathbf{F} = 3$ so

$$\iiint_D \operatorname{div}\mathbf{F}\,dV = \iiint_D 3\,dV = 3\,(\text{volume})$$

(b) If $\mathbf{F}$ were orthogonal to $\mathbf{n}$ at every point of S, then $\iint_S \mathbf{F}\cdot\mathbf{n}\,d\sigma = 0$, which contradicts part (a).

17. Let $\mathbf{F} = f\nabla f$. Then

$$\iint_S \mathbf{F}\cdot\mathbf{n}\,d\sigma = \iint_S (f\nabla f)\cdot\mathbf{n}\,d\sigma = \iint_S f\,(\nabla f\cdot\mathbf{n})\,d\sigma = \iint f\,\frac{\partial f}{\partial n}\,d\sigma$$

On the other hand,

$$\iiint_D \nabla\,(f\nabla f)\,dV = \iiint_D \left[(\nabla f)^2 + \nabla^2 f\right]dV = \iiint_D |\nabla f|^2\,dV$$

## 19.6 STOKE'S THEOREM

1. $\mathbf{F}(x,y,z) = x^2\mathbf{i} + 2x\mathbf{j} + z^2\mathbf{k}$. $\text{curl}\,\mathbf{F} = 2\mathbf{k}$

$$\iint_S \text{curl}\,\mathbf{F} \cdot \mathbf{n}\, d\sigma = 2\iint_S dx\,dy = 2\,(\text{area of ellipse}) = 4\pi$$

3. $\mathbf{F}(x,y,z) = y\mathbf{i} + xz\mathbf{j} + x^2\mathbf{k}$. $\text{curl}\,\mathbf{F} = -x\mathbf{i} - 2x\mathbf{j} + (z-1)\mathbf{k}$

We take as $\mathbf{n} = \frac{1}{\sqrt{3}}(\mathbf{i} + \mathbf{j} + \mathbf{k})$. $d\sigma = \sqrt{3}\,dx\,dy$

$$\iint_S \text{curl}\,\mathbf{F} \cdot \mathbf{n}\, d\sigma = \int_0^1\int_0^{1-y} (-3x + z - 1)\,dx\,dy = -\frac{5}{6}$$

5. $\mathbf{F}(x,y,z) = (y^2+z^2)\mathbf{i} + (x^2+y^2)\mathbf{j} + (x^2+y^2)\mathbf{k}$.

$$\iint\left(\frac{\partial N}{\partial x} - \frac{\partial M}{\partial y}\right)dx\,dy = \int_{-1}^1\int_{-1}^1 (2x - 2y)\,dx\,dy = 0$$

7. $\mathbf{F}(x,y,z) = x^2\mathbf{i} + 2x\mathbf{j} + z^2\mathbf{k}$. $\text{curl}\,\mathbf{F} = 2\mathbf{k}$

$$\iint_S \text{curl}\,\mathbf{F} \cdot \mathbf{n}\, d\sigma = 2\iint_S dx\,dy = 2\,(\text{area of ellipse}) = 4\pi$$

9. $\mathbf{F}(x,y,z) = -y\mathbf{i} + x\mathbf{j} + x^2\mathbf{k}$. Let C be $x = a\cos t$, $y = a\sin t$, $0 \le t \le 2\pi$.

Then $\displaystyle\iint_S \mathbf{F} \cdot dR = \oint_C -y\,dx + x\,dy$

$$= \int_0^{2\pi} (-a\sin t)(-a\sin t) + (a\cos t)(a\cos t)\,dt = 2\pi a^2$$

11. $\mathbf{F}(x,y,z) = x\mathbf{i} + y\mathbf{j} + z\mathbf{k}$.

(a) $\nabla \cdot \mathbf{F} = \left(\frac{\partial}{\partial x}\mathbf{i} + \frac{\partial}{\partial y}\mathbf{j} + \frac{\partial}{\partial z}\mathbf{k}\right) \cdot (x\mathbf{i} + y\mathbf{j} + z\mathbf{k}) = 1 + 1 + 1 = 3$

(b) $\nabla \times \mathbf{F} = \begin{vmatrix} \mathbf{i} & \mathbf{j} & \mathbf{k} \\ \frac{\partial}{\partial x} & \frac{\partial}{\partial y} & \frac{\partial}{\partial z} \\ x & y & z \end{vmatrix} = 0$

13. (a) $\nabla \cdot (g\mathbf{F}) = \frac{\partial}{\partial x}(gM) + \frac{\partial}{\partial y}(gN) + \frac{\partial}{\partial z}(gP)$

$$= \left(g\frac{\partial M}{\partial x} + M\frac{\partial g}{\partial x}\right) + \left(g\frac{\partial N}{\partial y} + N\frac{\partial g}{\partial y}\right) + \left(g\frac{\partial P}{\partial z} + P\frac{\partial g}{\partial z}\right)$$

$$= \left(M\frac{\partial g}{\partial x} + N\frac{\partial g}{\partial y} + P\frac{\partial g}{\partial z}\right) + g\left(\frac{\partial M}{\partial x} + \frac{\partial N}{\partial y} + \frac{\partial P}{\partial z}\right)$$

$$= \mathbf{F} \cdot \nabla g + g\,(\nabla \cdot \mathbf{F})$$

(b) $\nabla \times (g\mathbf{F}) = \left(\frac{\partial}{\partial y}(gP) - \frac{\partial}{\partial z}(gN)\right)\mathbf{i} + \left(\frac{\partial}{\partial z}(gM) - \frac{\partial}{\partial x}(gP)\right)\mathbf{j} + \left(\frac{\partial}{\partial x}(gN) - \frac{\partial}{\partial y}(gM)\right)\mathbf{k}$

$$= g\left(\left(\frac{\partial P}{\partial y} - \frac{\partial N}{\partial z}\right)\mathbf{i} + \left(\frac{\partial N}{\partial z} - \frac{\partial P}{\partial x}\right)\mathbf{j} + \left(\frac{\partial N}{\partial x} - \frac{\partial M}{\partial y}\right)\mathbf{k}\right) + \left(P\frac{\partial g}{\partial y} - N\frac{\partial g}{\partial z}\right)\mathbf{i}$$

$$+ \left(M\frac{\partial g}{\partial z} - P\frac{\partial g}{\partial x}\right)\mathbf{j} + \left(N\frac{\partial g}{\partial x} - M\frac{\partial g}{\partial y}\right)\mathbf{k}$$

$$= g(\nabla \times \mathbf{F}) + \nabla g \times \mathbf{F}$$

(c) Let $\mathbf{F}_1 = M_1\mathbf{i} + N_1\mathbf{j} + P_1\mathbf{k}$ and $\mathbf{F}_2 = \mathbf{M_2}iP + N_2\mathbf{j} + P_2\mathbf{k}$. Then

$$\nabla \cdot (\mathbf{F}_1 \times \mathbf{F}_2) = \frac{\partial}{\partial x}(N_1 P_2 - N_2 P_1) + \frac{\partial}{\partial y}(P_1 M_2 - M_1 P_2) + \frac{\partial}{\partial z}(M_1 N_2 - N_1 M_2)$$

$$= \left(N_1\frac{\partial P_2}{\partial x} + P_2\frac{\partial N_1}{\partial x} - N_2\frac{\partial P_1}{\partial x} - P_1\frac{\partial N_2}{\partial x}\right) + \left(P_1\frac{\partial M_2}{\partial y} + M_2\frac{\partial P_1}{\partial y} - M_1\frac{\partial P_2}{\partial y} - P_2\frac{\partial M_1}{\partial y}\right)$$

$$+ \left(M_1\frac{\partial N_2}{\partial z} + N_2\frac{\partial M_1}{\partial z} - N_1\frac{\partial M_2}{\partial z} - M_2\frac{\partial N_1}{\partial z}\right)$$

$$= M_2\left(\frac{\partial P_1}{\partial y} - \frac{\partial N_1}{\partial z}\right) + N_2\left(\frac{\partial M_1}{\partial z} - \frac{\partial P_1}{\partial x}\right) + P_2\left(\frac{\partial N_1}{\partial x} - \frac{\partial M_1}{\partial y}\right)$$

$$+ M_1\left(\frac{\partial N_2}{\partial z} - \frac{\partial P_2}{\partial y}\right) + N_1\left(\frac{\partial P_2}{\partial x} - \frac{\partial M_2}{\partial z}\right) + P_1\left(\frac{\partial M_2}{\partial y} - \frac{\partial N_2}{\partial x}\right)$$

$$= \mathbf{F}_2 \cdot \nabla \times \mathbf{F}_1 - \mathbf{F}_1 \cdot \nabla \times \mathbf{F}_2$$

15. (a) $\mathbf{F} = \nabla f = -(x^2 + y^2 + z^2)^{-3/2}(x\mathbf{i} + y\mathbf{j} + z\mathbf{k})$

Let C: $x = a\cos\theta$, $y = a\sin\theta$, $0 \le \theta \le 2\pi$. Then

$$\int \mathbf{F} \cdot d\mathbf{R} = -\frac{1}{a^3}\int_0^{2\pi} (a\cos\theta)(-a\sin\theta) + (a\sin\theta)(a\cos\theta)\,d\theta = 0$$

(b) $\int (\nabla \times \nabla F) \cdot \mathbf{n}\, d\sigma = 0$ by problem 14.

## 19.7 PATH INDEPENDENCE AND CONSERVATIVE FIELDS

1. $\mathbf{F} = yz\mathbf{i} + xz\mathbf{j} + xy\mathbf{k}$ is conservative.

$$\frac{\partial P}{\partial y} = x = \frac{\partial N}{\partial z} \qquad \frac{\partial M}{\partial z} = y = \frac{\partial P}{\partial x} \qquad \frac{\partial N}{\partial x} = z = \frac{\partial M}{\partial y}$$

3. $\mathbf{F} = y\mathbf{i} + (x + z)\mathbf{j} - y\mathbf{k}$ is not conservative.

$$\frac{\partial P}{\partial y} = -1 \quad \frac{\partial N}{\partial z} \quad \frac{\partial M}{\partial z} = 1$$

5. $\mathbf{F} = (z+y)\,\mathbf{i} + z\,\mathbf{j} + (y+x)\,\mathbf{k}$ is not conservative.

$$\frac{\partial N}{\partial x} = 0 \qquad \frac{\partial N}{\partial y} = 1$$

7. $\mathbf{F} = 2x\,\mathbf{i} + 3y\,\mathbf{j} + 4z\,\mathbf{k}$

$$f(x,y,z) = x^2 + \frac{3}{2}y^2 + 2z^2 + C$$

9. $\mathbf{F} = e^{y+2z}\,(\mathbf{i} + x\mathbf{j} + 2x\,\mathbf{k})$

$$f(x,y,z) = xe^{y+2z} + h(y,z)$$

$$\frac{\partial f}{\partial y} = xe^{y+2z} + \frac{\partial h}{\partial y} \qquad \frac{\partial f}{\partial z} = 2xe^{y+2z} + \frac{\partial h}{\partial z}$$

$$\frac{\partial h}{\partial y} = xe^{y+2z} - xe^{y+2z} = 0 \quad \frac{\partial h}{\partial z} = 2xe^{y+2z} - 2xe^{y+2z} = 0$$

$$\therefore \quad f(x,y,z) = xe^{y+2z} + C$$

11. $$\int_{(0,0,0)}^{(2,3,-6)} 2x\,dx + 2y\,dy + 2z\,dz = x^2 + y^2 + z^2 \Big]_{(0,0,0)}^{(2,3,-6)} = 49$$

13. $$\int_{(0,0)}^{(1,1)} x\,dx + y^2\,dy = \frac{1}{2}x^2 + \frac{1}{3}y^3 \Big]_{(0,0)}^{(1,1)} = \frac{5}{6}$$

15. $$\int_{(1,0)}^{(1,\pi/2)} 2x\sin y\,dx + x^2\cos y\,dy = x^2\sin y \Big]_{(1,0)}^{(1,\pi/2)} = 1$$

17. $$\int_{(1,1)}^{(2,3)} (y^2x + y)dx + (x^2y + x)\,dy = \frac{1}{2}y^2x^2 + yx \Big]_{(1,1)}^{(2,3)} = \frac{45}{2}$$

19. $$\int_{(0,1,1)}^{(2,2,1)} 3x^2\,dx + \frac{z^2}{y}\,dy + 2z\ln y\,dz = x^3 + z^2\ln y \Big]_{(0,1,1)}^{(2,2,1)} = 8 + \ln 2$$

21. The line is L: $x = 1+t,\ y = 1+2t,\ z = 1-2t,\ 0 \le t \le 1$

$$\int_{(1,1,1)}^{(2,3,-1)} y\,dx + x\,dy + 4\,dz = \int_0^1 (1+2t)\,dt + \int_0^1 (1+t)\,2\,dt + \int_0^1 4(-2\,dt) = -3$$

23. The line is L: $x = 0,\ y = 3t,\ z = 4t,\ 0 \le t \le 1$

$$\int_C x^2\,dx + yz\,dy + y^2\,dz = \int_0^1 (12t^2)\,3\,dt + (9t^2)\,4\,dt = 24$$

25. $$\oint \mathbf{F}\cdot d\mathbf{R} = \iint_R \nabla\times\mathbf{F}\cdot\mathbf{n}\,dA = \iint_R (0)\,dA = 0$$

27. $\mathbf{F} + -\frac{y}{x^2+y^2}\mathbf{i} + \frac{x}{x^2+y^2}\mathbf{j} + z\mathbf{k}$

$$\frac{\partial P}{\partial y} = \frac{\partial N}{\partial z} = \frac{\partial M}{\partial z} = \frac{\partial P}{\partial x} = 0; \quad \frac{\partial N}{\partial x} = \frac{\partial M}{\partial y} = \frac{y^2 - x^2}{(x^2+y^2)^2}. \quad \therefore\ \nabla \times \mathbf{F} = 0$$

$$\int \mathbf{F} \cdot d\mathbf{R} = \int_0^{2\pi} \sin^2 t + \cos^2 t \; dt = 2\pi$$

## 19.M MISCELLANEOUS

1. $f(x, y, z) = 2x - y^2 - 2z + 1$

Path 1: $\mathbf{R}(t) = t\mathbf{i} + t\mathbf{j} + t\mathbf{k}; \ |\mathbf{v}(t)| = \sqrt{3}$

$$\int_0^1 (2t - t^2 - 2t + 1)\sqrt{3}\, dt = \frac{2\sqrt{3}}{3}$$

Path 2: $\mathbf{R}_1(t) = t\mathbf{i} + t\mathbf{j}, \ |\mathbf{v}_1(t)| = \sqrt{2}$

$\mathbf{R}_2(t) = \mathbf{i} + \mathbf{j} + t\mathbf{k}, \ |\mathbf{v}_2(t)| = 1$

$$\int_0^1 (2t - t^2 + 1)\sqrt{2}\, dt + \int_0^1 (2 - 1 - 2t + 1)\, dt = \frac{5\sqrt{2} + 3}{3}$$

3. $\mathbf{R}(t) = (e^t \cos t)\mathbf{i} + (e^t \sin t)\mathbf{j} + e^t\mathbf{k}.$

$$ds = \sqrt{e^{2t}(1 - 2\sin t \cos t) + e^{2t}(1 + 2\sin t \cos t) + e^{2t}}\, dt = \sqrt{3}e^t\, dt$$

$$M = \delta\int_0^{\ln 2} \sqrt{3}e^t\, dt = \sqrt{3}\delta$$

$$I_z = \delta\int_0^{\ln 2} (e^{2t}\cos^2 t + e^{2t}\sin^2 t)\sqrt{3}\, e^t\, dt = \frac{\sqrt{3}}{3}\delta e^{3t}\Big]_0^{\ln 2} = \frac{7\sqrt{3}}{3}\delta$$

$$R_z = \sqrt{\frac{I_z}{M}} = \sqrt{\frac{7}{3}}$$

5. $\mathbf{R}(t) = (t\cos t)\mathbf{i} + (t\sin t)\mathbf{j} + \frac{2\sqrt{2}}{3}t^{3/2}\mathbf{k}, \ 0 \le t \le 1.$

$$ds = \sqrt{1 + t^2 + 2t}\, dt = |t + 1|\, dt = (t + 1)\, dt$$

$$M = \int_0^1 (t+1)\, dt = \frac{3}{2}; \quad M_{xy} = \int_0^1 \frac{2\sqrt{2}}{3}t^{3/2}(t+1)\, dt = \frac{16\sqrt{2}}{35}$$

$$\bar{z} = \frac{16\sqrt{2}}{35} \cdot \frac{2}{3} = \frac{32\sqrt{2}}{105}; \quad I_z = \int_0^1 t^2(t+1)\, dt = \frac{7}{12}; \quad R_z = \sqrt{\frac{I_z}{M}} = \sqrt{\frac{7}{18}}$$

7. The field at a point P is directed away from the origin in the direction of P, and has magnitude equal to the distance from P to the origin.

9. The direction of the field is accelerating in a counter-clockwise spiral about the origin.

11. $\mathbf{F}(x, y, z) = f(\rho)\,\mathbf{R}$ where $\rho = |\mathbf{R}|$ and $\mathbf{R} = x\mathbf{i} + y\mathbf{j} + z\mathbf{k}$.

(a) $\rho^{-n} = |f(\rho)|\rho \Rightarrow |f(\rho)| = \rho^{-n-1}$

$\therefore\ \mathbf{F} = \rho^{-n-1}\,\mathbf{R}$

(b) $2 = |f(\rho)|\rho \Rightarrow |f(\rho)| = \dfrac{2}{\rho}$

$\therefore\ \mathbf{F} = -\dfrac{2}{\rho}\mathbf{R}$

(c) $\dfrac{GM}{\rho^3} = |f(\rho)|\rho \Rightarrow |f(\rho)| = \dfrac{GM}{\rho^4}$

$\therefore\ \mathbf{F} = -\dfrac{GM}{\rho^4}\mathbf{R}$

13. View the surface as the same as $y^2 + x^2 = 2z$ cut by $z = 1$.

$d\sigma = \sqrt{1 + y^2 + x^2}\,dx\,dy$ and the surface area is

$$\int_0^{2\pi}\int_0^{\sqrt{2}} \sqrt{1 + r^2}\ r\,dr\,d\theta = \frac{2\pi}{3}(3\sqrt{3} - 1).$$

15. The projection of the surface onto the xy–plane is the triangular region bounded by the x–axis, y–axis and the line $\dfrac{x}{a} + \dfrac{y}{b} = 1$.

$\mathbf{n} = \dfrac{1}{a}\mathbf{i} + \dfrac{1}{b}\mathbf{j} + \dfrac{1}{c}\mathbf{k}$ is normal to the plane. $|\mathbf{n}\cdot\mathbf{k}| = \dfrac{1}{c}$ and

$|\mathbf{n}| = \dfrac{\sqrt{a^2b^2 + a^2c^2 + b^2c^2}}{abc}$. The surface area is

$$\frac{\sqrt{a^2b^2 + a^2c^2 + b^2c^2}}{abc}\cdot c\int_0^a\int_0^{(b/a)(a-x)} dy\,dx = \frac{\sqrt{a^2b^2 + a^2c^2 + b^2c^2}}{2}.$$

To check: Let $\mathbf{A} = a\mathbf{i} + c\mathbf{k}$ and $\mathbf{B} = a\mathbf{i} + b\mathbf{j}$. Then $\mathbf{A}\times\mathbf{B} = -bc\mathbf{i} + ac\mathbf{j} + ab\mathbf{k}$

and the area $= \dfrac{1}{2}|\mathbf{A}\times\mathbf{B}| = \dfrac{\sqrt{a^2b^2 + a^2c^2 + b^2c^2}}{2}$.

17. Let $f(x, y, z) = z + y^2 - a^2$. $\nabla F = 2y\mathbf{i} + \mathbf{k}$, $|\nabla F| = \sqrt{1 + 4y^2}$ and $\nabla F \cdot \mathbf{k} = 1$.

$$\text{Surface area} = \int_{-a}^{a}\int_{-\sqrt{a^2-y^2}}^{\sqrt{a^2-y^2}} \sqrt{1 + 4y^2}\,dx\,dy = \int_{-a}^{a} 2\sqrt{1 + 4y^2}\sqrt{a^2 - y^2}\,dy$$

19. We use the Theorem of Pappus: Area = $(2\pi a)(2\pi b) = 4\pi^2 ab$.

21. Let $F(x,y,z) = x^2 + y^2 + z^2 - 1$. $\nabla F = 2x\mathbf{i} + 2y\mathbf{j} + 2z\,\mathbf{k}$

$|\nabla F| = 2\sqrt{x^2 + y^2 + z^2} = 2$ and $\nabla F \bullet \mathbf{k} = 2z$.

$$\text{Surface area} = 4\iint_R \frac{1}{z}\,dA = 8\int_0^{\frac{\pi}{2}}\int_{\cos\theta}^{1} \frac{r}{\sqrt{1 - r^2}}\,dr\,d\theta = 8$$

23. Let $F(x,y,z) = x^2 + y^2 + z^2 - 4$. $\nabla F = 2x\mathbf{i} + 2y\mathbf{j} + 2z\,\mathbf{k}$

$|\nabla F| = 4\sqrt{x^2 + y^2 + z^2} = 4$ and $\nabla F \bullet \mathbf{k} = 4z$.

$$\text{Surface area} = 2\iint_R \frac{2}{z}\,dA = 2\int_0^{\frac{\pi}{2}}\int_0^{2\cos\theta} \frac{2r}{\sqrt{4 - r^2}}\,dr\,d\theta = 4\pi - 8$$

25. (a) Let $F(x,y) = x^2 + y^2$

$$\text{Surface area} = \iint_R \sqrt{4x^2 + 4y^2 + 1}\,dx\,dy$$

$$= \int_0^{2\pi}\int_0^{2} \sqrt{4r^2 + 1}\,r\,dr\,d\theta = \frac{\pi}{6}(17\sqrt{17} - 1)$$

(b) Let $F(y,z) = 1 - y^2 - z^2$

$$\text{Surface area} = \iint_R \sqrt{4z^2 + 4y^2 + 1}\,dy\,dz$$

$$= \int_0^{2\pi}\int_0^{1} \sqrt{4r^2 + 1}\,r\,dr\,d\theta = \frac{\pi}{6}(5\sqrt{5} - 1)$$

(c) Let $F(x,z) = \frac{1}{2}z^2$

$$\text{Surface area} = \int_0^{2} \sqrt{1 + z^2}\,dz = \sqrt{5} + \frac{1}{2}\ln(2 + \sqrt{5})$$

27. $$\text{Average distance} = \frac{1}{2\pi a^2}\int_0^{2\pi}\int_0^{\frac{\pi}{2}} (a\phi)\,a^2 \sin\phi\,d\phi\,d\theta = a$$

29. $\iint_S K\frac{\partial u}{\partial n}\,d\sigma = \iiint_D c\delta\frac{\delta u}{\delta t}\,dV$ (By Equation 1, Prob. 28).

By the Divergence Theorem, $\iint_S K\frac{\partial u}{\partial n}\,d\sigma = \iiint_D \nabla\bullet(K\,\nabla u)\,dV$.

$\therefore \iiint_D \left[\nabla\bullet(K\,\nabla u) - c\delta\frac{\delta u}{\delta t}\right]dV = 0$. Since the region D is arbitrary,

$\nabla\bullet(K\,\nabla u) - c\delta\frac{\delta u}{\delta t} = 0$ or $\nabla\bullet(K\,\nabla u) = c\delta\frac{\delta u}{\delta t}$.

31. $\iint_S u\,\nabla v\,\bullet d\sigma = \iiint_D \nabla\bullet(u\,\nabla v)\,dV = \iiint_D (u\,\nabla^2 v + \nabla u\bullet\nabla v)\,dV$

$= \iiint_D (u\nabla v + \nabla u\bullet\nabla v)\,dV$

33. $\iint_S u\frac{\partial u}{\partial n}\,d\sigma = \iint_S u\,(\nabla u)\bullet d\sigma = \iiint_D (u\,\nabla u + \nabla u\bullet\nabla u)\,dV$

$= \iiint_D (u\nabla \mathbf{u} + |\nabla u|^2)\,dV$ by Problem 31.

35. $\iint_S u\frac{\partial u}{\partial n}\,d\sigma = \;= \iiint_D (u\,\nabla u + |\nabla u|^2)\,dV$. If $n = o$ or $\frac{\partial u}{\partial n} = 0$ on S, then the left integral is zero, and hence so is the right. If u is harmonic, $\nabla u = 0$, so $|\nabla u| = 0$ and u is constant.

37. $\iint_S K\frac{\partial u}{\partial n}\,d\sigma = \;= \iiint_D \nabla u\;\;dV = 0$.

39. Let $f(x,y,z) = \frac{1}{2}(x^2+y^2+z^2)$. Then $\mathbf{F} = \nabla f$. and the starting and ending points are the same. $\therefore \int_A^A \mathbf{F}\bullet d\mathbf{R} = 0$.

41. $\nabla\times(x\mathbf{i} + y\mathbf{j} + z\mathbf{k}) = 0$. $\therefore \int \mathbf{F}\bullet d\mathbf{R} = 0$.

43. $\int_{(1,1,1)}^{(2,1,-1)} \nabla(xy^2z^3)\bullet d\mathbf{R} = xy^2z^3\Big]_{(1,1,1)}^{(2,1,-1)} = -3$

45. $f(x,y,z) = \int_{p_0}^{p(x,y,z)} \frac{1}{\rho}\,dp \Rightarrow f_x = \frac{1}{\rho}p_x,\; f_y = \frac{1}{\rho}p_y$ and $f_z = \frac{1}{\rho}p_z$.

$\therefore \nabla f = \frac{1}{\rho}\nabla p$

47. $A(R) = \int_C \frac{1}{2}(x\,dy - y\,dx)$

$$= \frac{1}{2}\int_{C'}\left[f(u,v)\left(\frac{\partial g}{\partial u}du + \frac{\partial g}{\partial v}dv\right) - g(u,v)\left(\frac{\partial f}{\partial u}du + \frac{\partial f}{\partial v}dv\right)\right]$$

Let $M = \frac{1}{2}\left(f\frac{\partial g}{\partial u} - g\frac{\partial f}{\partial u}\right)$ and $N = \frac{1}{2}\left(f\frac{\partial g}{\partial v} - g\frac{\partial f}{\partial v}\right)$. Then

$$\int_{C'} M\,du + N\,dv = \iint_{R'}\left(\frac{\partial N}{\partial u} - \frac{\partial M}{\partial v}\right)du\,dv = \iint_{R'}\left(\frac{\partial f}{\partial u}\frac{\partial g}{\partial v} - \frac{\partial f}{\partial v}\frac{\partial g}{\partial u}\right)du\,dv$$

$$= \iint_R \begin{vmatrix} f_u & f_v \\ g_u & g_v \end{vmatrix} du\,dv.$$

# CHAPTER 20

# DIFFERENTIAL EQUATIONS

## 20.1 INTRODUCTION

1. (a) $y = x^2 + C \Rightarrow y' = 2x$ and $y'' = 2$. $\therefore\ xy'' - y' = x(2) - 2x = 0$

   (b) $y = C_1 x^2 + C_2 \Rightarrow y' = 2C_1 x$ and $y'' = 2C_1$. $\therefore\ xy'' - y' = x(2C_1) - 2C_1 x = 0$

3. (a) $y = C \Rightarrow y' = y'' = 0$. $\therefore\ (y)(0) = 2(0)^2 - 2(0)$ or $0 = 0$

   (b) $C_1 y = \tan(C_1 x + C_2) \Rightarrow y' = \sec^2(C_1 x + C_2)$ and

   $y'' = 2C_1 \sec^2(C_1 x + C_2)\tan(C_1 x + C_2)$.

   $$y y'' = \left(\frac{1}{C_1}\tan(C_1 x + C_2)\right)(2C_1 \sec^2(C_1 x + C_2)\tan(C_1 x + C_2))$$

   $$= 2\sec^2(C_1 x + C_2)\tan^2(C_1 x + C_2)$$

   $$2(y')^2 - 2y' = 2\left(\sec^2(C_1 x + C_2)\right)^2 - 2\sec^2(C_1 x + C_2)$$

   $$= 2\sec^2(C_1 x + C_2)(\sec^2(C_1 x + C_2) - 1)$$

   $$= 2\sec^2(C_1 x + C_2)\tan^2(C_1 x + C_2)$$

5. $y = e^{-x} + Ce^{-(3/2)x} \Rightarrow y' = -e^{-x} - \frac{3}{2}Ce^{-(3/2)x}$.

   $\therefore\ 2y' + 3y = 2\left(-e^{-x} - \frac{3}{2}Ce^{-(3/2)x}\right) + 3\left(e^{-x} + Ce^{-(3/2)x}\right) = e^{-x}$.

## 20.2 FIRST ORDER DIFFERENTIAL EQUATIONS OF FIRST DEGREE

### Separable

1. $x(2y-3)\,dx + (x^2+1)\,dy = 0 \Rightarrow (x^2+1)\,dy = -x(2y-3)\,dx$

$$\int \frac{dy}{2y-3} = \int \frac{-x\,dx}{x^2+1} \Rightarrow \frac{1}{2}\ln|2y-3| = -\frac{1}{2}\ln|x^2+1| + C'$$

$$\ln|2y-3| = \ln\frac{1}{x^2+1} + \ln C' \quad \text{or} \quad y = \frac{C}{x^2+1}$$

3. $\dfrac{dy}{dx} = e^{x-y} = e^x e^{-y} \Rightarrow \int e^y\,dy = \int e^x\,dx \Rightarrow e^y = e^x + C$

5. $\sin x \dfrac{dx}{dy} + \cosh 2y = 0 \Rightarrow \int \sin x\,dx = \int -\cosh 2y\,dy \Rightarrow$

$$-\cos x = -\frac{1}{2}\sinh 2y + C' \quad \text{or } \sinh 2y - 2\cos x = C$$

7. $xe^y\,dy + \dfrac{x^2+1}{y}\,dx = 0 \Rightarrow \dfrac{x^2+1}{y}\,dx = -x e^y\,dy \Rightarrow \int\left(x+\dfrac{1}{x}\right)dx = -\int ye^y\,dy \Rightarrow$

$$\ln|x| + \frac{1}{2}x^2 = -ye^y + e^y + C$$

9. $\sqrt{1+x^2}\,dy + \sqrt{y^2-1}\,dx = 0 \Rightarrow \int \dfrac{dy}{\sqrt{y^2-1}} = -\int \dfrac{dx}{\sqrt{1+x^2}} \Rightarrow$

$$\cosh^{-1} y = -\sinh^{-1} x + C.$$

11. $\dfrac{dx}{dt} = 1000 + 0.1x \Rightarrow \dfrac{dx}{1000+0.1x} = dt \Rightarrow 10\ln(1000+0.1x) = t + C$

$1000 + 0.1x = Ae^{t/10} \quad (A = e^{C/10})$

$x(t) = Be^{t/10} - 10{,}000 \quad (B = 10A)$. Since $x(0) = 1000$, $B = 11{,}000$

$\therefore x(t) = 1000(11e^{t/10} - 10)$.

$100{,}000 = 1000(11e^{t/10} - 10)$ in $(10\ln 10) \approx 23.03$ years

13. $\dfrac{dT}{dt} = k(T - T_a) \Rightarrow \ln(T - T_a) = kt + C_1 \Rightarrow T - T_a = Ce^{kt} \quad (C = e^{C_1})$

$T(0) = 100 \Rightarrow 100 - 20 = C$, so $T = 20 + 80e^{kt}$

$T(20) = 80 \Rightarrow 80 = 20 + 80e^{20k}$ or $k = \dfrac{1}{20}\ln\dfrac{3}{4}$.

$T = 60$: $40 = 80e^{kt}$ or $\left(\dfrac{1}{20}\ln\dfrac{3}{4}\right)t = \ln\dfrac{1}{2} \Rightarrow t = \dfrac{20\ln 0.5}{\ln 0.75} \approx 48.2$ minutes

## Homogeneous

15. $x^2\,dy + (y^2 - xy)\,dx = 0 \Rightarrow \dfrac{dy}{dx} = -\dfrac{y^2 - xy}{x^2} = -\left(\dfrac{y}{x}\right)^2 + \dfrac{y}{x}.$

$F(v) = v - v^2$ with $v = \dfrac{y}{x}$. Then $\dfrac{dx}{x} + \dfrac{dv}{v - v + v^2} = 0.$

$\ln|x| - \dfrac{1}{v} = C \Rightarrow \ln|x| - \dfrac{x}{y} = C$ or $y = \dfrac{x}{\ln|x| + C}.$

17. $(x+y)\,dy + (x-y)\,dx = 0 \Rightarrow (x+y)\,dy = (y-x)\,dx \Rightarrow \dfrac{dy}{dx} = \dfrac{y-x}{x+y} = \dfrac{\frac{y}{x} - 1}{1 + \frac{y}{x}}.$

$F(v) = \dfrac{v-1}{v+1}$ so $\dfrac{dx}{x} + \dfrac{dv}{v - \frac{v-1}{v+1}} = 0 \Rightarrow \dfrac{dx}{x} + \dfrac{v+1}{v^2+1}\,dv = 0.$

$\ln|x| + \dfrac{1}{2}\ln(v^2+1) + \tan^{-1} v = C \Rightarrow \ln|x| + \dfrac{1}{2}\ln\left(\dfrac{y^2}{x^2} + 1\right) + \tan^{-1}\dfrac{y}{x} = C$

or $\dfrac{1}{2}\ln(x^2 + y^2) + \tan^{-1}\dfrac{y}{x} = C$

19. $\left(x \sin\dfrac{y}{x} - y\cos\dfrac{y}{x}\right)dx + \left(x\cos\dfrac{y}{x}\right)dy = 0 \Rightarrow \dfrac{dy}{dx} = \dfrac{y}{x} - \tan\dfrac{y}{x}.$

$F(v) = v - \tan v$ and $\dfrac{dx}{x} + \dfrac{dv}{v - v + \tan v} = 0 \Rightarrow \dfrac{dx}{x} + \cot v\,dv = 0$

$\ln|x| + \ln|\sin v| = C \Rightarrow \ln\left|\sin\dfrac{y}{x}\right| = \ln C - \ln|x| \Rightarrow \sin\dfrac{y}{x} = \dfrac{C}{x}.$

21. $x\,dy - 2y\,dx = 0 \Rightarrow \dfrac{dy}{y} = \dfrac{2\,dx}{x} \Rightarrow \ln|y| = 2\ln|x| + C$ or $y = C_1 x^2,$

a family of parabolas. The orthogonal trajectories are:

$2y\,dy + x\,dx = 0 \Rightarrow y^2 + \dfrac{1}{2}x^2 = C$, a family of ellipses.

23. $xy = C \Rightarrow x\,dy + y\,dx = 0.$ $\therefore\ y\,dy - x\,dx = 0 \Rightarrow \dfrac{1}{2}y^2 - \dfrac{1}{2}x^2 = C$

or $y^2 - x^2 = C'.$

## Linear

25. $2\dfrac{dy}{dx} - y = e^{x/2} \Rightarrow \dfrac{dy}{dx} - \dfrac{1}{2}y = \dfrac{1}{2}e^{x/2};\quad \int P(x)\,dx = \int -\dfrac{1}{2}dx = -\dfrac{1}{2}x.$

Let $\rho = e^{-x/2}$. Then $e^{-x/2}\dfrac{dy}{dx} - \dfrac{1}{2}e^{-x/2}y = \dfrac{1}{2} \Rightarrow e^{-x/2}y = \int \dfrac{1}{2}dx.$

$\therefore\ e^{-x/2}y = \dfrac{1}{2}x + C$ or $y = \dfrac{1}{2}xe^{x/2} + Ce^{x/2} = \dfrac{1}{2}e^{x/2}(x + C').$

27. $x\,dy + y\,dx = \sin x\,dx \Rightarrow \dfrac{dy}{dx} + \dfrac{1}{x}y = \dfrac{\sin x}{x}$

$\int P(x)\,dx = \int \frac{1}{x}\,dx = \ln x$. Let $\rho = e^{\ln x} = x$

Then $x\dfrac{dy}{dx} + y = \sin x \Rightarrow xy = \int \sin x\,dx$.

$\therefore\ xy = -\cos x + C$ or $y = \dfrac{1}{x}(C - \cos x)$.

29. $(x-1)^3\dfrac{dy}{dx} + 4(x-1)^2 y = x+1 \Rightarrow \dfrac{dy}{dx} + \dfrac{4}{x-1}y = \dfrac{x+1}{(x-1)^3}$

$\int P(x)\,dx = \int \frac{4}{x-1}\,dx = 4\ln(x-1)$. Let $\rho = (x-1)^4$

Then $(x-1)^4\dfrac{dy}{dx} + 4(x-1)^3 = x^2 - 1 \Rightarrow (x-1)^4 y = \int (x^2-1)\,dx$.

$\therefore\ (x-1)^4 y = \frac{1}{3}x^3 - x + C$ or $y = \dfrac{1}{(x-1)^4}\left(\dfrac{1}{3}x^3 - x + C\right)$

31. $e^{2y}\,dx + 2(xe^{2y} - y)\,dy = 0 \Rightarrow \dfrac{dx}{dy} + 2x = 2y\,e^{-2y}$

$\int P(y)\,dy = \int 2\,dy = 2y$. Let $\rho = e^{2y}$

Then $e^{2y}\dfrac{dx}{dy} + 2xe^{2y} = 2y \Rightarrow xe^{2y} = \int 2y\,dy$.

$\therefore\ xe^{2y} = y^2 + C$ or $x = e^{-2y}(y^2 + C)$

33. $(y^2+1)\,dx + (2xy+1)\,dy = 0 \Rightarrow \dfrac{dx}{dy} + \dfrac{2y}{y^2+1}x = -\dfrac{1}{y^2+1}$

$\int P(y)\,dy = \int \frac{2y}{y^2+1}\,dy = \ln(y^2+1)$. Let $\rho = y^2+1$

Then $(y^2+1)\dfrac{dx}{dy} + x = -1 \Rightarrow (y^2+1)x = \int -dy$.

$\therefore\ (y^2+1)x = -y + C$ or $x = \dfrac{1}{y^2+1}(C - y)$

35. $\dfrac{dx}{dt} = 1000 + 0.08x + 50t \Rightarrow \dfrac{dx}{dt} - 0.08x = 1000 + 50t$. Let $\rho = e^{-0.08t}$.

$e^{-0.08t}\dfrac{dx}{dt} - 0.08xe^{-0.08t} = 1000e^{-0.08t} + 50te^{-0.08t}$

$xe^{-0.08t} = -12{,}500e^{-0.08t} + 50(-12.5te^{-0.08t} - 156.25e^{-0.08t}) + C$

$x = -12{,}500 - 625t - 7{,}812.5 + Ce^{-0.08t}$

$x(0) = 1000 \Rightarrow C = 21{,}312.5$. Therefore,

$x = -20{,}312.5 - 625t + 21{,}312.5e^{-0.08t}$

## Exact

37. $y\,dx + x\,dy = 0$

(a) $\rho = \frac{1}{xy} \Rightarrow \frac{dx}{x} + \frac{dy}{y} = 0 \Rightarrow \ln|x| + \ln|y| = C$ or $xy = C$

(b) $\rho = \frac{1}{(xy)^2} \Rightarrow \frac{dx}{x^2y} + \frac{dy}{xy^2} = 0 \Rightarrow -\frac{1}{xy} = C$ or $xy = C$

39. $(x+y)dx + (x+y^2)\,dy = 0 \Rightarrow x\,dx + (y\,dx + x\,dy) + y^2\,dy = 0 \Rightarrow$

$\frac{1}{2}x^2 + xy + \frac{1}{3}y^3 = C$

41. $(2xy + y^2)\,dx + (x^2 + 2xy - y)dy = 0$

$(2xy\,dx + x^2\,dy) + (y^2\,dx + 2xy\,dy) - y\,dy = 0$

$x^2y + xy^2 - \frac{1}{2}y^2 = C$

43. $(x\,dy - y\,dx) + x^3\,dx = 0$. Let $\rho = x^2 \Rightarrow$

$\left(\frac{1}{x}dy - \frac{y}{x^2}dx\right) + x\,dx = 0 \Rightarrow \frac{y}{x} + \frac{1}{2}x^2 = C$ or $y = Cx - \frac{1}{2}x^3$

45. $(x^2 + x - y)\,dx + x\,dy = 0 \Rightarrow (x\,dy - y\,dx) + (x^2 + x)\,dx = 0$

$\frac{x\,dy - y\,dx}{x^2} + \left(1 + \frac{1}{x}\right)dx = 0 \Rightarrow \frac{y}{x} + x + \ln|x| = C$ or $y = Cx - x^2 - x\ln|x|$

47. $\left(\frac{y^2}{1+x^2} - 2y\right)dx + (2y\tan^{-1}x - 2x + \sinh y)\,dy = 0$

$\left(\frac{y^2}{1+x^2}dx + 2y\tan^{-1}x\,dy\right) - 2\,(x\,dy + y\,dx) + \sinh y\,dy = 0$

$\cosh y + y^2\tan^{-1}x - 2xy = C$

49. To be exact, we need $\frac{\partial}{\partial y}(ax^2 + by^2) = \frac{\partial}{\partial x}(cxy)$, or $2b = c$

Thus, $ax^2\,dx + (by^2\,dx + 2bxy\,dy) = 0 \Rightarrow \frac{a}{3}x^3 + bxy^2 = C$.

51. (a) $(\cos x + y\cos x)\,dx + dy = 0 \Rightarrow \frac{dy}{1+y} = -\cos x\,dx$

$\ln(1+y) = -\sin x + C$

(b) $y\left(\frac{\pi}{2}\right) = 0 \Rightarrow C = 1$. $\therefore \ln(1+y) = 1 - \sin x$ or $y = e^{1-\sin x} - 1$

53. (a) $\frac{dy}{dx} + 2y = x$; let $\rho = e^{2x}$. Then $ye^{2x} = \int xe^{2x}\,dx = \frac{1}{2}xe^{2x} - \frac{1}{4}e^{2x} + C$

$y = \frac{1}{2}x - \frac{1}{4} + C\,e^{-2x}$

(b) $y(0) = 1 \Rightarrow C = \frac{5}{4}$ $\therefore$ $y = \frac{1}{2}x - \frac{1}{4} + \frac{5}{4}e^{-2x}$

55. (a) $(1 + y^2)\,dx + e^{-x}\,dy = 0 \Rightarrow \frac{dy}{1 + y^2} = -e^{-x}\,dx$

$\tan^{-1} y = -e^{-x} + C$

(b) $y(0) = 1 \Rightarrow C = 1 + \frac{\pi}{4}$. $\therefore$ $\tan^{-1} y = -e^{-x} + 1 + \frac{\pi}{4}$

$y = \tan\left(1 + \frac{\pi}{4} - e^{-x}\right)$

57. (a) $(x + 2y)\,dx + (y + 2x)\,dy = 0 \Rightarrow x\,dx + (2y\,dx + 2x\,dy) + y\,dy = 0$

$\frac{1}{2}x^2 + 2xy + \frac{1}{2}y^2 = C$ or $x^2 + 4xy + y^2 = C$

(b) $y(1) = 1 \Rightarrow C = 6$. $\therefore$ $x^2 + 4xy + y^2 = 6$

59. (a) $x\frac{dy}{dx} + 2y = x^3 \Rightarrow \frac{dy}{dx} + \frac{2}{x}y = x^2$. Let $\rho = x^2$. Then

$x^2 y = \int x^4\,dx = \frac{1}{5}x^5 + C \Rightarrow y = \frac{1}{5}x^3 + \frac{C}{x^2}$

(b) $y(2) = 1 \Rightarrow C = -\frac{12}{5}$ $\therefore$ $y = \frac{1}{5}\left(x^3 - \frac{12}{x^2}\right)$

## 20.3 SECOND ORDER EQUATIONS REDUCIBLE TO FIRST ORDER

1. Let $p = \frac{dy}{dx}$ and $\frac{dp}{dx} = \frac{d^2y}{dx^2}$. Then $\frac{dp}{dx} + p = 0 \Rightarrow \frac{dp}{p} = -\,dx$

$\ln p = -x + C \Rightarrow p = e^{-x+C} = C_1 e^{-x}$. $\therefore$ $\frac{dy}{dx} = C_1 e^{-x} \Rightarrow y = -C_1 e^{-x} + C_2$

3. Let $p = \frac{dy}{dx}$ and $\frac{dp}{dx} = \frac{d^2y}{dx^2}$. Then $\frac{dp}{dx} + xp = 0 \Rightarrow \frac{dp}{p} = -x\,dx$

$\ln p = -\frac{x^2}{2} + C \Rightarrow p = C_1 e^{(-x^2/2)}$. $\therefore$ $\frac{dy}{dx} = C_1 e^{(-x^2/2)} \Rightarrow$

$y = C_1 \int e^{(-x^2/2)}\,dx + C_2$, which cannot be evaluated as a finite combination of elementary functions.

5. Let $p = \frac{dy}{dx}$ and $\frac{d^2y}{dx^2} = \frac{dp}{dx} = \frac{dp}{dy}\frac{dy}{dx} = p\frac{dp}{dy}$.

Then $p\frac{dp}{dy} - y = 0 \Rightarrow p\,dp = y\,dy \Rightarrow \frac{1}{2}p^2 = \frac{1}{2}y^2 + C$

$p = \pm\sqrt{y^2 + 2C} \Rightarrow \frac{dy}{dx} = \pm\sqrt{y^2 + 2C}$

Case I: $2C < 0$. Then $\frac{dy}{\sqrt{y^2 - 2C}} = \pm dx$. Let $B^2 = 2C$. We have

$$\cosh^{-1}\frac{y}{B} = \pm x + C_1 \quad \text{or } y = B\cosh(C_1 \pm x)$$

Case 2: $C = 0$. Then $\frac{dy}{dx} = \pm y \Rightarrow \ln y = \pm x + C_1$ or $y = C_2 e^{\pm x}$

Case 3: $C > 0$. Then $\frac{dy}{\sqrt{y^2 + 2C}} = \pm dx$. Let $B^2 = 2C$. Then

$$\sinh^{-1}\frac{y}{B} = C_2 \pm x \quad \text{or} \quad y = B\sinh(C_2 \pm x)$$

7. Let $\frac{d^2y}{dx^2} = q \Rightarrow \frac{d^3y}{dx^3} = \frac{dq}{dx}$

Then $x\frac{dq}{dx} - 2q = 0 \Rightarrow \frac{dq}{q} = \frac{2}{x}dx \Rightarrow \ln q = \ln x^2 + C$

$$q = C_1x^2 \Rightarrow \frac{d^2y}{dx^2} = C_1x^2 \Rightarrow \frac{dy}{dx} = \frac{1}{3}C_1x^3 + C_2 \Rightarrow y = \frac{1}{12}C_1x^4 + C_2x + C_3$$

9. (a) $y = C_1\sin(x + C_2)$; $y(0) = 0 \Rightarrow 0 = C_1\sin C_2 \Rightarrow C_2 = 0$

$$y\left(\frac{\pi}{2}\right) = 5 \Rightarrow 5 = C_1\sin\frac{\pi}{2} \Rightarrow C_1 = 5 \text{ and } y = 5\sin x$$

(b) $y' = C_1\cos(x + C_2)$; $y'(0) = 2 \Rightarrow 2 = C_1\cos 0 \Rightarrow C_1 = 3$ and $y = 2\sin x$

11. We have $m\frac{d^2x}{dt^2} = mg - k\frac{dx}{dt}$. Let $p = \frac{dx}{dt}$ and $\frac{d^2x}{dt^2} = \frac{dp}{dt}$

Then $m\frac{dp}{dx} + kp = 0 = mg \Rightarrow \frac{dp}{dx} + \frac{k}{m}p = g$. Let $\rho = e^{(k/m)t}$ so that

$$pe^{(k/m)t} = \int ge^{(k/m)t}\,dt = \frac{mg}{k}e^{(k/m)t} + C \Rightarrow p = \frac{mg}{k} + Ce^{-(k/m)t}$$

$\frac{dx}{dt} = \frac{mg}{k} + Ce^{-(k/m)t} \Rightarrow x = \frac{mg}{k}t - \frac{mC}{k}e^{-(k/m)t} + C_1$. $t = 0 \Rightarrow x = 0$

and $\frac{dx}{dt} = 0$, so $C = -\frac{mg}{k}$ and $C_1 = -\frac{m^2g}{k^2}$. Thus $x = \frac{mg}{k}t + \frac{m^2g}{k^2}[e^{-(k/m)t} - 1]$.

13. $u = x^2 \Rightarrow u' = 2x$ and $u'' = 2$ . $\therefore\ x^2 y'' - 2y = 2x^2 - 2x^2 = 0$

Let $y = uv = vx^2$ . Then $y' = 2xv + x^2 v'$ and

$y'' = 2xv' + 2v + x^2 v'' + 2xv'$. Substituting,

$2x^3 v' - 2vx^2 + x^4 v'' + 2x^3 v' - 2x^2 v = 0$ or $x^4 v'' + 4x^3 v' = 0$

Let $v' = p$ and $v'' = \dfrac{dp}{dx} \Rightarrow x^4 \dfrac{dp}{dx} + 4x^3 p = 0 \Rightarrow \dfrac{dp}{p} = -\dfrac{4}{x} dx$

$\therefore \ln p = -4 \ln x + C \Rightarrow p = Cx^{-4} \Rightarrow \dfrac{dv}{dx} = Cx^{-4} \Rightarrow v = -\dfrac{1}{3} C_1 x^{-3} + C_2$.

The general solution is $y = \dfrac{A}{x} + Bx^2$

15. $u = x^{1/2} \Rightarrow u' = \dfrac{1}{2} x^{-1/2}$ and $u'' = -\dfrac{1}{4} x^{-3/2}$ . $\therefore\ y'' + \dfrac{y}{4x^2} = -\dfrac{1}{4} x^{-3/2} + \dfrac{x^{1/2}}{4x^2} = 0$

Let $y = uv = vx^{1/2}$. Then $y' = \dfrac{1}{2} x^{-1/2} v + x^{1/2} v'$ and

$y'' = -\dfrac{1}{4} x^{-3/2} + x^{-1/2} v' + x^{1/2} v''$. Substituting,

we get $x^{1/2} v'' + x^{-1/2} v' = 0$ or $v'' + \dfrac{1}{x} v' = 0$.

Let $v' = p$ and $v'' = \dfrac{dp}{dx} \Rightarrow \dfrac{dp}{dx} + \dfrac{1}{x} p = 0 \Rightarrow \dfrac{dp}{p} = -\dfrac{dx}{x} \Rightarrow p = \dfrac{C}{x}$

$\therefore\ \dfrac{dv}{dx} = \dfrac{C}{x} \Rightarrow v = C \ln |x| + C_2$. The general

solution is $y = x^{1/2} (C \ln |x| + C_2)$

17. Let $y = uv$. Then $y' = uv' + vu'$ and $y'' = uv'' + 2v'u' + vu''$

Substituting into $y'' + Py' + Qy = F$ gives

$(u'' + Pu' + Qu) v + uv'' + (Pu + 2u')v' = F$ or $v'' + \left(P + \dfrac{2u'}{u}\right) v' = F$

Let $w = v'$ and $w' = v''$. Then $w' + \left(P + \dfrac{2u'}{u}\right) w = \dfrac{F}{u}$

Let $y = ve^x \Rightarrow y' = ve^x + v'e^x$ and $y'' = ve^x + 2v'e^x + v''e^x$.

Then $y'' - 2y' + y = e^x \Rightarrow ve^x + 2v'e^x + v''e^x - 2ve^x - 2v'e^x + ve^x = e^x$.

$v''e^x = e^x \Rightarrow v'' = 1$. Let $w = v'$ and $w' = v''$. Then $w' = 1 \Rightarrow$

$w = x + C_1 = v' \Rightarrow v = \dfrac{1}{2} x^2 + C_1 x + C_2 \Rightarrow y = e^x \left(\dfrac{1}{2} x^2 + C_1 x + C_2\right)$.

## 20.4 LINEAR SECOND ORDER HOMOGENEOUS EQUATIONS WITH CONSTANT COEFFICIENTS

1. $\frac{d^2y}{dx^2} + 2\frac{dy}{dx} = 0$ $r^2 + 2r = 0 \Rightarrow r(r+2) = 0$ or $r = 0$ or $-2$

$\therefore$ $y = C_1 + C_2e^{-2x}$

3. $\frac{d^2y}{dx^2} + 6\frac{dy}{dx} + 5y = 0$ $r^2 + 6r + 5 = 0 \Rightarrow (r+1)(r+5) = 0$ or $r = -1$ or $-5$

$\therefore$ $y = C_1e^{-x} + C_2e^{-5x}$

5. $\frac{d^2y}{dx^2} + \frac{dy}{dx} + y = 0$ $r^2 + r + 1 = 0 \Rightarrow r = \frac{-1 \pm \sqrt{1-4}}{2}$

or $r = -\frac{1}{2} \pm i\frac{\sqrt{3}}{2}$ $\therefore$ $y = e^{-(x/2)}\left(C_1 \cos\frac{\sqrt{3}}{2}x + C_2 \sin\frac{\sqrt{3}}{2}x\right)$

7. $\frac{d^2y}{dx^2} + 6\frac{dy}{dx} + 9y = 0$ $r^2 + 6r + 9 = 0 \Rightarrow r = -3, -3$

$\therefore$ $y = (C_1 + C_2x)e^{-3x}$

9. $\frac{d^2y}{dx^2} - 2\frac{dy}{dx} + 4y = 0$ $r^2 - 2r + 4 = 0 \Rightarrow r = \frac{2 \pm \sqrt{4-16}}{2}$

or $r = 1 \pm \sqrt{3}\,i$ $\therefore$ $y = e^x(C_1 \cos\sqrt{3}\,x + C_2 \sin\sqrt{3}\,x)$

11. $y'' - y = 0$ $r^2 - 1 = 0 \Rightarrow r = \pm 1$

$\therefore$ $y = C_1e^x + C_2e^{-x}$; $y' = C_1e^x - C_2e^{-x}$

$y(0) = 1 \Rightarrow 1 = C_1 + C_2$. $y'(0) = -2 \Rightarrow -2 = C_1 - C_2 \Rightarrow C_1 = -\frac{1}{2}$ and $C_2 = \frac{3}{2}$.

$\therefore$ $y = \frac{3}{2}e^{-x} - \frac{1}{2}e^x$.

13. $2y'' - y' - y = 0$ $2r^2 - r - 1 = 0 \Rightarrow (2r+1)(r-1) = 0$ $r = 1, -\frac{1}{2}$

$\therefore$ $y = C_1e^x + C_2e^{-x/2}$; $y' = C_1e^x - \frac{1}{2}C_2e^{-x/2}$

$y(0) = -1 \Rightarrow -1 = C_1 + C_2$. $y'(0) = 0 \Rightarrow 0 = C_1 - \frac{1}{2}C_2 \Rightarrow C_2 = -\frac{2}{3}, C_1 = -\frac{1}{3}$.

$\therefore$ $y = -\frac{2}{3}e^{-x/2} - \frac{1}{3}e^x$

15. $y'' - 4y = 0$ $r^2 - 4 = 0 \Rightarrow r = \pm 2$

$y = C_1e^{2x} + C_2e^{-2x}$ and $y' = 2C_1e^{2x} - 2C_2e^{-2x}$

$y(0) = 0 \Rightarrow 0 = C_1 + C_2$. $y'(0) = 3 \Rightarrow 3 = 2C_1 - 2C_2$

$C_1 = \frac{3}{4}$ and $C_2 = -\frac{3}{4}$ $\therefore$ $y = \frac{3}{4}e^{2x} - \frac{3}{4}e^{-2x}$

17. $y'' + 4y = 0 \qquad r^2 + 4 = 0 \Rightarrow r = \pm 2i$

$y = C_1\cos 2x + C_2 \sin 2x$ and $y' = -2\sin 2x + 2C_2\cos 2x$

$y(0) = 0 \Rightarrow 0 = C_1$ . $y'(0) = 2 \Rightarrow 2 = 2C_2 \Rightarrow C_2 = 1$

$\therefore\ y = \sin 2x$

## 20.5 LINEAR SECOND ORDER NONHOMOGENEOUS EQUATIONS WITH CONSTANT COEFFICIENTS

1. $\dfrac{d^2y}{dx^2} + \dfrac{dy}{dx} = x \qquad r^2 + r = 0 \Rightarrow r(r+1) = 0 \Rightarrow r = 0 \text{ or } -1$

Let $u_1 = 1$ and $u_2 = e^{-x}$. $D = \begin{vmatrix} 1 & e^{-x} \\ 0 & -e^{-x} \end{vmatrix} = -e^{-x}$

$v_1' = \dfrac{-xe^{-x}}{-e^{-x}} = x \Rightarrow v_1 = \dfrac{1}{2}x^2 + C_1$

$v_2' = \dfrac{x}{-e^{-x}} = -xe^{x} \Rightarrow v_2 = e^{x}(1-x) + C_2$

Then $y = \dfrac{1}{2}x^2 + C_1 + e^{-x}\left[ e^{x}(1-x) + C_2 \right] = 1 - x + \dfrac{1}{2}x^2 + C_2 e^{-x} + C_1$

3. $\dfrac{d^2y}{dx^2} + y = \sin x \qquad r^2 + 1 = 0 \Rightarrow r = \pm i$

Let $u_1 = \cos x$ and $u_2 = \sin x$. $D = \begin{vmatrix} \cos x & \sin x \\ -\sin x & \cos x \end{vmatrix} = 1$

$v_1' = -\sin^2 x \Rightarrow v_1 = \int -\sin^2 x\,dx = -\dfrac{1}{2}x + \dfrac{1}{4}\sin 2x + C_1$

$v_2' = \cos x \sin x \Rightarrow v_2 = \int \cos x \sin x\, dx = \dfrac{1}{2}\sin^2 x + C_2$

Then $y = \sin x\left(\dfrac{1}{2}\sin^2 x + C_2\right) + \cos x\left(-\dfrac{1}{2}x + \dfrac{1}{4}\sin 2x + C_1\right)$

$= \dfrac{1}{2}\sin^3 x - \dfrac{1}{2}x\cos x + \dfrac{1}{4}\cos x \sin 2x + C_1\cos x + C_2 \sin x$

$= C_1\cos x + C_2\sin x - \dfrac{1}{2}x\cos x + \dfrac{1}{2}\sin x(\cos^2 x + \sin^2 x)$

$= C_1\cos x + C_3 \sin x - \dfrac{1}{2}x\cos x$

5. $\frac{d^2y}{dx^2} + 2\frac{dy}{dx} + y = e^{-x}$ $\quad r^2 + 2r + 1 = 0 \Rightarrow r = -1, -1$

Let $u_1 = e^{-x}$ and $u_2 = xe^{-x}$ $\quad D = \begin{vmatrix} e^{-x} & xe^{-x} \\ -e^{-x} & -xe^{-x} + e^{-x} \end{vmatrix} = e^{-2x}$

$v_1' = -x \Rightarrow v_1 = \int -x\,dx = -\frac{1}{2}x^2 + C_1$

$v_2' = 1 \Rightarrow v_2 = \int dx = x + C_2$

Then $y = xe^{-x}\left(x + C_2\right) + e^{-x}\left(-\frac{1}{2}x^2 + C_1\right) = C_1 e^{-x} + C_2 xe^{-x} + \frac{1}{2}x^2 e^{-x}$

7. $\frac{d^2y}{dx^2} - y = e^x$ $\quad r^2 - 1 = 0 \Rightarrow r = \pm 1$

Let $u_1 = e^x$ and $u_2 = e^{-x}$. $D = \begin{vmatrix} e^x & e^{-x} \\ e^x & -e^{-x} \end{vmatrix} = -2$

$v_1' = \frac{1}{2} \Rightarrow v_1 = \int \frac{1}{2}\,dx = \frac{1}{2}x + C_1$

$v_2' = -\frac{1}{2}e^x e^x \Rightarrow v_2 = \int -\frac{1}{2}e^{2x}\,dx = -\frac{1}{4}e^{2x} + C_2$

Then $y = e^x\left(\frac{1}{2}x + C_1\right) + e^{-x}\left(-\frac{1}{4}e^{2x} + C_2\right)$

$= C_1 e^x + C_2 e^{-x} - \frac{1}{4}e^x + \frac{1}{2}xe^x = C_3e^x + C_2 e^{-x} + \frac{1}{2}xe^x$

9. $\frac{d^2y}{dx^2} + 4\frac{dy}{dx} + 5y = 10$ $\quad r^2 + 4r + 5 = 0 \Rightarrow r = -2 \pm i$

Let $u_1 = e^{-2x}\cos x$ and $u_2 = e^{-2x}\sin x$

$D = \begin{vmatrix} e^{-2x}\cos x & e^{-2x}\sin x \\ -e^{-2x}(2\cos x + \sin x) & e^{-2x}(\cos x - 2\sin x) \end{vmatrix} = e^{-4x}$ $\quad v_1' = -10\,e^{2x}\sin x$

$v_1 = \int -10\,e^{2x}\sin x\,dx = -2e^{2x}(2\sin x - \cos x) + C_1$

$v_2' = 10\,e^{2x}\cos x \Rightarrow v_2 = \int 10\,e^{2x}\cos x\,dx = 2e^{2x}(2\cos x + \sin x) + C_2$

$y = e^{-2x}\cos x\,(-2e^{2x}(2\sin x - \cos x) + C_1) +$

$e^{-2x}\sin x\,(2e^{2x}(2\cos x + \sin x) + C_2)$

$= e^{-2x}(C_1\cos x + C_2\sin x) + 2$

11. $\dfrac{d^2y}{dx^2} + y = \sec x, -\dfrac{\pi}{2} < x < \dfrac{\pi}{2}$ $\quad r^2 + 1 = 0 \Rightarrow r = \pm i$

Let $u_1 = \cos x$ and $u_2 = \sin x$ $\quad D = \begin{vmatrix} \cos x & \sin x \\ -\sin x & \cos x \end{vmatrix} = 1$

$v_1' = -\sin x \sec x = -\tan x \Rightarrow v_1 = \int -\tan x \, dx = \ln(\cos x) + C_1$

$v_2' = \cos x \sec x = 1 \Rightarrow v_2 = \int dx = x + C_2$

Then $y = \cos x(\ln(\cos x) + C_1) + \sin x(x + C_2)$

$= C_1 \cos x + C_2 \sin x + \cos x \ln(\cos x) + x \sin x$

13. $\dfrac{d^2y}{dx^2} - 3\dfrac{dy}{dx} - 10y = -3$ $\quad r^2 - 3r - 10 = 0 \Rightarrow r = 5, -2$

$\therefore y_h = C_1 e^{5x} + C_2 e^{-2x}$. Guess $y_p = A$. Then $y_p' = y_p'' = 0$

$y_p'' - 3y_p' - 10y_p = -3 \Rightarrow -10A = -3 \Rightarrow A = \dfrac{3}{10}$

Then $y = y_h + y_p = C_1 e^{5x} + C_2 e^{-2x} + \dfrac{3}{10}$

15. $\dfrac{d^2y}{dx^2} - \dfrac{dy}{dx} = \sin x$ $\quad r^2 - r = 0 \Rightarrow r = 0, 1$

$\therefore y_h = C_1 + C_2 e^x$. Guess $y_p = A\cos x + B\sin x$.

Then $y_p' = -A \sin x + B \cos x$, $y_p'' = -A\cos x - B \sin x$

$y_p'' - y_p' = \sin x \Rightarrow -A\cos x - B \sin x + A \sin x - B \cos x = \sin x$

$(A - B)\sin x - (A + B)\cos x = \sin x$; $A - B = 1$ and $A + B = 0 \Rightarrow A = \dfrac{1}{2}$ and $B = -\dfrac{1}{2}$

Then $y = y_h + y_p = C_1 + C_2 e^x + \dfrac{1}{2}(\cos x - \sin x)$

17. $\dfrac{d^2y}{dx^2} + y = \cos 3x$ $\quad r^2 + 1 = 0 \Rightarrow r = \pm i$

$\therefore y_h = C_1 \cos x + C_2 \sin x$. Guess $y_p = A\cos 3x + B\sin 3x$.

Then $y_p' = -3A \sin 3x + 3B \cos 3x$, $y_p'' = -9A\cos 3x - 9B \sin 3x$

$y_p'' + y_p = \cos 3x \Rightarrow -8A \cos 3x - 8B \sin 3x = \cos 3x$

$-8A \cos 3x = \cos 3x \Rightarrow A = -\dfrac{1}{8}$; $B = 0$

Then $y = y_h + y_p = C_1 \cos x + C_2 \sin x - \dfrac{1}{8}\cos 3x$

19. $\frac{d^2y}{dx^2} - \frac{dy}{dx} - 2y = 20\cos x \quad r^2 - r - 2 = 0 \Rightarrow r = 2, -1$

$\therefore y_h = C_1e^{2x} + C_2e^{-x}$. Guess $y_p = A\cos x + B\sin x$.

Then $y_p' = -A\sin x + B\cos x$, $y_p'' = -A\cos x - B\sin x$

$-A\cos x - B\sin x + A\sin x - B\cos x - 2A\cos x - 2B\sin x = 20\cos x$

$(A - 3B)\sin x + (-3A - B)\cos x = 20\cos x$; $A = -6$, $B = -2$

Then $y = y_h + y_p = C_1e^{2x} + C_2e^{-x} - 6\cos x - 2\sin x$

21. $\frac{d^2y}{dx^2} - y = e^x + x^2 \quad r^2 - 1 = 0 \Rightarrow r = \pm 1$

$\therefore y_h = C_1e^x + C_2e^{-x}$. Guess $y_p = Axe^x + Bx^2 + Cx + D$.

Then $y_p' = Ae^x + Axe^x + 2Bx + C$, $y_p'' = 2Ae^x + Axe^x + 2B$

$2Ae^x + Axe^x + 2B - Axe^x - Bx^2 - Cx - D = e^x + x^2$

$2Ae^x = e^x \Rightarrow A = \frac{1}{2}$, $B = -1$, $C = 0$, $D = -2$

Then $y = y_h + y_p = C_1e^x + C_2e^{-x} + \frac{1}{2}xe^x - x^2 - 2$

23. $\frac{d^2y}{dx^2} - \frac{dy}{dx} - 6y = e^{-x} - 7\cos x \quad r^2 - r - 6 = 0 \Rightarrow r = -2, 3$

$\therefore y_h = C_1e^{-2x} + C_2e^{3x}$. Guess $y_p = Ae^{-x} + B\cos x + C\sin x$

Then $y_p' = -Ae^{-x} - B\sin x + C\cos x$, $y_p'' = Ae^{-x} - B\cos x - C\sin x$

$Ae^{-x} - B\cos x - C\sin x + Ae^{-x} + B\cos x - C\sin x - 6Ae^{-x}$

$\qquad - 6B\cos x - 6A\sin x = e^{-x} - 7\cos x$

$-4Ae^{-x} = e^{-x} \Rightarrow A = -\frac{1}{4}$; $7B + C = 7$, $7C - B = 0 \Rightarrow B = \frac{49}{50}$, $C = \frac{7}{50}$

Then $y = y_h + y_p = C_1e^{-2x} + C_2e^{3x} - \frac{1}{4}e^{-x} + \frac{49}{50}\cos x + \frac{7}{50}\sin x$

25. $\frac{d^2y}{dx^2} + 5\frac{dy}{dx} = 15x^2$; $\quad r^2 + 5r = 0 \Rightarrow r = 0, -5$

$\therefore y_h = C_1 + C_2e^{-5x}$. Guess $y_p = Ax^3 + Bx^2 + Cx$

Then $y_p' = 3Ax^2 + 2Bx + C$; $y_p'' = 6Ax + 2B$

$6Ax + 2B + 15Ax^2 + 10Bx + 5C = 15x^2$; $A = 1, B = -\frac{6}{10}$, $C = \frac{6}{25}$

Then $y = y_h + y_p = C_1 + C_2e^{-5x} + x^3 - \frac{3}{5}x^2 + \frac{6}{25}x$

27. $\frac{d^2y}{dx^2} - 3\frac{dy}{dx} = e^{3x} - 12x$ ; $r^2 - 3r = 0 \Rightarrow r = 0, 3$

$\therefore y_h = C_1 + C_2 e^{3x}$. Guess $y_p = Axe^{3x} + Bx^2 + Cx$

Then $y_p' = Ae^{3x} + 3Axe^{3x} + 2Bx + C$ ; $y_p'' = 6Ae^{3x} + 9Axe^{3x} + 2B$

$3ae^{3x} - 6Bx + 2B - 3C = e^{3x} - 12x$; $A = \frac{1}{3}, B = 2, C = \frac{4}{3}$

Then $y = y_h + y_p = C_1 + C_2 e^{3x} + \frac{1}{3}xe^{3x} + 2x^2 + \frac{4}{3}x$

29. $\frac{d^2y}{dx^2} - 5\frac{dy}{dx} = xe^{5x}$ ; $r^2 - 5r = 0 \Rightarrow r = 0, 5$

$\therefore y_h = C_1 + C_2 e^{5x}$. $y_p = Ax^2e^{5x} + Bxe^{5x}$

Then $y_p' = 2Axe^{5x} + 5Ax^2e^{5x} + Be^{5x} + 5Bxe^{5x}$

$y_p'' = 2Ae^{5x} + 20Axe^{5x} + 25Ax^2e^{5x} + 10Be^{5x} + 25Bxe^{5x}$

$10Axe^{5x} + 5Be^{5x} + 2Ae^{5x} = xe^{5x}$ ; $A = \frac{1}{10}$

$2A + 5B = 0 \Rightarrow B = -\frac{1}{25}$

Then $y = y_h + y_p = C_1 + C_2 e^{5x} + \left(\frac{1}{10}x^2 - \frac{1}{25}x\right)e^{5x}$

31. $\frac{d^2y}{dx^2} + y = 2\cos x + \sin x$; $r^2 + 1 = 0 \Rightarrow r = \pm i$

$\therefore y_h = C_1\cos x + C_2 \sin x$. $y_p = x(A\cos x + B\sin x)$

Then $y_p' = (A\cos x + B\sin x) + x(-A\sin x + B\cos x)$

; $y_p'' = 2(-A\sin x + B\cos x) - x(A\cos x + B\sin x)$

$-2A\sin x + 2B\cos x = 2\cos x + \sin x \Rightarrow A = -\frac{1}{2}$ and $B = 1$

Then $y = y_h + y_p = C_1\cos x + C_2\sin x + x\left(\sin x - \frac{1}{2}\cos x\right)$

33. $\frac{d^2y}{dx^2} - \frac{dy}{dx} = e^x + e^{-x}$; $r^2 - r = 0 \Rightarrow r = 0, 1$

$\therefore y_h = C_1 + C_2 e^x$.

(a) $u_1 = 1$, $u_2 = e^x$, $F(x) = e^x + e^{-x}$

$$D = \begin{vmatrix} 1 & e^x \\ 0 & e^x \end{vmatrix} = e^x ;\ v_1' = -(e^x + e^{-x}) \Rightarrow v_1 = e^{-x} - e^x$$

$v_2' = 1 + e^{-2x} \Rightarrow v_2 = x - \frac{1}{2}e^{-2x}$. Thus $y_p = (x-1)e^x + \frac{1}{2}e^{-x}$

(b) Let $y_p = Axe^x + Be^{-x}$. Then $y_p' = Axe^x + Ae^x - Be^x$ and

$y_p'' = 2Ae^x + Axe^x + Be^{-x}$

$y_p'' - 4y_p' + 4y_p = 2e^{2x} \Rightarrow Ae^x + 2Be^{-x} = e^x + e^{-x} \Rightarrow A = 1$ and $B = \frac{1}{2}$

$\therefore y = (C_1 + C_2 e^x) + xe^x + \frac{1}{2}e^{-x}$

35. $\frac{d^2y}{dx^2} - 4\frac{dy}{dx} - 5y = e^x + 4;\quad r^2 - 4r - 5 = 0 \Rightarrow r = 5, -1$

$\therefore y_h = C_1e^{5x} + C_2e^{-x}$

(a) $u_1 = e^{5x}$, $u_2 = e^{-x}$, $F(x) = e^x + 4$

$$D = \begin{vmatrix} e^{5x} & e^{-x} \\ 5e^{5x} & -e^{-x} \end{vmatrix} = -6e^{4x};\quad v_1' = \frac{1}{6}e^{-4x} + \frac{2}{3}e^{-5x} \Rightarrow v_1 = -\frac{1}{24}e^{-4x} - \frac{2}{15}e^{-5x}$$

$v_2' = -\frac{1}{6}e^{2x} - \frac{2}{3}e^x \Rightarrow v_2 = -\frac{1}{12}e^{2x} - \frac{2}{3}e^x$. Thus $y_p = -\frac{1}{8}e^x - \frac{4}{5}$

(b) Let $y_p = Ae^x + B$. Then $y_p' = Ae^x$ and $y_p'' = Ae^x$

$Ae^x - 4Ae^x - 5Ae^x - 5B = e^x + 4 \Rightarrow A = -\frac{1}{8}$ an d $B = -\frac{4}{5}$. Thus $y_p = xe^{9x}$

$\therefore y = C_1e^{5x} + C_2e^{-x} - \frac{1}{8}e^x - \frac{4}{5}$

37. $\frac{d^2y}{dx^2} + y = \cot x,\ 0 < x < \pi \qquad r^2 + 1 = 0 \Rightarrow r = \pm i$

Let $u_1 = \cos x$, $u_2 = \sin x$. $D = \begin{vmatrix} \cos x & \sin x \\ -\sin x & -\cos x \end{vmatrix} = 1$

$v_1' = -\sin x \cot x = -\cos x \Rightarrow v_1 = -\sin x + C_1$

$v_2' = \cos x \cot x = \csc x - \sin x \Rightarrow v_2 = -\ln|\csc x + \cot x| + \cos x + C_2$

$\therefore\ y = C_1 \cos x + C_2 \sin x - \sin x \ln|\csc x + \cot x|$

39. $\frac{d^2y}{dx^2} - 8\frac{dy}{dx} = e^{8x} \qquad r^2 - 8r = 0 \Rightarrow r = 0, 8$

$y_h = C_1 + C_2e^{8x} \qquad$ Let $y_p = Axe^{8x}$

Then $y_p' = Ae^{8x} + 8xe^{8x}$ and $y_p'' = 16Ae^{8x} + 64Axe^{8x}$

$16Ae^{8x} + 64Axe^{8x} - 8Ae^{8x} - 64xe^{8x} = e^{8x} \Rightarrow A = \frac{1}{8}$

$\therefore y = C_1 + C_2e^{8x} + \frac{1}{8}xe^{8x}$

41. $\dfrac{d^2y}{dx^2} - \dfrac{dy}{dx} = x^3$ $\qquad r^2 - r = 0 \Rightarrow r = 0, 1$

$y_h = C_1 + C_2 e^x$ Let $y_p = Ax^4 + Bx^3 + Cx^2 + Dx$

Then $y_p' = 4Ax^3 + 3Bx^2 + 2Cx + D$ and $y_p'' = 12Ax^2 + 6Bx + 2C$

$4Ax^3 + 3Bx^2 + 2Cx + D - 12Ax^2 - 6Bx - 2C = x^3 \Rightarrow A = -\dfrac{1}{4}, B = -1, C = -3, D = -6$

$\therefore y_h = C_1 + C_2 e^x - \dfrac{1}{4}x^4 - x^3 - 3x^2 - 6x$

43. $\dfrac{d^2y}{dx^2} + 2\dfrac{dy}{dx} = x^2 - e^x$ $\qquad r^2 + 2r = 0 \Rightarrow r = 0, -2$

$y_h = C_1 + C_2 e^{-2x}$. Let $y_p = Ax^3 + Bx^2 + Cx + De^x$

Then $y_p' = 3Ax^2 + 2Bx + C + De^x$ and $y_p'' = 6Ax + 2B + De^x$

$6Ax + 2B + De^x + 2Ax^3 + 2Bx^2 + 2Cx + 2De^x = x^2 - e^x$

$6Ax^2 + (6A + 4B)x + (2B + 2C) + 3De^x = x^2 - e^x \Rightarrow A = \dfrac{1}{6}, B = -\dfrac{1}{4}, C = \dfrac{1}{4}, D = -\dfrac{1}{3}$

$\therefore y = C_1 + C_2 e^{-2x} + \dfrac{1}{6}x^3 - \dfrac{1}{4}x^2 + \dfrac{1}{4}x - \dfrac{1}{3}e^x$

45. $\dfrac{d^2y}{dx^2} + y = \sec x \tan x, -\dfrac{\pi}{2} < x < \dfrac{\pi}{2}$ $\qquad r^2 + 1 = 0 \Rightarrow r = \pm i$

$u_1 = \cos x \quad u_2 = \sin x \quad F = \sec x \tan x$

$D = \begin{vmatrix} \cos x & \sin x \\ -\sin x & \cos x \end{vmatrix} = 1$

$v_1' = -\sin x \sec x \tan x \Rightarrow v_1 = -\int \tan^2 x\, dx = x - \tan x + C_1$

$v_2' = \cos x \sec x \tan x \Rightarrow v_2 = \int \tan x\, dx = \ln(\sec x) + C_2$

$\therefore y = C_1 \cos x + C_2 \sin x + x\cos x - \sin x + \sin x \ln(\sec x)$

47. $\dfrac{dy}{dx} - 3y = e^x$ $\qquad r - 3 = 0 \Rightarrow r = 3$

$y_h = Ce^{3x}$ Let $y_p = Ae^x$. Then $y_p' = Ae^x$

$Ae^x - 3Ae^x = e^x \Rightarrow A = -\dfrac{1}{2} \quad \therefore y = Ce^{3x} - \dfrac{1}{2}e^x$

49. $\dfrac{dy}{dx} - 3y = 5e^{3x}$ $\qquad r - 3 = 0 \Rightarrow r = 3$

$y_h = Ce^{3x}$ Let $y_p = Axe^{3x}$. Then $y_p' = 3Axe^{3x} + Ae^{3x}$

$3Axe^{3x} + Ae^{3x} - 3Axe^{3x} = 5e^{3x} \Rightarrow A = 5 \quad \therefore y = Ce^{3x} + 5xe^{3x}$

51. $\dfrac{d^2y}{dx^2} + y = \sec^2 x,\ -\dfrac{\pi}{2} < x < \dfrac{\pi}{2}$ $\quad r^2 + 1 = 0 \Rightarrow r = \pm i$

Let $u_1 = \cos x$ and $u_2 = \sin x$

$D = \begin{vmatrix} \cos x & \sin x \\ -\sin x & \cos x \end{vmatrix} = 1 \quad v_1' = -\sin x \sec^2 x = -\sec x \tan x$

$v_1 = \int -\sec x \tan x\, dx = -\sec x + C_1$

$v_2' = \cos x \sec^2 x = \sec x \Rightarrow v_2 = \int \sec x\, dx = \ln|\sec x + \tan x| + C_2$

Then $y = C_1 \cos x + C_2 \sin x - 1 + \sin x \ln|\sec x + \tan x|$

$y(0) = 1 \Rightarrow C_1 = 2;\ y'(0) = 1 \Rightarrow C_2 = 1$

$y = 2\cos x + \sin x - 1 + \sin x \ln|\sec x + \tan x|$

53. $y(x) + \int_0^x y(t)\, dt = x \Rightarrow \dfrac{d}{dx}\left[y(x) + \int_0^x y(t)\, dt\right] = 1$

$\dfrac{dy}{dx} + y(x) = 1 \Rightarrow y_h = Ce^{-x}$. Let $y_p = A = 1$. $\therefore y = Ce^{-x} + 1$

$y(0) = 1 \Rightarrow C = -1$. Thus $y = -e^{-x} + 1$

## 20.6 VIBRATIONS

1. From Equation 5, $x = C_1 \cos \omega t + C_2 \sin \omega t$. $x(0) = x_0 \Rightarrow C_1 = x_0$.

$x'(0) = v_0 \Rightarrow C_2 = \dfrac{v_0}{\omega}$. $\therefore x = x_0 \cos \omega t + \dfrac{v_0}{\omega} \sin \omega t$.

Also, $x = C \sin(\omega t + \phi)$ with $C = \sqrt{x_0^2 + \left(\dfrac{v_0}{\omega}\right)^2}$ and $\phi = \tan^{-1}\left(\dfrac{\omega x_0}{v_0}\right)$

3. (a) v a constant $\Rightarrow \dfrac{dV}{dt} = 0$. We have $\dfrac{d^2 i}{dt^2} + \omega^2 i = 0$

$\therefore i = C_1 \cos \omega t + C_2 \sin \omega t$

(b) $i_h = C_1 \cos \omega t + C_2 \sin \omega t$ from part (a).

$v = V \sin \alpha t \Rightarrow \dfrac{dv}{dt} = \alpha V \cos \alpha t$. $\dfrac{d^2 i}{dt^2} + \omega^2 i = \dfrac{\alpha V}{L} \cos \alpha t$

Guess $i_p = A \cos \alpha t + B \sin \alpha t$. We get $B = 0$, $A = \dfrac{\alpha V}{L(\omega^2 - \alpha^2)}$

$\therefore i = C_1 \cos \omega t + C_2 \sin \omega t + \dfrac{\alpha V}{L(\omega^2 - \alpha^2)} \cos \alpha t$

(c) $i_h = C_1 \cos \omega t + C_2 \sin \omega t$ from part (a).

$v = V \sin \omega t \Rightarrow \frac{dv}{dt} = \omega V \cos \varpi t$. $\frac{d^2 i}{dt^2} + \omega^2 i = \frac{V\omega}{L} \cos \omega t$

Guess $i_p = A t \cos \omega t + B t \sin \omega t$. We get $B = 0$, $A = \frac{V}{2L}$

$\therefore i = C_1 \cos \omega t + C_2 \sin \omega t + \frac{V}{2L} t \sin \omega t$

(d) $5 \frac{d^2 i}{dt^2} + 50 \frac{di}{dt} + \frac{10^6}{9} i = 0 \Rightarrow r = -5 \pm 149\,i$

$\therefore i = e^{-5t} (C_1 \cos 149\,t + C_2 \sin 149t$

5. $\frac{d^2\theta}{dt^2} + \omega^2 \theta = 0$, where $\omega = \sqrt{\frac{2k}{mr^2}} \Rightarrow r = \pm \omega i$. $\theta = C_1 \cos \omega t + C_2 \sin \omega t$.

$\theta(0) = 0 \Rightarrow C_1 = \theta_0$. $\frac{d\theta}{dt} = v_0$ at $t = 0 \Rightarrow C_2 = \frac{v_0}{\omega}$.

$\therefore \theta = \theta_0 \cos \omega t + \frac{v_0}{\omega} \sin \omega t$, $\omega = \sqrt{\frac{2k}{mr^2}}$

7. $m\frac{d^2x}{dt^2} + kx = k f(t)$ $\quad r^2 + \frac{k}{m} = 0 \Rightarrow r = \pm i \sqrt{\frac{k}{m}}$. Let $\omega^2 = \frac{k}{m}$

Then $x_h = C_1 \cos \omega t + C_2 \sin \omega t$

(a) $f(t) = A \sin \alpha t$, $\alpha \neq \omega$. Guess $x_p = B \cos \alpha t + C \sin \alpha t$

Then one finds $B = 0$, $C = \frac{A\omega^2}{\omega^2 - \alpha^2} \Rightarrow$

$x = C_1 \cos \omega t + C_2 \sin \omega t + \frac{A\omega^2}{\omega^2 - \alpha^2} \sin \alpha t$

$x = x_0$ and $\frac{dx}{dt} = 0$ when $t = 0 \Rightarrow C_1 = x_0$ and $C_2 = -\frac{\alpha\omega A}{\omega^2 - \alpha^2}$

(b) $f(t) = A \sin \alpha t$, $\alpha = \omega$. Guess $x_p = t(B \cos \alpha t + C \sin \alpha t)$

Then one finds $C = 0$, $B = -\frac{\omega A}{2} \Rightarrow$

$x = C_1 \cos \omega t + C_2 \sin \omega t - \frac{\omega A}{2} \cos \alpha t$

$x = x_0$ and $\frac{dx}{dt} = 0$ when $t = 0 \Rightarrow C_1 = x_0$ and $C_2 = \frac{A}{2}$

## 20.7 HIGHER ORDER LINEAR EQUATIONS WITH CONSTANT COEFFICIENTS

1. $\frac{d^3y}{dx^3} - 3\frac{d^2y}{dx^2} + 2\frac{dy}{dx} = 0 \qquad r^3 - 3r^2 + 2r = r(r-2)(r-1) = 0$

   $y = C_1e^x + C_2e^{2x} + C_3$

3. $\frac{d^4y}{dx^4} - 4\frac{d^2y}{dx^2} + 4y = 0 \qquad (r^2-2)^2 = 0 \Rightarrow r = \pm\sqrt{2}, \pm\sqrt{2}$

   $y = e^{\sqrt{2}x}(C_1 + C_2x) + e^{-\sqrt{2}x}(C_3 + C_4x)$

5. $\frac{d^4y}{dx^4} + 16y = 0 \qquad r = \sqrt{2} \pm i\sqrt{2}, -\sqrt{2} \pm i\sqrt{2}$ (See Ex. 5, Page A-56)

   $y = e^{\sqrt{2}x}(C_1\cos\sqrt{2}x + C_2\sin\sqrt{2}x) + e^{-\sqrt{2}x}(C_3\cos\sqrt{2}x + C_4\sin\sqrt{2}x)$

7. $\frac{d^4y}{dx^4} - 4\frac{d^3y}{dx^3} + 6\frac{d^2y}{dx^2} - 4\frac{dy}{dx} + y = 7 \qquad r^4 - 4r^3 + 6r^2 - 4r + 1 = (r-1)^4$

   $y_h = e^x(C_1 + C_2x + C_3x^2 + C_4x^3)$ ; Try $y_p = 7$. Then

   $\therefore\ y = e^x(C_1 + C_2x + C_3x^2 + C_4x^3) + 7$

## 20.8 APPROXIMATION METHODS: POWER SERIES

1. $y = 2e^{x-1} - 2 - (x-1) \Rightarrow y' = 2e^{x-1} - 1$

   $x + y = x + 2e^{x-1} - 2 - (x-1) = 2e^{x-1} - 1$. Also $y(1) = 0$

3. $y(x) = y(0) + y'(0)x + \frac{y''(0)}{2!}x^2 + \ldots$

   $y' + y = 0 \Rightarrow y' = -y. \quad \therefore y'(0) = -y(0) = -1$

   $y'' = -y' \Rightarrow y''(0) = -y'(0) = 1$

   $\therefore\ y = 1 + x - \frac{1}{2}x^2 + \ldots = \sum_{n=0}^{\infty}(-1)^n\frac{x^n}{n!}$

5. $y(x) = y(0) + y'(0)(x-1) + \frac{y''(0)}{2!}(x-1)^2 + \ldots$

$y' = -2y. \quad \therefore y'(1) = -2y(1) = 2$

$y'' = -2y' \Rightarrow y''(1) = 2y'(1) = -2^2$

$$\therefore y = -(x-1) + 2(x-1) - \frac{2^2}{2!}(x-1)^2 \ldots = \sum_{n=0}^{\infty} (-1)^{n+1} \frac{2^n}{n!}(x-1)^n$$

7. $y(x) = y(0) + y'(0)x + \frac{y''(0)}{2!}x^2 + \ldots; y'(0) = 0$ and $y(0) = 1$

$y'' = -y \Rightarrow y''(0) = -1.$

$y''' = -y' \Rightarrow y'''(0) = y'(0) = 0; \; y^{iv} = -y'' = 1$

$$\therefore y = 1 - \frac{1}{2}x^2 + \frac{1}{4!}x^4 - \ldots = \sum_{n=0}^{\infty} (-1)^n \frac{x^{2n}}{(2n)!}$$

9. $y(x) = y(0) + y'(0)x + \frac{y''(0)}{2!}x^2 + \ldots$

$y'' = y + x. \quad y'(0) = 2$ and $y(0) = -1 \Rightarrow y''(0) = -1$

$y''' = y' + 1 \Rightarrow y'''(0) = 2 + 1 = 3$

$y^{iv} = y'' = -1; \; y^{v} = y''' = 3; \; y^{vi} = y^{iv} = -1$

$$\therefore y = -1 + 2x - \frac{1}{2!}x^2 + \frac{3}{3!}x^3 - \frac{1}{4!}x^4 + \frac{3}{5!} + \ldots$$

$$= 3\sum_{n=0}^{\infty} \frac{x^{2n+1}}{(2n+1)!} - \sum_{n=0}^{\infty} \frac{x^{2n}}{(2n)!} - x$$

11. $y(x) = y(0) + y'(0)x + \frac{y''(0)}{2!}x^2 + \ldots$

$y'' = x^2 y. \quad y' = y_1$ and $y = y_0; \; y'' = 0$

$y''' = 2xy + x^2 y' \Rightarrow y''' = 0$

$y^{iv} = 2xy' + 2y + 2xy' + x^2 y'' = 2y_0$

$y^{v} = 2xy'' + 2y' + 2y' + 2xy'' + 2y' + 2xy'' + x^2 y''' = 6y_1$

$y^{vi} = y^{vii} = 0; \; y^{viii} = 60y_0$

$$\therefore y = y_0 + y_1 x + \frac{2y_0}{4!}x^4 + \frac{6y_1}{5!} + \ldots$$

$$= \sum_{n=0}^{\infty} a_n x^n, \text{ where } a_0 = y_0, a_1 = y_1, a_2 = a_3 = 0, a_n = \frac{1}{n(n-1)}a_{n-4} \text{ for } n \geq 4.$$

12. $y(x) = y(0) + y'(0)x + \frac{y''(0)}{2!}x^2 + \ldots$

$y'' = -x^2 y + x$. $y' = y_1$ and $y = y_0$; $y'' = 0$

$y''' = 2xy + x^2 y' \Rightarrow y''' = 1$

$y^{iv} = 2xy' + 2y + 2xy' + x^2 y'' = -2y_0$

$y^{v} = 2xy'' + 2y' + 2y' + 2xy'' + 2y' + 2xy'' + x^2 y''' = -6y_1$

$y^{vi} = 0;\ y^{vii} = -20$

$\therefore\ y = y_0 + y_1 x + \frac{1}{3!} - \frac{2y_0}{4!}x^4 - \frac{6y_1}{5!}x^5 + \ldots$

$= \sum_{n=0}^{\infty} a_n x^n$, where $a_0 = y_0, a_1 = y_1, a_2 = 0, a_3 = \frac{1}{6}, a_n = \frac{1}{n(n-1)}a_{n-4}$ for $n \ge 4$.

## 20.9 DIRECTION FIELDS AND PICARD'S THEOREM

1. The isoclines are the vertical lines $x$ = constant

(See graph in answer section of textbook)

3. If $\frac{1}{x} = C$, then $x = \frac{1}{C} = C_1$. The isoclines are the vertical lines $x$ = constant. (See graph in answer section of textbook)

5. The isoclines are the curves $xy$ = constant.

(See graph in answer section of textbook)

7. Let $u = x + y \Rightarrow \frac{du}{dx} = 1 + \frac{dy}{dx}$. Hence $y' = (x+y)^2$ becomes

$\frac{du}{dx} = 1 + u^2 \Rightarrow \frac{du}{1+u^2} = dx$ or $\tan^{-1} u = x + C$.

$\therefore\ y = \tan(x + C) - x$. This passes through $(0, 0)$ when $C = 0$

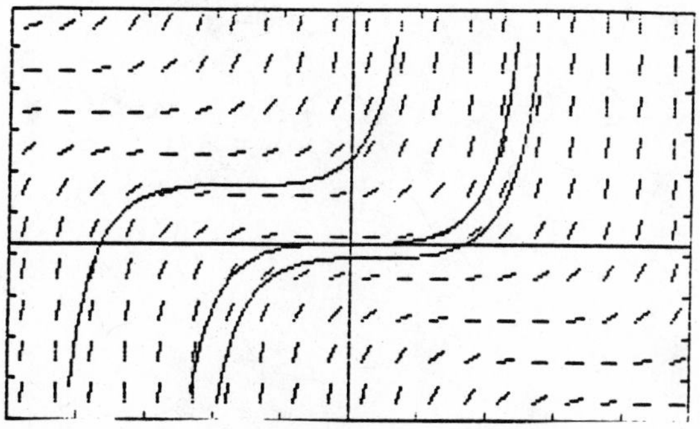

9. $\frac{dy}{dx} + y = x$. Let $\rho = e^{\int dx} = e^x$. Then $e^x y = \int xe^x\,dx$

$e^x y = xe^x - e^x + C \Rightarrow y = x - 1 + Ce^{-x}$

(a) If $C = 0$, then $y = x - 1$ is a solution.

(b) If $y' = x - y$ then $y'' = 1 - y' = 1 - (x - y)$

Concave up ($y'' > 0$) if $y > x - 1$ and concave down ($y'' < 0$) if $y < x - 1$

(See graph in answer section of textbook)

11. $y = -1 + \int_1^x t - y(t)\,dt \Rightarrow y' = x - y,\ y(1) = -1$

13. $y = 2 - \int_0^x (1 + y(t))\sin t\,dt \Rightarrow y' = -(1 + y)\sin x,\ y(0) = 2$

15. $y_0 = 2,\ y_1 = 2 + \int_1^x t\,dt = 2 + \frac{1}{2}x^2 - \frac{1}{2} = \frac{1}{2}x^2 + \frac{3}{2}$

$y_2 = y_3 = 2 + \int_1^x t\,dt = \frac{1}{2}x^2 + \frac{3}{2}$

17. $y_0 = 1,\ y_1 = 1 + \int_1^x t\,dt = \frac{1}{2}(1 + x^2)$

$y_2 = 1 + \int_1^x \frac{1}{2}(1 + t^2)\,t\,dt = \frac{5}{8} + \frac{1}{4}x^2 + \frac{1}{8}x^4$

$y_3 = 1 + \int_1^x \left(\frac{5}{8} + \frac{1}{4}t^2 + \frac{1}{8}t^4\right)t\,dt = \frac{29}{48} + \frac{5}{16}x^2 + \frac{1}{16}x^4 + \frac{1}{48}x^6$

19. $y_0 = 1,\ y_1 = 1 + \int_0^x (t + 1)\,dt = 1 + x + \frac{1}{2}x^2$

$y_2 = 1 + \int_0^x \left[t + \left(1 + t + \frac{1}{2}t^2\right)\right]dt = 1 + x + x^2 + \frac{1}{6}x^3$

$y_3 = \int_0^x \left[t + \left(1 + t + t^2 + \frac{1}{6}t^3\right)t\,dt = 1 + x + x^2 + \frac{1}{3}x^3 + \frac{1}{24}x^4\right.$

21. $y' - y = x$. Let $\rho = e^{-x}$. Then $e^{-x}y = \int xe^{-x} = -xe^{-x} - e^{-x} + C$

$y = -x - 1 + Ce^x$. $y(x_0) = y_0 \Rightarrow y_0 = Ce^{x_0} - x_0 - 1$ or $C = x_0 + y_0 + 1$

$\therefore\ y = (x_0 + y_0 + 1)e^{x - x_0} - (x + 1)$

## 20.10 NUMERICAL METHODS

1.

| i | $x_i$ | $y_i$ | $y_{i+1} = y_i(h+1)$ |
|---|---|---|---|
| 0 | 0 | 1 | 1.2 |
| 0 | 0 | 1 | 1. |
| 1 | 0.2 | 1.2 | 1.44 |
| 2 | 0.4 | 1.44 | 1.728 |
| 3 | 0.6 | 1.728 | 2.0736 |
| 4 | 0.8 | 2.0736 | 2.48832 |

The exact value is $e^x$

3.

| i | $x_i$ | $y_i$ | $z_i = y_i(1+h)$ | $y_{i+1} = y_i + 0.1(y_i + z_{i+1})$ |
|---|---|---|---|---|
| 0 | 0 | 1 | 1.2 | 1.22 |
| 1 | 0.2 | 1.22 | 1.464 | 1.4884 |
| 2 | 0.4 | 1.4884 | 1.78608 | 1.815848 |
| 3 | 0.6 | 1.815848 | 2.1790176 | 2.2153346 |
| 4 | 0.8 | 2.2153346 | 2.6584015 | 2.7027082 |

5. $\frac{dy}{dx} = a^2 + y^2 \Rightarrow \frac{dy}{a^2+y^2} = dx \Rightarrow \frac{1}{a}\tan^{-1}\frac{y}{a} = x + C$

$$y(a) = f(a) \Rightarrow C = \frac{1}{a}\tan^{-1}\frac{f(a)}{a} - a. \therefore y = a\tan\left[a\left(x + \frac{1}{a}\tan^{-1}\frac{f(a)}{a} - a\right)\right].$$

$$a\left[x + \frac{1}{a}\tan^{-1}\frac{f(a)}{a} - a\right] = \frac{\pi}{2} \Rightarrow x = a + \frac{1}{a}\left[\frac{\pi}{2} - \tan^{-1}\frac{f(a)}{a}\right]$$

For $a = 2.0$ and $f(a) = 317.2244$, $x^* = 2.0031523$

7. $y(0) = 1 \Rightarrow a_0 = 1$

$c_0 = a_0^2 = 1$ $\qquad a_1 = c_0 = 1$

$c_1 = 2a_0 a_1 = 2$ $\qquad a_2 = \frac{1}{2}c_1 = 1$

$c_2 = 2a_0 a_2 + a_1^2 = 3$ $\qquad a_3 = \frac{1}{3}(1 + c_2) = \frac{4}{3}$

$c_3 = 2a_0a_3 + 2a_1a_2 = \frac{14}{3}$ $\qquad a_4 = \frac{14}{12} = \frac{7}{6}$

## 20.M MISCELLANEOUS

1. $y\ln y\,dx + (1+x^2)\,dy \Rightarrow (1+x^2)\,dy = -y\ln y\,dx \Rightarrow$

$$\frac{dy}{y\ln y} = -\frac{dx}{1+x^2} \Rightarrow \ln|\ln y| = -\tan^{-1}x + C$$

3. $e^{x+2y}\,dy - e^{y-2}\,dx = 0 \Rightarrow e^{x+2y}\,dy = e^{y-2}\,dx$

$e^{y+2}\,dy = e^{-x}\,dx \Rightarrow e^{y+2} = -e^{-x} + C$ or $y = -2 + \ln(C - e^{-x})$

5. $y\,dy = \sqrt{1+y^4}\,dx \Rightarrow \dfrac{y\,dy}{\sqrt{1+y^4}} = dx \Rightarrow \dfrac{1}{2}\sinh^{-1}(y^2) = x + C$

7. Let $v = \dfrac{y}{x}$, $\dfrac{dy}{dx} = v + x\dfrac{dv}{dx}$. Then $\dfrac{dy}{dx} = \dfrac{x^2+y^2}{2xy} \Rightarrow 2xy\dfrac{dy}{dx} = x^2 + y^2$

$$2\left(\frac{y}{x}\right)\frac{dy}{dx} = 1 + \left(\frac{y}{x}\right)^2 \text{ so } 2v\left(v + x\frac{dv}{dx}\right) = 1 - v^2 \Rightarrow \frac{2v\,dv}{1-v^2} = \frac{dx}{x}$$

$$\ln|1-v^2| = -\ln|x| + C \Rightarrow 1 - v^2 = \frac{1}{x} + C \Rightarrow y^2 = x^2 - Cx$$

9. $x\,dy = \left(y + x\cos^2\dfrac{y}{x}\right)dx \Rightarrow x\,dy - y\,dx = x\cos^2\dfrac{y}{x}\,dx$

$$(x\,dy - y\,dx)\sec^2\frac{y}{x} = x\,dx \Rightarrow \frac{(x\,dy - y\,dx)}{x^2}\sec^2\frac{y}{x} = \frac{dx}{x}$$

$$\therefore\ \tan\frac{y}{x} = \ln|x| + C \text{ or } y = x\tan^{-1}(\ln|x| + C)$$

11. $x\,dy + (2y - x^2 - 1)\,dx = 0 \Rightarrow \dfrac{dy}{dx} + \dfrac{2}{x}y = x + \dfrac{1}{x}$.

Then $\rho = e^{\int 2/x\,dx} = x^2$, so $x^2 y = \int (x^3 + x)\,dx = \dfrac{1}{4}x^4 + \dfrac{1}{2}x^2 + C$

$$y = \frac{1}{4}x^2 + \frac{1}{2} + Cx^{-2}$$

13. $\cosh x\,dy - (y + \cosh x)\sinh x\,dx = 0$

$$\cosh x\frac{dy}{dx} - (\sinh x)\,y = \cosh x\sinh x \Rightarrow \frac{dy}{dx} - (\tanh x)\,y = \sinh x$$

$$\rho = e^{-\ln(\cosh x)} = \operatorname{sech} x, \text{ so } y\operatorname{sech} x = \int \tanh x\,dx = \ln(\cosh x) + C$$

$$y = \cosh x\,[\ln(\cosh x) + C]$$

15. $(1+y^2)\,dx + (2xy + y^2 + 1)\,dy = 0 \Rightarrow \dfrac{dx}{dy} + \dfrac{2y}{1+y^2}x = -1$

$$\rho = 1 + y^2 \text{ so } x(1+y^2) = -\int (1+y^2)\,dy = -y - \frac{1}{3}y^3 + C$$

$$3x(1+y^2) + 3y + y^3 = C$$

17. $(x^2+y^2)\,dx + (2xy + \cosh y)\,dy = 0 \Rightarrow x^2\,dx + (2xy\,dy + y^2\,dx) + \cosh y\,dy = 0$

$$\frac{1}{3}x^3 + xy^2 + \sinh y = C$$

19. $x(1+e^y)\,dx + \dfrac{1}{2}(x^2+y^2)e^y\,dy = 0$

$$x\,dx + \left(xe^y\,dx + \frac{1}{2}x^2e^y\,dy\right) + \frac{1}{2}y^2e^y\,dy = 0.$$

$$\frac{1}{2}x^2 + \frac{1}{2}x^2e^y + \left(\frac{1}{2}y^2e^y - ye^y + e^y\right) = C$$

$$x^2 + e^y(x^2 + y^2 - 2y + 2) = C$$

21. $\frac{d^2y}{dx^2} - 2y\frac{dy}{dx} = 0$. Let $p = \frac{dy}{dx}$ so $\frac{d^2y}{dx^2} = p\frac{dp}{dy}$. Then $p\frac{dp}{dy} - 2yp = 0 \Rightarrow$

$p = 0$ or $dp = 2y\,dy \Rightarrow p = C$ or $p = y^2 + C \Rightarrow \frac{dy}{dx} = y^2 + C$ or $y = C$.

For $\frac{dy}{dx} = y^2 + C$ there are three cases to consider.

$C = 0$: $\frac{dy}{y^2} = dx \Rightarrow -y^{-1} = x + K$ or $y = -\frac{1}{x+K}$

$C = B^2 > 0$: $\frac{dy}{B^2 + y^2} = dx \Rightarrow \frac{1}{B}\tan^{-1}\frac{y}{B} = x + K \Rightarrow y = B\tan(Bx + K')$

$C < 0$, $C = -B^2$ : $\frac{dy}{y^2 - B^2} = dx \Rightarrow \frac{1}{2B}\ln\left|\frac{y-B}{y+B}\right| = x + K$

23. $\frac{d^2y}{dx^2} = 1 + \left(\frac{dy}{dx}\right)^2$. Let $p = \frac{dy}{dx}$. Then $\frac{dp}{dx} = 1 + p^2 \Rightarrow \frac{dp}{1+p^2} = dx$

$\tan^{-1}p = x + C \Rightarrow p = \frac{dy}{dx} = \tan(x + C) \Rightarrow y = \ln|\sec(x + C)| + K$

25. $x^2\frac{d^2y}{dx^2} + x\frac{dy}{dx} = 1$. Let $p = \frac{dy}{dx}$. Then $x^2\frac{dp}{dx} + xp = 1$

$\frac{dp}{dx} + \frac{1}{x}p = x^{-2} \Rightarrow xp = \int x^{-1}\,dx = \ln x + C$.

$\frac{dy}{dx} = \frac{\ln x}{x} + \frac{C}{x} \Rightarrow y = \frac{1}{2}(\ln x)^2 + C\ln x + K$

27. $\frac{d^3y}{dx^3} - 2\frac{d^2y}{dx^2} + \frac{dy}{dx} = 0$ $\quad r^3 - 2r^2 + r = 0 \Rightarrow r = 0, 1, 1$

$y = C_1 + C_2e^x + C_3\,x\,e^x$

29. $\frac{d^2y}{dx^2} - \frac{dy}{dx} - 2y = e^{2x}$ $\quad r^2 - r - 2 = 0 \Rightarrow r = 2, -1$

$y_h = C_1e^{2x} + C_2e^{-x}$ . Try $y_p = Axe^{2x}$. Then $3Ae^{2x} = e^{2x} \Rightarrow A = \frac{1}{3}$

$y = C_1e^{2x} + C_2e^{-x} + \frac{1}{3}xe^{2x}$

31. $4x^2\frac{d^2y}{dx^2} + 4x\frac{dy}{dx} - y = 0$. If $y = x^c$ is a solution then

$\frac{dy}{dx} = cx^{c-1}$ and $\frac{d^2y}{dx^2} = c(c-1)x^{c-2}$ satisfy the equation.

$4c(c-1)x^2\,x^{c-2} + 4cx\,x^{c-1} - x^c = 4c(c-1)\,x^c + 4cx^c - x^c = 0$

$x^c(4c^2 - 1) = 0$ or $c = \pm\frac{1}{2} \Rightarrow y = C_1x^{1/2} + C_2\,x^{-1/2}$

33. $x^2 = Cy^3 \Rightarrow 3Cy^2\frac{dy}{dx} = 2x \Rightarrow 3\left(\frac{x^2}{y^3}\right)y^2\frac{dy}{dx} = 2x \Rightarrow \frac{dy}{dx} = \frac{2y}{3x}$.

The orthogonal trajectories should have slope $\frac{dy}{dx} = -\frac{3x}{2y}$

Then $y^2 = -\frac{3}{2}x^2 + A$ or $2y^2 + 3x^2 = B$

35. $y^2 = 4C(C-x) \Rightarrow 2y\frac{dy}{dx} = -4C \Rightarrow y^2\left(\frac{dy}{dx}\right)^2 = 4C^2$

$$y^2\left(\frac{dy}{dx}\right)^2 = y^2 + 4Cx = y^2 - x\left(2y\frac{dy}{dx}\right).$$

$$y^2\left(\frac{dy}{dx}\right)^2 + 2xy\frac{dy}{dx} - y^2 = 0 \Rightarrow \left(\frac{dy}{dx}\right)^2 + \frac{2x}{y}\frac{dy}{dx} - 1 = 0$$

$$\frac{dy}{dx} = \frac{-\frac{2x}{y} \pm \sqrt{\frac{4x^2}{y^2} + 4}}{2} = -\frac{x}{y} \pm \sqrt{\left(\frac{x}{y}\right)^2 + 1}$$. The orthogonal trajectories

satisfy $\frac{dx}{dy} = -\frac{x}{y} \pm \sqrt{\left(\frac{x}{y}\right)^2 + 1}$ also. Let $v = \frac{x}{y}$, so $\frac{dx}{dy} = v + y\frac{dv}{dy}$.

$$v + y\frac{dv}{dy} = -v \pm \sqrt{v^2+1} \Rightarrow \frac{dv}{\pm\sqrt{v^2+1}} = \frac{dy}{y} \Rightarrow \pm \ln|v + \sqrt{v^2+1}| = \ln y + B$$

$$v \pm \sqrt{v^2+1} = By \Rightarrow \frac{x}{y} \pm \sqrt{\left(\frac{x}{y}\right)^2 + 1} = By \Rightarrow x \pm \sqrt{x^2+y^2} = B$$

$x^2 - 2Bx + B^2 = x^2 + y^2$ or $y^2 = B^2 - 2Bx$.

37. $\frac{dy}{dx} - y = x$. Let $\rho = e^{-x}$. Then $ye^{-x} = \int xe^{-x}\,dx = -xe^{-x} - e^{-x} + C$.

$y = Ce^x - x - 1$. $y(0) = 0 \Rightarrow C = 1$. $\therefore y = e^x - x - 1$. The series is

$$y = \left(1 + x + \frac{1}{2}x^2 + \ldots\right) - x - 1 = \sum_{n=2}^{\infty}\frac{x^n}{n!}$$

39. (a) $y' = x + \sin y$ $\quad y(0) = \frac{\pi}{2}$, $y'(0) = 1$

$y'' = 1 + (\cos y)y'$ $\quad y''(0) = 1$

$y''' = (-\sin y)y' + (\cos y)y''$ $\quad y'''(0) = -1$

$y^{iv} = (-2\sin y)y'' + (-\sin y)y' + (\cos y)y'''$ $\quad y^{iv}(0) = -3$

$y = \frac{\pi}{2} + x - \frac{1}{2}x^2 - \frac{1}{6}x^3 - \frac{3}{8}x^4 + \ldots$

(b) $y' = x + \sin y$ $\quad y(0) = -\frac{\pi}{2}$, $y'(0) = -1$

$y'' = 1 + (\cos y)y'$ $\quad y''(0) = 1$

$y''' = (-\sin y)y' + (\cos y)y''$ $\quad y'''(0) = 1$

$y^{iv} = (-2\sin y)y'' + (-\sin y)y' + (\cos y)y'''$ $\quad y^{iv}(0) = -3$

$y = -\frac{\pi}{2} - x + \frac{1}{2}x^2 + \frac{1}{6}x^3 - \frac{3}{8}x^4 + \ldots$